The Complete UrbanBuzz

The
Complete
UrbanBuzz

Published by University College London

Printed in England by Midway Colour Print

ISBN: 0-9561323-0-8

Copyright © UCL, Bartlett Faculty of the Built Environment, 2009

Welcome to UrbanBuzz

In 2007, University College London (UCL) received an unprecedented £5 million of public funds from the Higher Education Innovation Fund, and leveraged this to create the £7.75 million UrbanBuzz: Building Sustainable Communities knowledge exchange 'impact' programme. This book describes how UrbanBuzz used this risk capital to unlock potential; funding 27 projects over an intense two-year period. UrbanBuzz has delivered a portfolio of new tools and processes grounded in the evidence base; targeting those charged with placemaking and shaping our world in a more inclusive and sustainable manner.

UrbanBuzz set out to challenge the 'conventional' approach to disbursing funds by creating a system that brought together unlikely stakeholders in an open and collaborative manner. This process aimed to deliver real outcomes and real legacies of benefit to end-users. *The Complete UrbanBuzz* captures the learning and successes of this unique enterprise, and provides clear signposts directing the reader to its many free outputs.

This book will become an essential reference for practitioners in the professional, trade, policy, academic and community sectors – in particular where the acquisition of new techniques and processes are key to personal and professional development. It will make a valuable contribution to learning at every level, and will contribute to a greater understanding of the real issues in this domain.

UCL was delighted to have the University of East London (UEL) as its prime partner for the UrbanBuzz programme, thereby creating a powerful pan-London collaborative axis.

As demonstrated so emphatically in the 2008 Research Assessment Exercise, UCL has world-class expertise in architecture, planning, civil engineering, transportation, geography, environmental science, health and social sciences, all of which impact on sustainable development. UEL also has key strengths in these areas, in addition to excellent community links and regional networks: it is a strategic partner in the Thames Gateway and Olympic regeneration areas, the largest programme of new urban development since post-war reconstruction.

The Complete UrbanBuzz tells a story of improbable working relationships, risky ventures and triumph over unreasonable deadlines. The programme will be remembered by many of the 150-plus participating organisations for its unique culture of openness (for example, it was not even possible to bid for funding without sharing ideas publicly on the programme website), and for its focus on outcomes. The enduring human and virtual networks created by UrbanBuzz will be harnessed by UCL and UEL to help deliver future aspirations: the UCL Grand Research Challenge on Sustainable Cities, to be launched during 2009, and the planned new Thames Gateway Institute for Sustainability.

All enquiries regarding this publication and its contents should, in the first instance, be directed to David Cobb, UrbanBuzz Programme Director, at d.cobb@ucl.ac.uk

How to use this book

Section one: the UrbanBuzz programme
UrbanBuzz operated on two levels: the programme, which took care of strategy, administration, communications, awareness-raising and evaluation; and the projects – the 27 innovative working partnerships supported by the programme.

The first part of the book focuses on the UrbanBuzz programme: its aims, its conception, its operation, the context in which the projects were progressed, and its legacy. See page 8.

Section two: the UrbanBuzz projects
The second section is dedicated to the projects. Each of the 27 projects is summarised, and its context, process, outputs, outcomes and resources detailed. See page 76.

And finally…
In all cases, the opinions expressed in this book are those of the editors, referenced in experience and evidence derived from the UrbanBuzz community.

Navigating this book
Because the 27 projects address such a wide variety of complex issues, the editors have introduced:

01   a range of pie charts, tables and graphics on pages 78-86, designed to illustrate key programme and project impacts and audiences;

02   at-a-glance guide (between pages 88-89), offering an overview of each project's objectives, outputs, outcomes, impacts and expected areas of influence, along with page references and links to further information;

03   a project classification table on pages 90-91, outlining the scope and likely audiences for each project;

04   a useful list of keywords and project references on page 216.

Contents

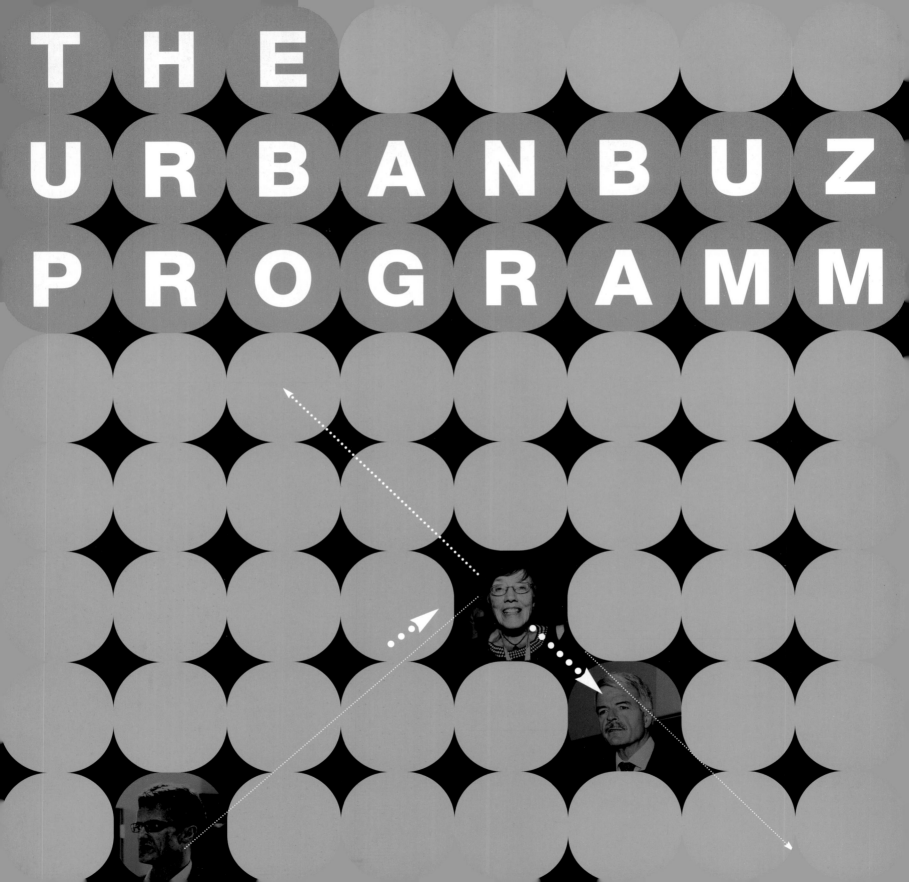

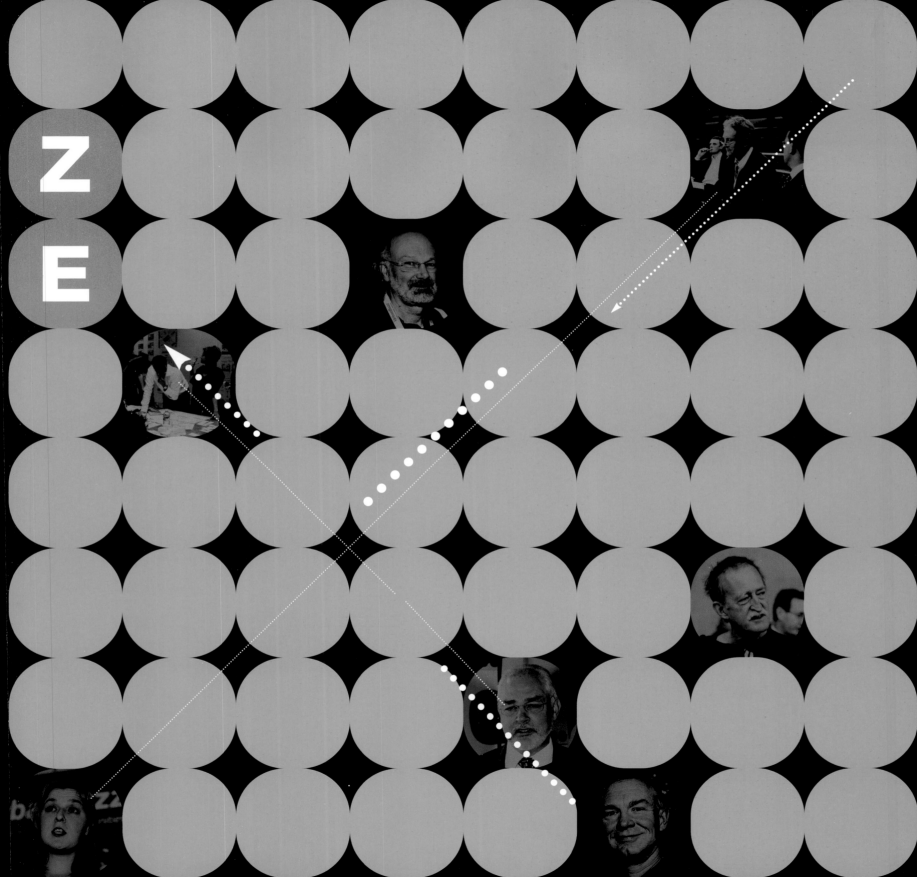

The UrbanBuzz programme

There often seems to be a gap between people's ingenuity and their capacity to act. In times of crisis this first becomes obvious to all, and then a point comes where the social conditions inhibiting action change, and action takes place.

The question facing us at present is whether the time is yet ripe for action in the face of the crisis of sustainability. UrbanBuzz follows a proposition: that universities hold a strategic position and a special responsibility with respect to catalysing action in the face of the unsustainable behaviours of humanity.

This is for two reasons. First, that universities are heavily implicated in the construction of the problem. Academia and the pursuit of science under a western model have, in essence, divided the world in order to understand it. Their products, in terms of technology and understanding, have been immense.

However, alongside these advances has come a series of social divides within the culture of science, engineering and the world at large. These divides now inhibit our ability to coordinate understanding to tackle the complex real-world interactions that characterise our relationship to the physical and natural environment. Effectively, our knowledge of the world has become segmented, and the structure of academia defines this segmentation and works actively to reproduce it. University departmental structures are defined according to these segmented domains of understanding, while the professions that we train define themselves according to bodies of knowledge that these produce. In effect, universities produce and reproduce the segmented structure of our contemporary knowledge-based society.

Second, universities hold the keys to constructing the solution. It is exactly these segments of in-depth domain knowledge that first identified the problems facing the planet: climate change, global warming, the ozone hole and the globalisation of culture and the economy, for example, all have been identified through academic research. It is these bodies of knowledge, and the technologies they make possible, that are necessary for solutions to be defined.

It will be up to the professionals and policymakers that we train to take the lead in resolving the problems facing us in the coming years. As active producers of knowledge, and reproducers of the social structures of our professions, it is the universities that must take a lead in developing solutions.

New fields of science, in domains as diverse as ecology, spatial planning and complexity mathematics, that investigate the systemic interactions between multiple levels of the domains concerned with sustainability, are developing rapidly, and this knowledge of systems and emergent dynamics will be critical to success.

UrbanBuzz sits in this context. It was defined in recognition of the strategic position that universities hold, and framed its processes of action against this background. What we aimed to do was intervene in a complex social structure, and to spawn a reconfiguration of the social networks involved in the production and reproduction of dominant bodies of knowledge relating to sustainable communities. This involved both internal reconfiguration of communication networks within and between universities (UCL worked with UEL, Oxford University, Oxford Brooks University and others), and external reconfiguration amongst organisations in the public, private and voluntary sectors. Most importantly, it involved academics opening up their good 'within discipline' external contacts to others outside their department and discipline.

Essentially, this involved building a shared vocabulary, a shared vision and a degree of trust between individuals and organisations in knowledge domains that historically have not interacted well. Cultural change at this level is a risky venture. For individuals, much is at stake.

It is too soon to say whether or not the UrbanBuzz adventure has succeeded in its aim to catalyse widespread change, and whether the risks have paid off. If it does succeed, it will not be easy to disentangle the effects of the programme from those of the flavour of the times. What can be said is that this novel approach to intervening in academia's relations with its public and user communities has succeeded in constructing a wealth of personal contacts and new shared understanding.

Amongst the projects sponsored by the programme, all have delivered different kinds of lasting change to their target communities. Some have succeeded beyond expectation; others have faced insuperable challenges. The accounts in this book give some idea of what has been achieved, and the lessons learned.

A time for action?
Do universities, through programmes such as UrbanBuzz, have a responsibility to act as a catalyst in the face of the unsustainable behaviours of humanity? Professor Alan Penn, lead academic on the UrbanBuzz programme, considers the issues

Professor Alan Penn

Professor of Architectural and
Urban Computing at The Bartlett
School of Graduate Studies,
University College London, and
UrbanBuzz lead academic

A lasting legacy

It has been my privilege to chair the Programme Board of UrbanBuzz. This board has helped shape the range of activities undertaken within the UrbanBuzz programme by developing and implementing the governance procedures that underpinned the ways that proposals were sought, projects were managed and dissemination was conducted. A privilege certainly, but also a big responsibility. Get it right and we would allow UrbanBuzz to fulfil its potential as a short-term 'impact' programme through which £5m of public money would be used wisely: both to transfer knowledge and to build a lasting legacy of new methods and, more importantly, novel networks of people and organisations. Get it wrong, and we would have wasted both money and opportunity.

It is perhaps early days, but the indications are that UrbanBuzz has succeeded. A well-balanced programme of 27 individual projects was developed, many of which have included innovative groupings of people from academia, public and private organisations and the voluntary sector. The projects, all of which have been externally audited, have led to a range of knowledge transfer activities, but have also provided a number of exciting new insights on how more sustainable communities might be nurtured and managed.

I would like to thank my colleagues on the Programme Board for turning a privilege into a real pleasure – the individuals concerned have without exception provided wise counsel, dedication and great cheerfulness. I would also like to thank the academic and Programme Office staff at UCL and UEL for their great willingness to advocate and work in what were, at times, quite scary ways to ensure that UrbanBuzz 'hit the spot'.

Finally, I would like to thank my employer, Halcrow, for its strong support of my UrbanBuzz activities. The company's strapline has for a number of years been 'sustaining and improving the quality of people's lives'. UrbanBuzz has provided, is providing and will continue to provide, part of the means by which we can 'walk our talk'.

Professor Tim Broyd

Chair, UrbanBuzz Programme Board
Group Director of Technology &
Innovation, Halcrow

Making an impact

We need to be able to draw upon any and all disciplines in coping with the complex problems of the modern world. I well recall three years ago, along with other leaders of the UrbanBuzz programme, contemplating the bid that we should make to the Higher Education Innovation Fund (HEIF). The purpose of HEIF is to draw universities more into the 21st century and to open their vistas into the transfer of knowledge – not just the understanding, creation and development of knowledge targeting the next generation of scholars – but, as with UCL's bid, to spin it out laterally to impact on the way communities and individuals lead their lives.

One of the great challenges facing universities is overcoming the barriers of our own construction that confine knowledge within artificial silos. Only universities are able to do this, and so UCL has announced four Grand Research Challenges across the whole institution: 'Global Health'; 'Human Wellbeing', including healthy ageing; 'Intercultural Interactions' and finally 'Sustainable Cities' – of which UrbanBuzz's legacy will become a vital component.

We accept the obligation that goes with the privilege of being a university – an obligation that ensures our talent is used for social good. The close of this programme marks the end of 'phase one' of this process, beyond which lies a longer process of dissemination and engagement with partners, including the recently-formed Homes and Communities Agency, the agenda of which strongly resonates with all that is good about UrbanBuzz.

I'd like to pay a particular tribute to those who have led the programme; both in its conception and inception, and here in particular I mention my colleagues David Cobb and Alan Penn, but also those involved in its implementation over the two years of funding.

During this phase, UrbanBuzz not only engaged scholars from The Bartlett Faculty of the Built Environment, which has been the lead programme faculty at UCL, it has engaged 53 members of academic staff across 10 departments. More than 150 people worked directly on projects from outside UCL, including 15 local authorities. It has engaged with the University of East London, UCL's prime partner, and has proved to be an outstanding example of inter-university cooperation. It has generated and engaged with, in just two years, a much bigger community – a virtual community – comprising a staggering 3,000 members!

Thank you to everyone who has made this programme possible, most of whom are listed at the back of this publication (see page 212). To those of you to whom it is a new experience; I commend to you the new tools and processes developed by UrbanBuzz.

Professor Malcolm Grant

President and Provost,
University College London

Crossing boundaries

UrbanBuzz has been successful because it has used institutional diversity as an asset in fostering partnership and innovation, responding to demand and in the creation of new ideas. I think this is how higher education should work; breaking down silos and crossing boundaries to apply expertise to the solution of real-life problems.

Universities are unique organisations. They have the ability to work almost anywhere, and on any subject. They are not bounded in the way that many organisations are. UrbanBuzz has enabled UCL and UEL together to demonstrate that crossing boundaries adds value. Some of those boundaries exist historically between universities with different missions and between the professions whose staff we train. UrbanBuzz has provided us with excellent examples of the fact that it is in both the public and commercial interest for us to create expert partnerships that break down such barriers.

The Thames Gateway Institute for Sustainability, in which both UEL and UCL are partners, was launched at the 2008 Thames Gateway Forum by Communities Secretary Hazel Blears. This body is an excellent illustration of what UrbanBuzz has been about. It is very much the fruit of collaboration in the sustainability field between government, the private sector, institutions of international research standing such as UCL and institutions like UEL, a key player in, and critical element of, the London and Thames Gateway regeneration infrastructure. The trail blazed by UrbanBuzz will have practical legacy in the creation of sustainable communities.

Professor Susan Price

Acting Vice-Chancellor,
University of East London

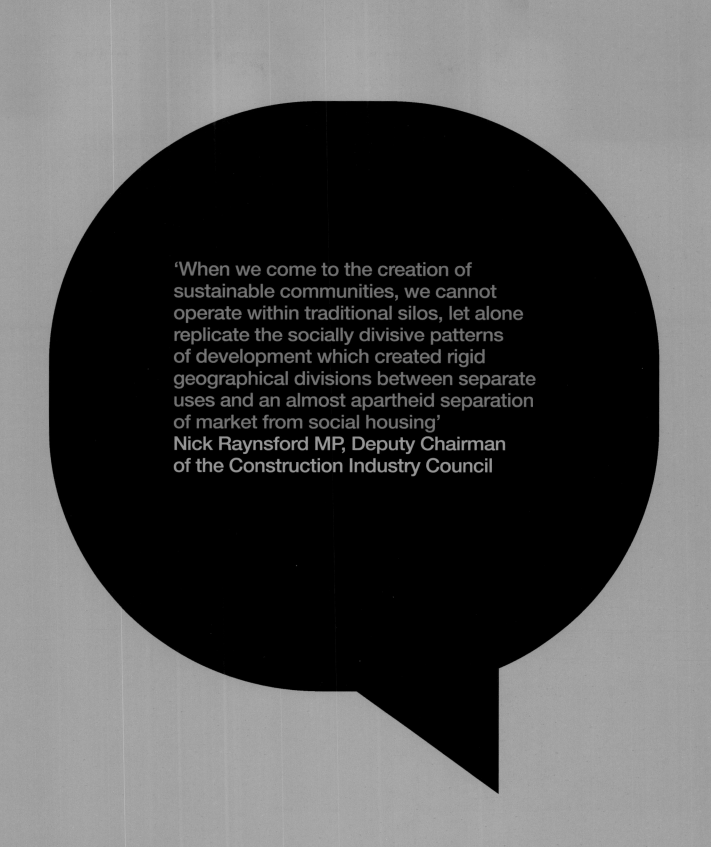

'When we come to the creation of sustainable communities, we cannot operate within traditional silos, let alone replicate the socially divisive patterns of development which created rigid geographical divisions between separate uses and an almost apartheid separation of market from social housing'
Nick Raynsford MP, Deputy Chairman of the Construction Industry Council

'UrbanBuzz was an experiment. We dared to do something different, and I have been excited to follow its progress and to celebrate its success. It has been an exemplar of university commitment to interdisciplinary working and disseminating knowledge in wholly innovative ways.

'Sustainability is the one big challenge for all professions associated with land, property and development. It has to be the issue that cracks the walls of the professional silos and allows interdisciplinary activity to take place'
Professor Malcolm Grant, UCL

UrbanBuzz: every revolution needs a catalyst
The UrbanBuzz programme, supporting 27 knowledge exchange projects, was created with one key aim in mind: to overcome the barriers inherent in creating sustainable communities

The UrbanBuzz knowledge exchange programme was designed to support new partnerships, stimulate new thinking and bring the ideal of building sustainable communities within our grasp.

The innovative two-year, government-funded 'impact' programme was led by University College London (UCL), with University of East London (UEL) as its prime partner. The programme funded, supported and administered 27 collaborative projects, each addressing key sustainability issues such as community empowerment, access to information, low carbon lifestyles and planning for new settlements.

Each project has built on the research evidence base and, through partnership working, has developed new tools, processes and techniques to help build sustainable communities, for example:

01	simulating the impact of the Mayor of London's transportation strategy on CO_2 emissions;
02	spatial mapping techniques relating to anti-social behaviour and designing-out crime;
03	energy-use reduction through retrofitting the existing housing stock;
04	tools and techniques to engage communities in local decision-making and social infrastructure planning;
05	urban agriculture demonstration for the Thames Gateway, incorporating a challenge to local governance.

The programme involved more than 150 partner organisations from the worlds of academia, finance, management, design, policy, planning and the third sector. 'It was UrbanBuzz's ambition to unlock professional "silos" and ways of thinking, and to create an intellectual and skills mix as rich and complex as the problems it sets out to resolve,' says UCL's Professor Alan Penn, the UrbanBuzz lead academic. To this end UrbanBuzz encouraged new activity, free from the limitations of expert labels and narrow professional competencies, by bringing two types of people together: business fellows (from the academic world) and innovation fellows (from the world beyond academia).

'The professionalisation of knowledge and knowledge domains reduces the autonomy of individuals,' says Penn. 'People feel so detached from the exercise of knowledge that they have no way of understanding why the professionals are getting it wrong. Currently institutions, regulation, and the professions that create our communities, operate in silos. Universities have to accept responsibility in this respect because it is

academics that invented, generated and continue to reproduce professional disciplines.'

UCL's President and Provost Professor Malcolm Grant agrees that universities must play a key role in developing new ways of thinking, seeing and practising. 'Only universities have the multiplicity of discipline, the multiplicity of talent at all levels, the willingness and the curiosity to engage with new challenges,' he says. 'UrbanBuzz has been an outstanding example of inter-university cooperation, where usually we experience inter-university rivalry and competition. It has been about the transfer of knowledge, and impacting upon the way in which communities and individuals lead their lives.'

'What is the clever way of reinventing partnerships, the procurement process, the incentives between the public and private sector? Innovation is the very basis of the common sense moves that have to be taken forward in the next few years' Tim Williams, Navigant Consulting, speaking at the launch of the UrbanBuzz Showcase

UrbanBuzz has also, says Grant, gone a long way towards opening up a completely different vision of what a modern university should be about.

As Lord Rogers, amongst others, has made very clear, we are already in danger of creating tomorrow's slums in the emerging Thames Gateway. Instead, we need to create communities that support healthy living, social cohesion and prosperity, and that encourage people to live low-carbon lifestyles. UrbanBuzz has highlighted the power of innovative collaborative thinking, rooted in existing knowledge of what really works. In regard to sustainable communities, the programme has aimed to ensure that, in future, new questions do not meet with old answers.

Funding innovation, mitigating risk

UrbanBuzz accepted the challenge of unlocking potential by boldly going where other funders do not go. This innovative approach has enabled many new ideas to take root, and wide-ranging academic-private-public partnerships to thrive.

UrbanBuzz was funded jointly by The Higher Education Funding Council for England (HEFCE) and the Department for Innovation, Universities and Skills (DIUS). UCL was one out of 11 universities that received funding under the auspices of the Higher Education Innovation Fund-round 3 (HEIF).

UrbanBuzz received £5 million as 'risk capital'. The diagram below illustrates the risk profile and time dimension. UrbanBuzz's financial contribution to all projects has had a catalytic effect by stimulating evidence-based development and enquiry. The 'investor' threshold equally could mean the 'early adopter' threshold, as this is the point at which value, in the eyes of the user/investor, becomes inexorable and therefore represents money well spent.

UrbanBuzz: mitigating investor risks

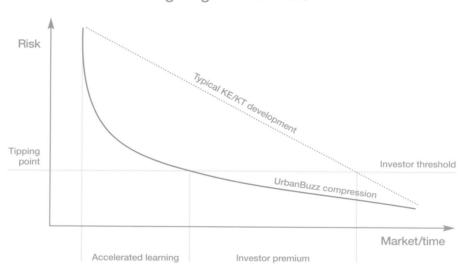

KE = knowledge exchange
KT = knowledge transfer

Risk

Typical KE/KT development

Tipping point

Investor threshold

UrbanBuzz compression

Market/time

Accelerated learning

Investor premium

'UrbanBuzz was an innovative, forward thinking programme. It filled a funding gap by investing in high-risk ideas with the potential to have a major impact in the longer term. There's no way that I could have gone to any other institution or bank for funds to develop our type of tool.' **Michael Kohn, Slider Studio (ESP-SIM project, page 120)**

'UrbanBuzz has funded projects that wouldn't normally receive funding, but which have delivered real innovation in the sustainable communities area. Many of the projects will continue long-term because those running them have a vested interest in doing so.' **Julian Hart, Lancefield Consulting (Sustainable Training project, page 194)**

'If we only spend public money on complete certainty, we'll never do anything interesting. The issue is intelligent management of risk. The rigorous processes the UrbanBuzz programme had in place to evaluate individual project proposals reflected intelligent risk management.' **John Lock, Development Director, UEL**

'The way traditional funding streams operate relies on dissemination between partners, rather than actually encouraging collaboration and effective partnership building. UrbanBuzz has 'built in' time and opportunity for people to work together.' **Gemma Moore, UCL (RETILE project, page 172)**

'UrbanBuzz was open to projects that enabled us to get a coalition of different bodies to work together, so creating a really viable project team. A typical research council may have found this a bit far-fetched, but bringing together an eclectic mix was possible with UrbanBuzz.' **Muki Haklay, UCL (MCSC project, page 154)**

'UrbanBuzz encouraged a mix of academia, industry and local authority partners. This allowed us to source the best people for our projects, which were successful because of these inputs. With traditional funding streams, it would have been a lot more difficult.' **Professor Allan Brimicombe, UEL (EASY and SEDUC projects, pages 112 and 180)**

UrbanBuzz recognised the immediate opportunity for leveraging the HEFCE/DIUS contribution and pledged a further £1.79 million to augment the real value of the programme. In the final analysis the 'contribution in kind' (CIK) total was around £2.75 million, which represented matched funding on a par with the core project funding.

The single largest 'overhead' for the programme was the running costs of the programme office – but at around 11 per cent of the total value of the programme, this was considered lean. Additional support was outsourced as and when required and followed UCL procurement guidelines. The largest allocations, 72.5 per cent of the total value of the programme, were directed at the 27 projects themselves. Contributions in kind were verified by the project monitors with the same level of scrutiny as that applied to the public funds.

£7.75 million: total value of the programme

Funding allocation

- Outreach and events
  £513,205
- Education and training
  £103,463
- Webmaster
  £165,000
- Programme Office: staff and accommodation
  £870,959
- Programme Office: monitoring and outsourcing
  £246,202
- Oxford Institute for Sustainable Development evaluation
  £230,000
- Projects
  £2,871,170
- Projects contribution in kind (CIK)
  £2,750,000

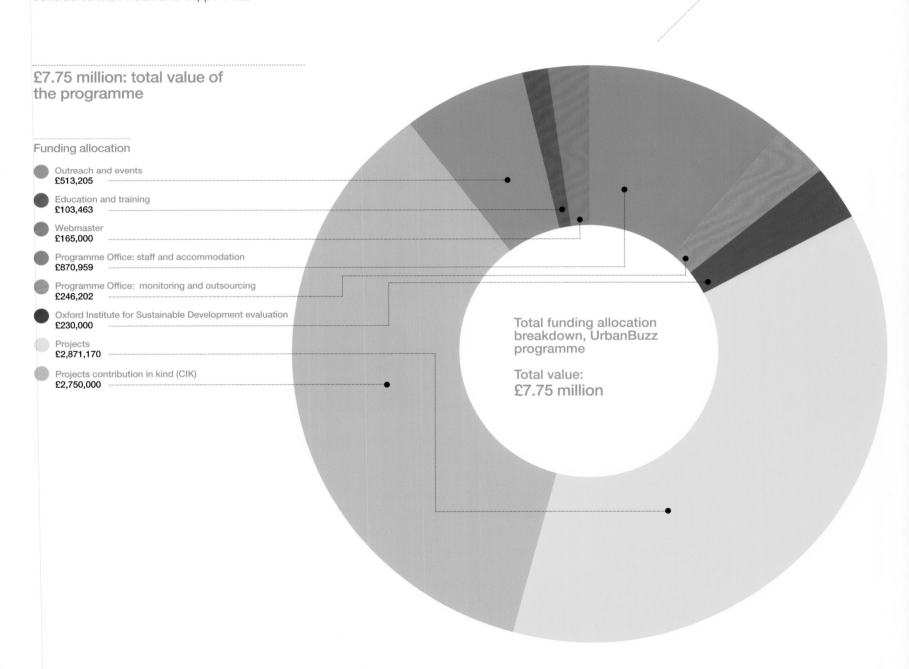

Total funding allocation breakdown, UrbanBuzz programme

Total value:
£7.75 million

The UrbanBuzz programme
Every revolution needs a catalyst

A programme to make a difference

UrbanBuzz was effectively born on the London Underground late in 2005. UCL's then Commercial Director, Dr Jeff Skinner, casually mentioned to Professor Alan Penn of the Bartlett that UCL was looking for ideas to support a bid for knowledge transfer funding. The rest is history. David Cobb, then Bartlett Business Development Manager with UCL Business, joined Jeff and Alan and the trio began the two-stage bidding journey.

Early on, the advantage of constructing a pan-London academic axes was recognised. UEL quickly recognised the potential of bringing staff and regional connections together to address sustainability problems. UEL's Development Director John Lock helped forge stronger links between the two institutions and UEL formally became UCL's prime partner.

Winning funding in the face of stiff competition from 94 other universities required an innovative and creative approach. One of the more compelling factors that no doubt helped UCL's bid was the significant number of organisations from diverse stakeholder sectors (more than 70), cited in the bid. Each organisation pledged to engage with the knowledge exchange programme.

Upon being awarded funding, UCL focused on creating a new 'community of practice' with its own strong identity. A unique, inspirational name was sought to convey the innovative nature of the developing network.

Within weeks, UrbanBuzz was born – with the hope that the name would reflect the energy and 'buzz' of the networks of academics, industry experts, practitioners and community groups that were the programme's lifeblood.

Background and barriers

There is a significant gap in knowledge transfer associated with building sustainable communities. This is recognised as a pressing strategic objective by government. The price of unsustainable development is high – not only in economic terms, but also in terms of quality of life, health, security, social cohesion and environmental impact. UrbanBuzz has risen to this challenge by constructing innovative mechanisms that create unlikely partnerships and foster unprecedented types of collaboration, seeking to bridge the professional silos endemic in the public, private, academic and voluntary sectors.

Much of UrbanBuzz's success can be attributed to its bottom-up, collaborative approach. An inclusive style of consultation was adopted from the outset, from the workshops that established the barriers to be overcome to the bidding process itself.

Barriers to overcome

01	policy, legislation and regulation
02	conceptual understanding
03	existing knowledge and practice
04	resources (time, finance, space, tools)
05	accessibility (funding streams, projects, information)
06	communication and engagement (lack of, means and ways)
07	perceptions, expectations and cultures
08	organisational frameworks and structures
09	measurements and metrics

Governance and management

Delivering a programme that would be completed inside two years required an agile and flexible management and governance system. The diagram below summarises the major components of UrbanBuzz operations.

The Programme Board

Professor Tim Broyd, former chief executive of CIRIA (an organisation dedicated to improvement in the construction industry) and now Group Technology Director for Halcrow, chaired the Programme Board. Broyd helped to shape the board membership to ensure the broadest engagement of sectoral interests (a list of board members can be found on page 212). The board provided an excellent sounding board and a basis for discussing activities and options for programme management consideration.

Independent evaluator

HEFCE required that the programme be independently evaluated. Professor Mike Jenks and Dr Carol Dair from the Oxford Institute for Sustainable Development (OISD) both have extensive knowledge in the sustainability field and were appointed to evaluate the projects' contributions to sustainability and knowledge transfer. More details can be found on page 26.

The Programme Office

A six-strong, flexible core team (see page 24) was assembled at the outset of the programme to administer the necessary legal, financial, project management, marketing and dissemination aspects of the programme.

The management of UrbanBuzz was undertaken by UCL Business, which handles the wealth of innovation and intellectual property emanating from UCL, and offers services from consultancy through to collaborative research, IP licensing and the creation of spinout companies and joint ventures. Consultants were outsourced as required for design, web and event management, media and editorial activities (see page 212 for details).

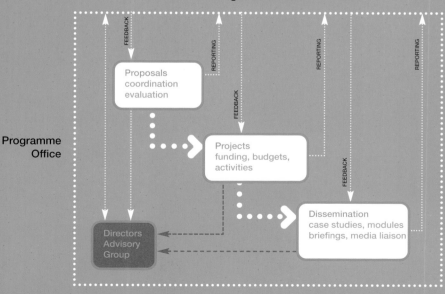

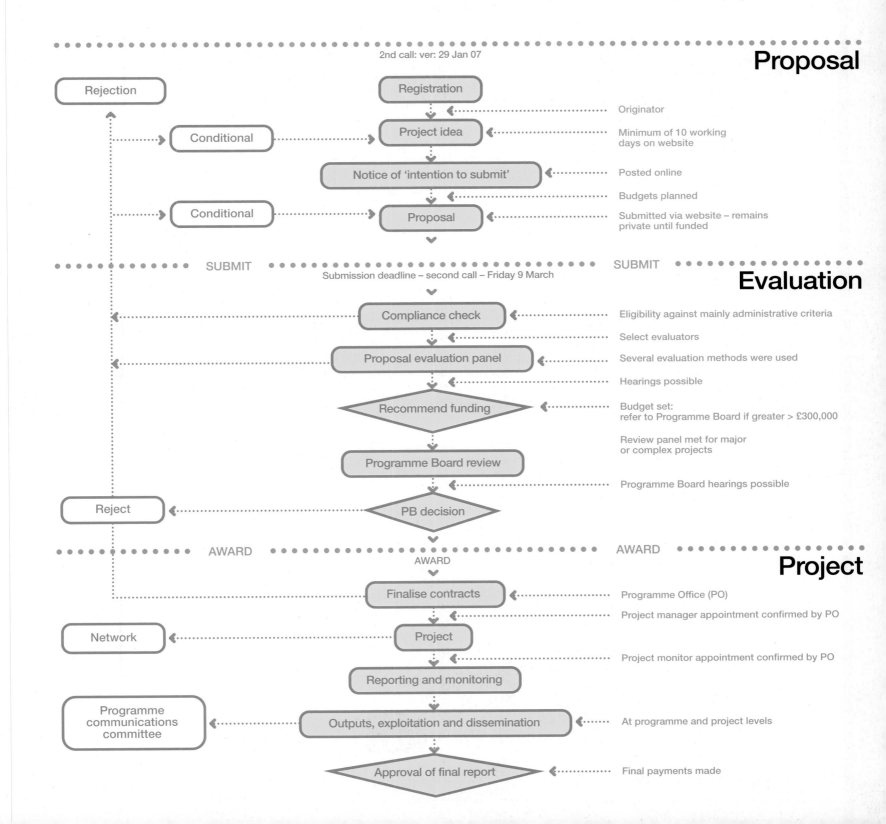

Selecting the projects:
collaboration, not competition
The programme's initial workshops revealed that both the reality and the perception of the barriers to creating sustainable communities were notably wide-ranging. Responding to this diversity of opinion, UrbanBuzz opted to follow a collaborative, not competitive, route to funding

2nd call: ver: 29 Jan 07

Proposal

Rejection

Registration

Conditional .... Project idea ← .... Originator

Notice of 'intention to submit' ← .... Minimum of 10 working days on website

Conditional .... Proposal ← .... Posted online

Budgets planned

Submitted via website – remains private until funded

SUBMIT .... SUBMIT

Submission deadline – second call – Friday 9 March

Evaluation

Compliance check ← .... Eligibility against mainly administrative criteria

Select evaluators

Proposal evaluation panel ← .... Several evaluation methods were used

Hearings possible

Recommend funding ← .... Budget set: refer to Programme Board if greater > £300,000

Programme Board review ← .... Review panel met for major or complex projects

Programme Board hearings possible

Reject ← .... PB decision

AWARD .... AWARD

AWARD

Project

Finalise contracts ← .... Programme Office (PO)

Project manager appointment confirmed by PO

Network ← .... Project

Project monitor appointment confirmed by PO

Reporting and monitoring

Programme communications committee ← .... Outputs, exploitation and dissemination ← .... At programme and project levels

Approval of final report ← .... Final payments made

'Social and economic life happens in surprising places. As communities' appropriate space for their own use, interesting things begin to happen. UrbanBuzz is interested in how we allow people to create innovative, creative, culturally exciting forms of urban development in their communities' Professor Alan Penn, UCL

projects. In all, three calls for proposals were held. The final call included an 'adventurous' category in which the level of funding was considerably less than for the previous two funding rounds, and the risks much higher.

Proposals had to clearly identify their proposed networks of business and innovation fellows, and cite which barriers to sustainable communities their proposal was addressing. They were also required to complete a 'project resource spreadsheet' (PRS) giving detailed costings and showing where 'contributions in kind' (CIK) were offered, as UrbanBuzz had pledged to raise £1.69 million CIK.

All calls were communicated to website registrants who then were invited to submit an idea online – 385 of these were received and remain fully searchable on the UrbanBuzz website. All project ideas remain accessible such that collaboration – even outside of UrbanBuzz – opportunities can be harnessed by anyone.

Once a project idea had been posted on the website for at least 10 working days, and the proposers intended to progress to a final submission, the proposal was 'upgraded' to a notice of 'intention to submit'.

All information remained fully accessible and available to those seeking to collaborate. The actual proposals were submitted via online forms, and could be updated any time prior to the deadline.

Post deadline, proposals were checked for basic compliance and then assigned to an evaluator. The process of selecting evaluators was complex. Following a 'call for evaluators', around 45 were shortlisted.

A process involving keywords and algorithms was used to provide the best 'fit', in addition to taking other factors such as potential conflicts of interest into account. In most cases, three evaluators were assigned to each project,

and all remained anonymous to each other and to the proposers.

The evaluation process involved both collective examination-style assessment sessions and reflective electronic review.

The evaluation process itself was both quantitative and qualitative. Once a ranking list emerged, a Proposal Evaluation Panel comprising Programme Board members further considered each project's merits and noted issues for further clarification.

In the few cases where such issues could not be resolved by negotiation, a hearing was held to clarify the way forward.

Particularly important aspects of the reviews were value for money and risk profiles. UrbanBuzz was releasing 'risk capital', but did not intend to fund the progress of any new 'product' to market.

UrbanBuzz thus established a 'tipping point' with several projects, at which the project's financial risk had been reduced to levels that could reasonably attract investors/adopters of the proposed technology (see page 18).

The final option, used only once, was for higher-cost projects to make a presentation to the Programme Board, for further review.

Once a project had been recommended for funding, and 27 fell into this category, the project moved forward to contract stage. All potential fellows were required to register on the website, taking the total to around 360 from more than 150 organisations.

A project monitor, representing the Programme Office, was assigned to each project and, where deemed necessary due to particularly complex subject characteristics, independent expert assistance was enlisted to provide support.

The projects were monitored on an ongoing basis, with funding released in stages relating to performance and delivery.

Spreading the word: the outreach phase

The final stages of the project saw a shift towards the development of education and training material, and the dissemination of project outputs to relevant stakeholders. For some projects, this meant a series of workshops sharing practical advice. For others, it meant the testing and evaluation of software tools and associated training programmes. All projects were encouraged to address a portfolio of dissemination mechanisms, in particular conference papers, professional and trade journals and local and national press.

The issue of 'outreach' in all its forms was recognised as a critical activity. A Programme Communications Committee (PCC) worked closely with the Programme Board, incorporating key external consultants. Due to the back-loaded nature of the programme, many projects are generating their 'final' reports as the funding period ends. The project chapters (see page 76) detail how the latest information can be accessed (as do the project web pages on the UrbanBuzz website: www.urbanbuzz.org).

The overriding outreach objective was to secure active engagement in the legacy of each of the 27 projects. This meant connecting practitioners and others with an interest in sustainable communities with project outputs and outcomes, so ensuring that momentum will be preserved. Outcomes arising from projects will continue to be associated with the UrbanBuzz brand, which represents quality and probity, and will be seen as valuable additions to the toolkits of those involved in regeneration and development at all levels.

The legacy: the spirit lives on

UCL made it very clear in its original bid that UrbanBuzz has been devised as an 'impact' programme, concentrating resources on supporting projects for its two-year lifespan. Inevitably, however, there are strong pressures for a more enduring network coming from those involved. At the same time, it is clear that the majority of the projects have created sustainable networks that will see their work continue via stakeholders and partners.

The ABUNDANCE urban agriculture plot, for example, will be developed further by project partners Transition Towns and groups of local residents. Other project teams have used the two years of UrbanBuzz funding to establish new tools and processes that only now, as the programme closes and funding ends, are being adopted into real-world workflows: the CARBONBUZZ online platform, for example, which enables architects to benchmark and monitor actual energy performance in buildings, is attracting new users with each week that passes.

Both UCL and UEL recognise the potential value of the human and virtual networks created by UrbanBuzz, as well as its many outputs (see page 30 for more on the UrbanBuzz networks). At the time of writing, dialogue with interested parties regarding the UrbanBuzz legacy continued. Commission for Architecture and the Built Environment (CABE), the Academy of Urbanism, the Sustainable Development Commission, the British Urban Regeneration Association (BURA), Urban Design London, the Greater London Authority (GLA), London Sustainability Exchange, CITB-ConstructionSkills and other professional institutions are exploring ways in which they can 'endorse' UrbanBuzz's various outputs.

The new UK Homes and Community Agency (HCA), led by Sir Bob Kerslake, incorporates the former Academy for Sustainable Communities and is developing the HCA Academy as the place where knowledge, skills and capacity existing within the housing and regeneration sector comes together. 'We want to use our substantial resources to raise the game across the country. The key is for us to invest in transferring knowledge and skills through the HCA Academy, which I believe can be a very powerful transmission mechanism for learning, including that which has come from UrbanBuzz,' says Sir Bob. 'I think that some of the UrbanBuzz outcomes would be an extremely good fit. It's particularly important at this difficult time that we build on existing learning.'

Finally, during 2009, UCL will be launching its Research Grand Challenges – one with the title 'Sustainable Cities'. It is entirely serendipitous that UrbanBuzz should draw to a close in the start-up phase to this major new UCL initiative which will embrace cross-faculty collaborations in addressing global issues in the built environment. Over in east London, UEL will be seeking to build on partnerships developed during UrbanBuzz projects, and aims to participate actively in the proposed Thames Gateway Institute for Sustainability.

'The key is for us to invest in transferring knowledge and skills through the HCA Academy, which I believe can be a very powerful transmission mechanism for learning, including that from UrbanBuzz. Some of the UrbanBuzz outcomes would be an extremely good fit. It's particularly important at this difficult time that we build on existing learning' **Sir Bob Kerslake, HCA**

‹ Tina Crombie
Projects coordination
'I supported the project monitors, liaised with the external evaluator and contributed to outreach activities. I've led negotiations with consortia to help UrbanBuzz minimise its risk exposure and, at the same time, capture the most value from each project. ›

‹ David Cobb
Programme Director
'I have created a temporary operational and governance infrastructure to evaluate, deliver and communicate UrbanBuzz's diverse portfolio of new tools and processes. We have focused on those who will benefit most from the UrbanBuzz outputs and outcomes. ›

The greatest challenge for me has been stepping back during busy periods and applying foresight in order to "tool-up" for the continually changing skill-sets required in managing and supporting the central aims and outputs of the programme.'

The UrbanBuzz team
The six-strong Programme Office team supported the 27 projects and handled programme management and administration

LOWCARB4REAL (page 146), for example, has engaged people across the construction cycle and worked out where influence and training is needed for low carbon buildings. RETILE (page 172) has provided a framework for evaluation that will pervade a national regeneration charity. These outcomes are brilliant, real and wonderful to be part of.'

**< Chris Anderson
Project monitor**
'Based at the University of East London, I was the project monitor for 13 UrbanBuzz projects, responsible for supporting, monitoring and providing guidance for the project teams and ensuring their successful delivery. >

Working on such a wide variety of projects has been challenging and rewarding. The MCSC project (page 154) has engaged local community groups, and it was great to see the enthusiasm and pride in the work shown by the people involved.'

**< Daniel Gilbert
Marketing coordination**
'I worked on all aspects of marketing UrbanBuzz at a programme level, for example using the website, www.urbanbuzz.org, regular e-newsletters, events, posters and written materials. Getting the message right in the first place, and then effectively >

communicated, was a key part of my role. I have a background in regeneration and worked in this field for nearly 10 years at UEL. I think the partnership between UCL and UEL, two very different universities offering contrasting but complementary strengths, is one of the most interesting and fruitful aspects of the UrbanBuzz programme.'

**< Gemma Moore
Project monitor**
'I was responsible for supporting, monitoring and providing guidance for projects funded within the programme. I worked on the programme part-time, also working as a research fellow at The Bartlett School of Graduate Studies, University College London. >

Despite the numerous challenges that come with effective collaboration, many of the projects have created new, fruitful partnerships. It has been a pleasure to support the development of these relationships over the life of the programme.'

**< Jon Davis
Administrator and
project monitor**
'As the programme administrator, I have been responsible for budgeting and payment, and have acted as project monitor for four projects. It has been great to work with teams who are so keen to take their work forward. >

For instance, the MOBILISING KNOWLEDGE team (page 164) has done convincing work and is in a position to take its ideas on consultation with older people forward as part of much wider "no voice goes unheard" training initiative with Lewisham council.'

The Oxford Institute for Sustainable Development (OISD) was appointed to evaluate UrbanBuzz due to its pre-eminent expertise and knowledge in the field of urban sustainability and sustainable development. OISD reviewed and assessed:

01 performance in relation to the achievement of sustainability objectives, based on a fundamental appraisal of the impact of the projects and the programme;

02 the effectiveness of knowledge transfer and exchange, requiring stakeholder engagement and courses, tools and media activity appropriate to the subject matter and the target groups for engagement;

03 the effectiveness of programme processes, such as the commissioning of projects and operation of the network, as with regards probity and performance.

OISD provided evaluation plans for projects, monitored project progress and reported on a regular basis to the Programme Board. Through relationships established with the UrbanBuzz Programme Office and with project participants, this work formed a vital part of the programme.

Professor Alan Penn, UCL, the lead academic for UrbanBuzz, recognised at the time of proposal to HEFCE for initial funding that knowledge is transferred by people, working together to solve problems. Trust and understanding is fundamental to such collaborative working, and one of best ways to encourage this is for the programme itself to foster transparency and probity in all its dealings. The appointment of an independent evaluator was part of this mission.

'The evaluation is very much to do with the projects' contribution to environmental, social, environmental and economic sustainability and governance,' says Dr Carol Dair, principal OISD evaluator. 'Knowledge transfer and knowledge exchange is key. One of the successes of UrbanBuzz has been to break down knowledge silos between professionals and universities, and between professional groups. It has brought them together to share understanding.'

Capturing knowledge

In finalising evaluation frameworks (see Sustainability evaluation framework opposite) OISD, the programme office and project teams worked together to ensure that not only were project methods likely to be effective, but that evidence of activity and efficacy could be captured. This allowed reflection and learning on the part of the project groups.

Dair communicated regularly with project coordinators during the two-year programme, encouraging them to discuss and refine their draft evaluation criteria. 'UrbanBuzz was all about overcoming barriers to sustainability knowledge transfer,' she says. 'Of interest to OISD is both the content (and quality) of the sustainable development knowledge being transferred, and also the processes (methods and strategies) needed for successful knowledge transfer.'

To assess each project, OISD established a generic evaluation framework. This was designed to enable projects to capture aspects of sustainability and knowledge exchange, and to report progress in a flexible, but structured, manner. The framework is made up of five sustainability principles and a knowledge transfer principle. The five sustainability principles are:

01 living within environmental limits;
02 ensuring a strong, healthy and just society;
03 achieving a sustainable economy;
04 promoting good governance;
05 using sound science.

Monitoring progress, probity and transparency
The Higher Education Funding Council for England required all projects funded under their Higher Education Innovation Fund 3 scheme to be subjected to independent external evaluation

Sustainability evaluation framework

Five key sustainability principles to be addressed by projects: outlined by OISD

Living within environmental limits	Ensuring a strong, healthy and just society	Achieving a sustainable economy	Promoting good governance	Using sound science	Principles
Respecting the limits of the planet's environment, resources and biodiversity – to improve our environment and ensure that the natural resources needed for life are unimpaired and remain so for future generations.	Meeting the diverse needs of all people in existing and future communities, promoting personal well-being, social cohesion and inclusion and creating equal opportunity.	Building a strong, stable and sustainable economy that provides prosperity and opportunities for all, and in which environmental and social costs fall on those who impose them (polluter pays), and efficient resource use is incentivised.	Actively promoting effective, participative systems of governance at all levels of society – engaging people's creativity, energy and diversity.	Ensuring policy is developed and implemented on the basis of strong scientific evidence, whilst taking into account scientific uncertainty, as well as public attitudes and values.	Criteria/considerations
UrbanBuzz projects have: created an online carbon monitoring tool for architectural practices; provided policy makers with low-carbon transport strategies for London; introduced urban agriculture to urban green spaces; enabled a monitoring process for the energy performance of a renovated 'low energy' Victorian home.	UrbanBuzz projects have: established an online searchable database of resources to raise awareness of gender issues in the built environment; increased urban designers' and planners' knowledge about the needs of old and young people through specialised training activities; provided planning authorities with computer modelling systems and up-to-date data to help that will help them target social infrastructure provision and reduce anti-social behaviour.	UrbanBuzz projects have: established an online cross-cutting mega-network (combining job seekers, employers and an environmental network) that has improved the environmental performance of some small and medium enterprises and has helped disadvantaged jobseekers; created a student internship scheme resulting in several students being offered permanent positions with employers.	UrbanBuzz projects have: brought together practitioners, professionals and academics in projects that have broken down many institutional barriers, especially between planning authorities and universities. Community participation was a key focus for several projects. A great deal has been learnt about which engagement strategies are effective and under what circumstances, and which are not.	UrbanBuzz projects have: ensured that they used reliable data sources and validated data so as to be fit for purpose; referred to expert advice and verification, and applied recognised methodologies. For many projects, the object was to bring experts together in appropriate forums or to post expert information to accessible platforms. Reliable data sources, for example Ordnance Survey data and London borough FLARE data, have been used and manipulated by academic and practitioner experts.	Examples of application

Evaluation criteria selected (in the form of sustainability objectives)

For each sustainability principle, project teams worked with OISD to determine a set of meaningful sustainability objectives. For instance, the REBOPSE team, considering the principle 'living within environmental limits', selected the following sustainability objective: to improve awareness of green issues including resource and biodiversity constraints, and to foster the sharing of knowledge and understanding.

Indicators: meeting sustainability objectives

The REBOPSE team identified sustainability indicator(s) including: deployment of a cross-cutting green network; absorption between linked networks; number of supported connections and new and sustained network membership. During the project, the team gathered data that would indicate whether the objectives were being met: REBOPSE monitored the numbers of new network members, the number of connections and the length of connections.

The framework also includes a series of example evaluation criteria designed to provide suggestions as to how each principle can be met. These took the form of 'objectives'.

Unlike tick-box approaches to measurement and assessment, objectives offer the flexibility to work with evaluation criteria that are meaningful at the local community scale, and appropriate for each project. This was important given the scale and range of facets of sustainability addressed by the projects.

Two examples from project evaluation frameworks demonstrate how different project teams selected different sustainability objectives under the 'living within environmental limits' sustainability principle:

LSTS: elected to minimise the use of resources involved in delivering the project;

VIBAT: elected to address climate change through reducing carbon emissions, and to provide low-carbon realistic and viable emissions transport strategies based on a range of potential transport-related policy packages for London.

Knowledge transfer principle

The knowledge transfer principle aimed to ensure that barriers to knowledge and communication are minimised, and that 'silo thinking' is avoided. In this way, evaluation by OISD goes to the heart of the UrbanBuzz programme. Knowledge transfer and exchange applies to all activities, involving the exchange of information, the direction of flow, and the general content with respect to sustainability.

A knowledge exchange objective for the REBOPSE project team, for example, was to expand sustainable development knowledge transfer and knowledge exchange. The team intended to meet this challenge by holding a number of events to raise awareness and interest amongst employee and volunteering organisations and jobseekers in joining a social network. Each event provided information on the capabilities and advantages of the network.

Flexibility and innovation

OISD felt that giving project groups the freedom to define the nature of their contribution to building sustainable communities and knowledge transfer would encourage innovation and new thinking. The project groups were asked to draw up evaluation plans, using the generic framework as a guide, but based on the actual activities they planned to undertake during the

lifetime of the project. The project groups were also asked to advise OISD as to which supporting evidence they planned to include in the evaluation process. Once agreed upon, the plans then formed the basis for future reporting on progress.

The evaluation was designed to be enabling and open-minded. Project teams were encouraged to highlight areas of innovation, and of speculative and/or new thinking that they saw as being important to their project activity. For example, within the MCSC project, Muki Haklay of UCL and Chris Church of London21 proposed the production of an online GIS-based 'planning' map of east London and the Thames Gateway. Achieving this meant engaging people in the development of four local maps, and building their skills and confidence around the planning process and their use of ICT.

Evaluation processes in this case supported a reflective approach to the assessment of a range of engagement strategies. The team agreed to describe the engagement strategies, the responses and type of respondents to each, and to provide reflections on how effective each

approach turned out to be. OISD was interested to learn about what did not work, as well as what did, and this kind of framework encouraged the reporting of participant feedback and practitioner reflections. Questionnaires used before and after workshops captured feedback on particular knowledge exchange aspirations, and their use was encouraged in many projects.

Measuring sustainability

The OISD approach to creating the evaluation criteria followed the internationally endorsed Bellagio Principles (IISD, 1987) for the measurement and assessment of progress towards sustainability (see *Resources* at the end of this article for more information).

Setting the conceptual boundaries for 'sustainability' was the next step. OISD favoured a sustainability evaluation that is commonly understood and, although not without controversy, is widely used in Britain. The 'quadruple bottom line' met these criteria and was adopted. It encapsulates environmental sustainability, social advancement, economic prosperity and institutional sustainability, and

'Evaluation is to do with each project's contribution to sustainability. This includes not only the environment, but also social, environmental and economic sustainability and governance. Knowledge transfer and exchange is key. One of the successes of UrbanBuzz has been to break down knowledge silos between professionals and universities, and between professional groups. It has brought them together to share understanding'
Dr Carol Dair, The Oxford Institute for Sustainable Development (OISD)

forms the basis of the UK Government's sustainability policy (see SOSEFRA, 2005).

A rich information mix

OISD took an initial assessment of the expected sustainability contribution arising from the projects. This assessment is shown in the graph below. Firstly, it became clear that there were differences between project groups in grasping evaluation requirements. Some teams found the process troublesome; others found it useful. OISD concluded that the most effective way forward was to agree the proposed plan with each project group through discussion.

Secondly, it took time for some project teams to grasp the importance of providing information on *processes* – such as ways of engaging people in projects – as well as *outcomes*. The engagement strategies used were of interest to OISD, as part of the effectiveness of knowledge exchange, and so knowledge relating to processes was as important as any 'hard' data.

For example, the LSTS project established a network for sustainable development knowledge transfer, comprising students and employers interested in brokered internships. Activities within the network included a continuously modified recruitment strategy, interactive events for network members, a bulletin for network members, a range of communication channels for all partners including the web, email, telephone and a website, and an LSTS Facebook group. There were clear forms, guidelines and procedures for both students and employers. Valuable detail on the process and effectiveness of all these initiatives was captured by this flexible evaluation, in addition to the usual hard data such as the number of network members engaged.

While some projects may have found a tick-box approach to reporting easier, the rich information of the process element would not have been captured. Collectively, the projects have provided a comprehensive source of evidence on which engagement strategies work, those that are less successful and which circumstances support engagement.

The final assessment of the projects has yet to take place. However, there is clear evidence that all have helped to overcome knowledge barriers between professionals.

The overall conclusion is that, despite problems and given the programme's short time-span, the results have been, and continue to be, surprisingly good. Professor Mike Jenks, OISD evaluation team leader, is pleased with progress to date: 'This has been a very successful programme. We've been extremely impressed with the way that it has developed, and encouraged that such a complex programme has worked.'

OISD plans to publish a review of the evaluation during 2009, highlighting particular examples of good practice. For information on updates, please visit www.urbanbuzz.org.

Resources
IISD (International Institution for Sustainable Development). Complete Bellagio Principles International Institution for Sustainable Development, 1997.
http://www.iisd.org/measure/principles/progress/bellagio_full.asp
SOSEFRA (Secretary of State for the Environment, Food and Rural Affairs). The UK Government Sustainable Development Strategy; Securing the Future London: The Stationery Office, 2005.

How the combined UrbanBuzz projects approached sustainable development (SD) and knowledge transfer (KT) objectives

● combined SD and KT relative approaches tackled by projects

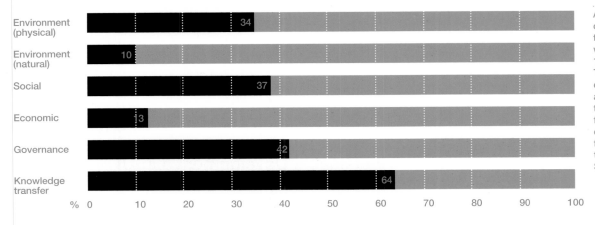

All of the possible objectives under each of the SD and KT principles were combined to give 100% for each principle. This graph shows the combined relative approaches tackled by the 27 projects. Clearly, far more emphasis was directed towards KT, and fewer objectives tackled the natural environment SD principle (source: OISD)

'UrbanBuzz has been about creating networks,' says Professor Alan Penn, UCL, the programme's lead academic. 'We recognised that universities are well-engaged with their disciplinary groups across the built environment sector, but that engagement tends to be vertical,' he says. 'It goes from the architecture faculty to the architectural practice; from the engineering faculty to engineering firms. We set out to create networks that do something quite different.'

UrbanBuzz has been about crossing barriers to sustainability. It has brought 'unusual suspects' from industry, local authorities, the voluntary sector and academia together, and enabled them to work collaboratively across barriers. 'We've been collaborating as a network of fellows,' says Penn. 'The success of UrbanBuzz will be the sustainability of these diverse networks, or "communities", that it has brought together.'

Creating such collaborative networks, and keeping the developing UrbanBuzz community interested and engaged, presented a significant challenge. UrbanBuzz focused on bringing two types of people together: business fellows (from the academic world) and innovation fellows (from the world beyond academia). Their 'fellow' titles were designed to encourage new activitiy, free from the limitations of expert labels and narrow professional competencies. All fellows ›

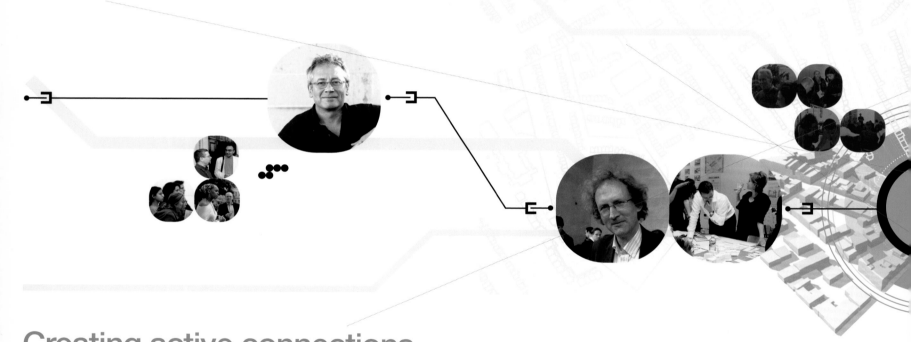

Creating active connections
During its two-year programme, UrbanBuzz brought together a diverse range of professionals, academics and communities through its website, its programme of events and its project activity, creating strong and active online and offline networks

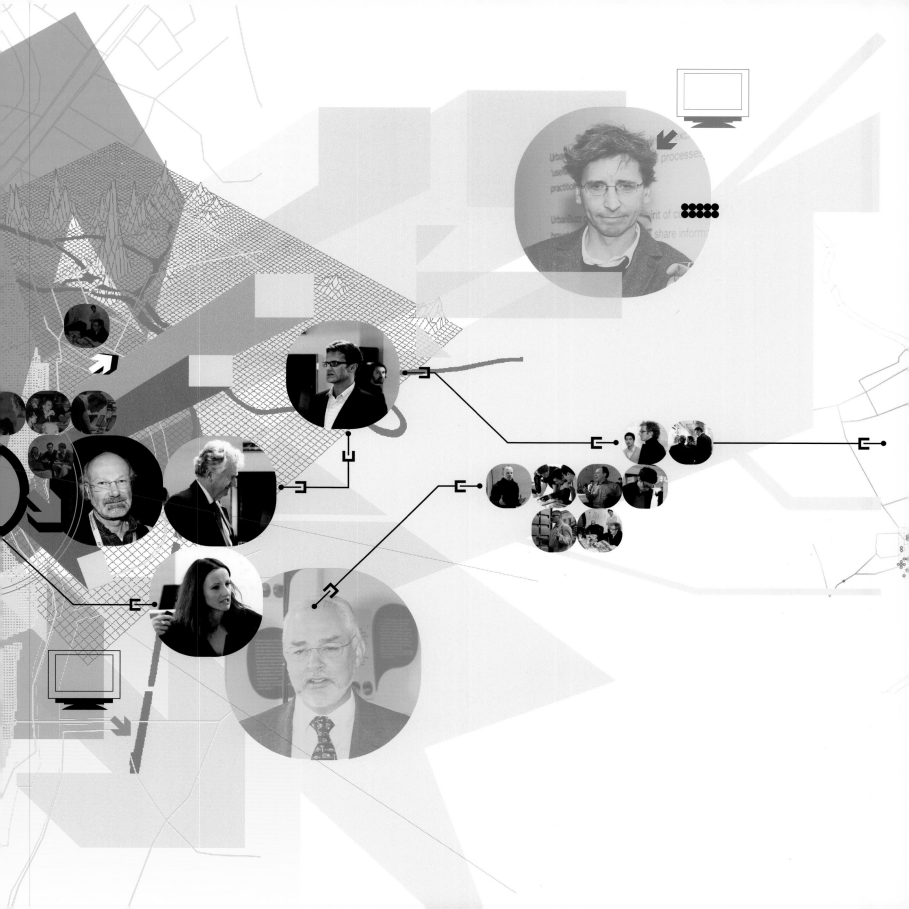

'The network that we've built up keeps growing; it now tops 800 and we haven't done any active recruitment. Our highly interactive events have been key to this success. We've brought students and professionals together at events and now, not only do we have a student network, we have a professional network too. These networks continue to interact and this helps both groups to define their skills and sustainability agendas, as well as to keep sustainability on the radar'

Kirsty Balmer, LSTS project coordinator

were required to register on the programme website, where they could characterise their interests and outline what they were seeking in terms of potential collaborators or associates.

In creating such active networks, UrbanBuzz sought to capitalise on the internet and the capabilities of virtual networking. The internet was regarded from the beginning as an active communications channel, rather than a simple information repository.

Encouraging online collaboration

An online network of 3,000 registered UrbanBuzz members has been created. Although not large by the standards of commercial social networking sites, the level of interest indicates that professionals and academics are keen to get involved with the work of building sustainable communities.

Independent research was conducted on the website, particularly with respect to its social networking usage. Initially, this feature of the website was created to bring together potential collaborators. During the three bidding rounds, users wishing to submit bids were required to do so on an open, collaborative basis via the website. Bidders were required to publicise their proposal ideas online prior to submission, with a view to attracting additional contributors.

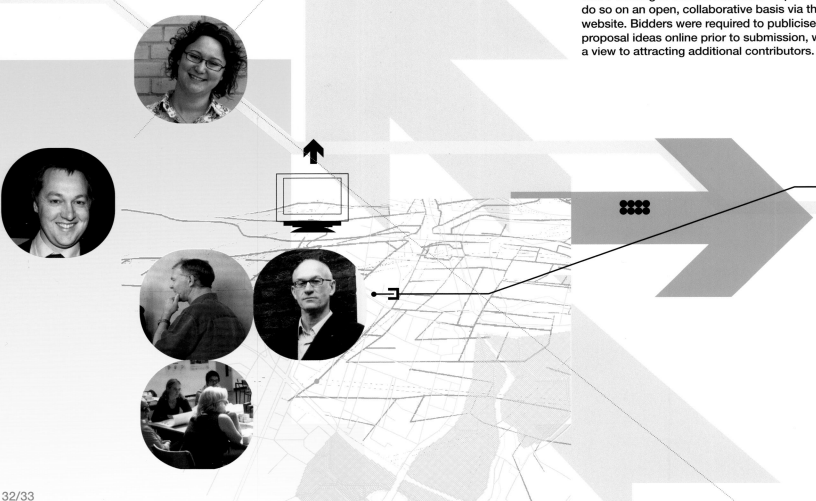

The independent research examined how the online networking facility was used as the programme developed. The qualitative research findings were fed back at regular stages during the programme's lifetime, and provided an invaluable evidence base to inform the programme's website management. Google Analytics provide quantitative data on web hits and website usage patterns.

Predictably, the statistics showed that usage of the site peaked in the phases prior to the three calls for funding. Outside of these periods, most visitors to the website were seeking the timing and location of events.

It had been hoped that those linked into the network would create an active forum for discussion around building sustainable communities, inputting as well as accessing information. Regrettably, no such active online forum developed following the funding phase. As the projects developed, project teams reported pressure on time and resources for updating online communication or online networking, resulting in the network becoming increasingly passive. A second force for change was user feedback, as part of a growing appreciation of what was working well for the developing community – and what was not.

Establishing a web portal

From January 2008, the website was managed as an information hub, linking to project websites and blogs, and with the facility for users to post comments. An e-newsletter kept members updated on programme and project level progress. Other, established sites such as YouTube were also used to spread news and information on UrbanBuzz projects, with video content uploaded to YouTube linking back to the UrbanBuzz website. Several project videos found sizable audiences within the established YouTube viewership, and were taken up and distributed to websites around the globe.

Active doing: bringing people together

It was an UrbanBuzz objective that its online networks be supported by networking events – both during and after the two years of funded UrbanBuzz programme activity. A key legacy of UrbanBuzz will be the networks or 'communities' it has brought together.

UrbanBuzz was about activity; it was created for 'active doing' that increased the knowledge and mutual understanding of everyone with an interest in building sustainable communities. As the projects progressed and began holding seminars and workshops for their partners, at the same time supporting other project events and making presentations at relevant external events, the level of 'active doing' grew. The programme's networking focus increasingly developed a practical knowledge-sharing focus. UrbanBuzz was involved centrally in at least 60 events, not including those organised at project level. The six-week UrbanBuzz Showcase (see page 36), held at central London's The Building Centre, played a key role in exposing new audiences to innovative thinking on sustainable communities, and the final conference (see page 40) brought key industry leaders together to discuss the reality of creating sustainable communities with UrbanBuzz project teams.

More than 800 people attended 10 major UrbanBuzz-organised events, aimed at a range of student, academic, public, private and third sector audiences.

The many individuals and organisations involved with UrbanBuzz have helped to break new ground, and have created a blueprint for future initiatives of this kind. Already, across the UK, the success of UrbanBuzz is inspiring universities, colleges and professional bodies to team up with public and private partners for the purpose of creating new ways of doing things. The UrbanBuzz website will remain online, ensuring that the programme's information hub remains active: www.urbanbuzz.org.

Page views: 62,907
Unique visits: 44,259
Web visits took place during week days, with the website registering around 170 unique visits on any given week day. Site usage peaked in March 2008 at 500 unique visits per week day, due to the online ESP-SIM competition

89 per cent of visits are from the UK
2 per cent are from the USA
1 per cent are from Italy, followed by France, Holland, Portugal, India, Russia, Australia and Canada in close order. Visitors came from 105 countries in total

The five most popular project pages on the site, in terms of visits, are:
01 LEVH
02 ABUNDANCE
03 ESP-SIM
04 FEfUR
05 GBE

'We were able to find potential collaborators through the online network, connecting with new colleagues to build our team. We formed a team with a better range of academic, business and technology skills to create a winning bid. It was a very effective system'
Dan Brown, project coordinator, REBOPSE

Wikis, websites and social networks: how the projects connected

Each of the 27 project teams has built up internal and external networks, using various channels and strategies. In several cases, teams came together to discuss cross-project issues. The project teams involved in spatial analysis and mapping, for example, met several times to discuss emerging common themes such as data accessibility and data consistency. Improvements to data quality and accessibility, the project teams agreed, could be greatly beneficial to researchers and policymakers working in the sustainability field. These common findings led to the creation of a paper on data access in the UK, a version of which is published on page 52.

The SSSP team used a wiki to support such collaborative discussions, and it became 'instrumental for communication between the project partners', says project coordinator Paul Coates (see page 184). 'A number of project activities have taken place or been agreed via the wiki, including establishing parameters for the simulations, and setting out all the data for discussion in one place.'

Creating active social networks
REBOPSE is addressing sustainability by widening access to employment opportunities for the socially excluded and disadvantaged (see page 168). 'Our aim is to support a sustainable economy using a social networking model,' says project coordinator Dan Brown. 'We worked with "green" networks because research and experience suggests that these are particularly strong.'

Green networks, says Brown, are densely populated, independent and range across socio-economic divides. The project's Green Maniac social networking website has registered 149 jobless people and 148 businesses. It appears evident from the activity on Green Maniac that the virtual network was active and vibrant in cases when people had something to gain from network activity, and there were opportunities for personal communications.

The project team collected data on 15,335 socially excluded workless individuals, primarily in Camden, north London. The project has successfully engaged these individuals, using personal email contacts and follow-up phone calls, with businesses and voluntary programmes, through both the online network and offline volunteering opportunities.

'People who have been without jobs for a long time might be richly connected to other people,' says project partner Sue Batty from UCL. 'But usually the people they're connected with are exactly the same as them. Our idea is to get jobless people to connect with people who do have jobs and opportunities.

'The volunteering sessions bring the jobless into contact with people who have opportunities. We've already seen cases where trust builds through voluntary work – employers tell us that they are more confident about offering somebody a job after seeing them working in a voluntary situation,' says Batty.

The network members are actively engaged in environmental activities, such as street cleaning, graffiti removal and helping out at green events. The project's most successful event so far has been the Camden Green Fair. 'We provided hundreds of volunteers, and made a huge impact, both on the event and on our network members. It's been a triumph for us,' says Brown.

The participants were also enthusiastic about the event. One commented: 'I would love to take part in events like these more often, plus it's great experience to put on your CV.'

Networking to spread sustainability
The LSTS project (see page 150) has developed a network that supports London's sustainability agenda by connecting students from all academic disciplines with opportunities for sustainability-related internships. The network has registered almost 730 students and 46 organisations offering internships, and has consistently grown since the start of the project. It now promotes key sustainability factors to employers and potential employees across the south-east.

London Sustainability Exchange (LSx), the project coordinator, has supported the network by providing individual responses to applications for internships. A total of 20 placements have been offered. The students were recruited initially through freshers' fairs, events, university liaison departments and, importantly, word of mouth. LSTS created a Facebook group, but, to date, only 24 people are signed up and the site is used primarily to post information.

Monthly e-bulletins, produced by network members, raise key issues of sustainability across the network. Students have contributed positive reports, detailing ways in which the internship experience has helped them with research work and job-seeking, or simply added to their knowledge of the sustainability issues facing London and the region.

Several students have reported that the network has helped them to develop partnerships with the 'real world', helping to bridge the gap between academic knowledge and practical skills.

The GBE project
This focused on developing Gendersite (www.gendersite.org), a comprehensive online resource for gender and the built environment that will help the planning and development community to create inclusive environments that meet the needs of both women and men (see page 130). To avoid the need to develop expensive online functionality, GBE used existing Web 2.0 service SurveyMonkey to carry out a baseline survey to measure professional knowledge on issues regarding gender and the built environment, to be followed up by susbsequent surveys after the Gendersite launch. SurveyMonkey is an open source questionnaire tool, used by a variety of organisations (mostly academic).

The survey results, following the site launch, suggest that it may be helping to inform users about gender and built environment issues: on the second survey, 59.4 per cent of respondents thought that women experienced the built environment differently from men, compared to 42.2 per cent for the first survey.

The ESP-SIM project
This set out to define a viable model of Enabled Self Procurement housing delivery concept, and to create a virtual world for testing and progressing the concepts (see page 120). To populate the virtual world, the Royal Institute of British Architects (RIBA) supported an open design competition for 'pattern book' housing designs.

The RIBA and the ESP project team encouraged the public to vote on the UrbanBuzz website for their preferred schemes. Registration details were taken from hundreds of voters, many of whom remained active members of the UrbanBuzz community for the duration of the programme.

Creating networks that really work: what can we learn from UrbanBuzz?

There is little doubt that the UrbanBuzz website successfully encouraged active collaboration during the initial proposals process. Indeed, several project submissions, notably that of REBOPSE, were put together via the website by people who had never previously met, and who benefited greatly from the different competencies that were consequently focused on the original idea. 'We were able to find potential collaborators through the online network, connecting with new colleagues to build our team,' says Dan Brown, project coordinator, REBOPSE. 'We formed a team with a better range of academic, business and technology skills to create a winning bid. It was a very effective system.'

From February 2008 onwards, and against quite different yardsticks, the UrbanBuzz website proved successful as a communications hub, keeping project teams, UrbanBuzz members and the wider public up to date on programme and project development. The popular e-newsletter was being circulated weekly by autumn 2008, and the YouTube experiment, with short project videos uploaded to the video-sharing website, while limited in the number of projects participating, was helping to raise awareness of project activity internationally.

Research at the programme's outset might have identified the 'disconnect' between social networking aspirations, so prominent at the start of the programme, and the lack of appetite for this type of service from its users.

In terms of harnessing the power of real and virtual networks, the programme team has drawn several conclusions:

01 Successful online strategies require dedicated resource, and programme teams without these specific skillsets will need to outsource to an organisation for which online communications is a core requirement – and to dedicate time and effort to the brief and selection of any partner.

02 UrbanBuzz attempted the outsourcing route, but quickly realised that the choice of online partner also requires a serious investment of resource in terms of initial research, brief and selection process. The gap between the team's expectations and the delivery offered by the selected company was, in this case, unmanageable, due to lack of clarity in the brief and poor response on the part of the webmaster partner. The programme responded by scaling down the functionality of the website, and by using effective and free Web 2.0 applications such as SurveyMonkey, with links to the UrbanBuzz website, to perform key tasks.

03 Know your likely audiences. Are they known for being active social networkers? If not, do you have the resource, skills and platform to encourage them to become so?

04 Use appropriate communication and delivery channels for the information to be communicated. Even potentially useful information may not be welcome if it is made available using inappropriate means.

05 Virtual contacts frequently need to be supported with real-world interaction. A combination of proactive communications, interactive events, an interactive website/information hub and the ability to connect to, and make use of, existing web tools and services is a useful starting point.

'The bad news is that we build the worst, smallest, most expensive houses in Europe. The good news is that we've stopped!' With this wry comment, Tim Williams, Director of Navigant Consulting, former special advisor to Government minister David Miliband and a Homes and Communities agency strategist, launched the UrbanBuzz Showcase in October 2008.

The audience of more than 100 people was packed into the venue's 'Launchpad' space, home to the six-week UrbanBuzz exhibition and series of 25-plus free knowledge exchange events.

New thinking called for

Williams followed his black humour with a rallying call for new thinking in the creation of sustainable communities. 'There is a huge role for local authorities and the

Practical knowledge exchange: the UrbanBuzz Showcase

For six weeks in October and November 2008, the 27 UrbanBuzz projects were showcased at The Building Centre, central London. Several hundred professionals, academics, policy makers and practitioners visited the exhibition and took part in the 25-plus free seminars and knowledge-sharing events that supported it

Tim Williams (right): 'We should avoid the "build it and bugger off" model of speculative housing... This is not a moment for timidity'

Professor Tim Broyd (far right): 'The programme's challenge was not lack of policy but lack of coordination – to get the right knowledge where it can be channelled'

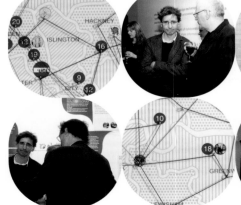

public sector moving forward,' he enthused. 'If the private sector doesn't want to take risks with land, we may move towards a leasehold and licensing approach, rather than selling freehold.' Williams derided the 'build it and bugger off' model of speculative housing popular in the UK, and suggested that we 'use our hold on land to have a better working relationship with the private sector, and a long-term engagement with the care and the management of a place'.

Appealing to the built environment professionals in the room, Williams suggested redoubled effort, more action and better results: 'As many as 223,000 households are forming in England every year. We are now producing 80,000 homes to be delivered by the end of 2008. The gap grows exponentially. There are one and a half million people on social housing waiting lists. There will probably be four million people on waiting lists in four years' time. This is not a moment for timidity.'

Project knowledge sharing

A key aim of the Showcase was to deliver practical knowledge sharing. Not all UrbanBuzz project outputs lend themselves to physical demonstrations but, using models, print, multimedia, seminars and discussion groups, the Showcase was able to communicate the emerging body of knowledge being developed by project teams, and enabled a comparative review of all 27 projects.

The Building Centre was chosen as the Showcase venue based on its appeal to practitioners and professionals responsible for delivering regeneration and development – verified by a weekly footfall of 2,000 visitors. During the six-week event, 16 knowledge-sharing sessions were run by 11 UrbanBuzz project teams, attracting hundreds of visitors from the public and private sectors.

Tim Williams' outspoken comments were echoed many times during this series of events. Several UrbanBuzz projects picked up on his views, for example ESP-SIM project coordinator Michael Kohn. At his Showcase event, Kohn emphasised both the demonstrable advantages of self-procured housing, and the degree to which it is under-valued in the UK compared to continental Europe.

Kohn's workshop on Enabled Self Procurement: a viable alternative for housing in the UK, enabled him finally to reach private-sector audiences. The response to his workshop, plus that to the ESP project's stand during the 2008 London Festival of Architecture, has confirmed that 'the psychological barriers to self-procurement are coming down', says Kohn. 'ESP offers a combination of community self-realisation, pragmatic use of off-the-shelf pattern book designs and a practical response to the › credit crisis which is afflicting speculative housing construction projects.'

The SCREAM project, led by UCL, focuses on media screens as a potential means of communication. The project team held several knowledge-sharing events at the Showcase, attended by a wide range of interested parties from the Arts Council, body>data>space, Art2Architecture, Live Sites, FACT, University of Salford and Smartslab. The in-depth debate focused on ways in which screens could support urban regeneration, or inhibit it by degrading the urban environment if handled insensitively, failing to include community-generated input and balanced content reflecting the diversity of any urban area.

Influencing the policymakers

The launch of the CARBONBUZZ online carbon emissions monitoring platform attracted a wide range of architects and engineers. The new tool was received warmly, and the positive audience response made it clear that CARBONBUZZ is well placed to influence the development of public energy policy.

Transport policy is another key area that UrbanBuzz targeted. The Showcase's VIBAT London project workshop focused on the project's interactive simulation model and findings with respect to transport in London, for instance the degree to which the effects of carbon emissions savings achieved in people's day-to-day transport choices could be wiped out by our increasing propensity to travel by airplane.

VIBAT project coordinator Dr Robin Hickman has run a number of VIBAT sessions over the two-year UrbanBuzz programme, often to over-subscribed audiences. However, the distinguishing factor in terms of the audience attracted to this VIBAT session was the high quality of interaction he achieved in this more intimate setting.

'There was a very good discussion with senior members from Commission for Architecture and the Built Environment (CABE), Transport for London (TfL) and the Greater London Authority (GLA) as to how VIBAT London might contribute to the capital's future policy development, and the depth of these discussions was greater in light of the tightness of the group,' said Hickman.'

Using models, print, multimedia, seminars and discussion groups, the Showcase was able to demonstrate the new tools and processes developed by the project teams

Working together

The Showcase spirit of collaboration was highlighted by Gayle Burgess, innovation fellow on the LSTS project team. Indeed, Burgess was one of many people to single out the way in which UrbanBuzz Showcase events had placed information about other projects 'up front and personal', with the net result that mutual understanding about project missions and achievements became widespread. This helped to forge a shared sense of purpose amongst project teams, and cohesion across the programme as a whole. This feeling was ably articulated by Judit Kimpian, CARBONBUZZ project coordinator. 'It has been a boon launching our project here in such familiar context, alongside the other UrbanBuzz projects. This creates a much more rounded story,' she said at the CARBONBUZZ launch event.

Joined-up development

A creeping change to the UK DNA is well under way in the form of suburban densification, all too often resulting from a series of separate developments, separately considered, whose combined impact on an area is overlooked. The result can be a decrease in the quality of life for local residents, and an understandable antipathy to the idea of development in their neighbourhood.

However, if urban areas are to operate efficiently, with housing located close to rail and other infrastructure, and any serious attempt is to be made to meet the UK's housing need, then suburban densification is something that simply has to happen.

In response to this key policy issue, UrbanBuzz ran a major seminar, 'Securing successful densification in our suburbs', during the Showcase event. Discussions at the seminar revolved around a key tension in planning policy between securing brownfield development through high-density infill and maintaining the character of existing suburban areas.

The seminar heard that various local planning authorities are carrying out characterisation studies. But, according to an analysis carried out by Bill Erikson from the University of Westminster,

few of these studies have been done in a way in which they usefully can be used to influence planning policy. An exception to this is a recent characterisation study carried out by the London Borough of Sutton, good practice that was discussed during the seminar.

At the end of the seminar, one attendee commented: 'I want to take all these presenters back home with me to sort out the mess we have in our deprived locality.'

Families: the litmus test?

The importance of community ties in the building of sustainable communities was recognised at the second major UrbanBuzz seminar held during the Showcase: 'Rethinking sustainable cities', a precursor to the UCL launch of the second 'Grand Research Challenge' focused on sustainable cities, due to begin around mid-2009. Many of the contributors to this seminar will be participating actively in helping UCL to address global issues impacting on the quality and design of urban communities.

A longstanding member of the UrbanBuzz community, Nick Gallent from the Bartlett School of Planning, quoting the London School of Economics' Anne Power, got the audience thinking from the outset: 'Families are the litmus test of whether a city is really working.' He went on to pose the following question: 'Is housing working for families, or have families been

forgotten as government pursues the efficient and effective use of land?' Gallent argued persuasively that, contrary to current practice, 'The starting point of residential development should not be a concern for land (density), but a concern for people and broader social objectives: work out what people (and communities) need and then think about how these needs can be met.'

Speakers at this event considered the complex and systemic problems facing the urban environment today, and focused on ways in which the latest urban and environmental research at UCL is contributing towards the building of sustainable cities and communities. This focus was chosen as a conscious echo of the UrbanBuzz final conference, 'The reality of creating sustainable communities' held in December 2008 (see page 40).

'Families are the litmus test of whether a city is really working. Is housing working for families, or have families been forgotten as government pursues the efficient and effective use of land?'
Nick Gallent, Bartlett School of Planning, UCL

The reality of creating sustainable communities

UrbanBuzz has confirmed that the academic world can work with private and public partners to create effective tools and processes to support the creation of inclusive societies. At the programme's final conference, an impressive selection of influential keynote speakers reflected on how partnership working will underpin sustainable communities

'The UrbanBuzz programme has been a major success, and has shown that the academic world can cooperate to organise an intense programme of activities across all sectors which interest our stakeholders,' said Dr Jean Venables, President of the Institution of Civil Engineers, and an UrbanBuzz Programme Board member. 'Perhaps', she asked, 'this is a new paradigm for public funding disbursement?'

Venables was speaking at the Westminster-based conference organised by UrbanBuzz as the programme's funded period drew to a close in December 2008. The conference had several aims: specifically, to bring outcomes and outputs from the 27 supported projects to the attention of those who could benefit from them, and to those who will develop and build on their initial work; and to communicate key learning from the programme relating to the demonstrable success of knowledge exchange and partnership working. Specifically, the event targeted, both in terms of speakers and delegates, the leaders and innovators who will be tasked with influencing, developing and implementing policy in the coming years.

UrbanBuzz has 'conclusively demonstrated the ability of a modern institution, such as UCL, to be outward-looking, agile and capable of engaging with a major social issue and with a multiplicity of partners,' said UCL's President and Provost Malcolm Grant. 'The outputs and outcomes from the UrbanBuzz projects,' he stressed, 'indicate that academia can create outputs and outcomes that are not only sustainable in name, but sustainable in reality.'

Professor Alan Penn, originator of UrbanBuzz, outlined the the programme's objectives. 'We recognised that while universities are well-engaged with their disciplinary groups across the built environment sector, engagement tends to be vertical,' says Penn. 'It tends to go from architecture to the architectural practice, or from engineering to engineering firms.

'UrbanBuzz has,' said Penn, 'overcome these barriers by bringing people together to work collaboratively on projects, by creating a "social network" to aid collaboration, and by creating a practical mechanism to engage non-academics in sustainability projects and their implementation.'

Several keynote speakers at the event discussed how the knowledge, skills and practices unlocked by UrbanBuzz through its partnership approach will contribute to creating the climate of social cohesion and innovation that investors, including the Government, require before large-scale regeneration can take place.

Conference speakers

01 Peter Bishop
Group Director, London Development Agency and University College London (UCL) Honorary Fellow

02 Professor Allan Brimicombe
Centre for Geo-Information Studies, University of East London

03 Professor Tim Broyd
Group Technology Director, Halcrow and Chair, UrbanBuzz Programme Board

04 Paul Finch
UCL Honorary Fellow and Editor, *Architectural Review*

05 Professor Malcolm Grant
President and Provost, UCL

06 Julian Hart
Lancefield Consulting

07 Sir Bob Kerslake
Chief Executive, Homes and Communities Agency

08 Professor Bob Lowe
Professor of Energy and Building Science, UCL

09 Roger Madelin
Joint Chief Executive of the Argent Group plc

10 Sir Simon Milton
Deputy Mayor of London

11 Gemma Moore
UCL and UrbanBuzz

12 Professor Alan Penn
The Bartlett Faculty of the Built Environment, UCL and UrbanBuzz lead academic

13 Sunand Prasad
President, Royal Institute of British Architects

14 Nick Raynsford MP
Deputy Chairman, Construction Industry Council

15 Matthew Taylor
Royal Society of Arts (RSA) Chief Executive

16 Dr Jean Venables OBE
President, Institution of Civil Engineers

The lunch break provided delegates with the opportunity to visit the UrbanBuzz Showcase in the ICE's impressive Great Hall. Paul Finch, UCL Honorary Fellow and editor of the *Architectural Review*, engaged delegates in conversation about the projects with several project fellows around the room. Edited highlights from this session are available to view from the multimedia section of www.urbanbuzz.org

The UrbanBuzz programme
The reality of creating sustainable communities

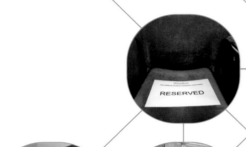

Roger Madelin outlined the ways in which the right socio-economic framework, including active local partnerships and plans for new jobs and training in the area, has been developed for the ongoing King's Cross regeneration, led by Argent plc. He focused on the need for a collective view that represents a wide range of local interests. 'Misinformation is the cancer of democracy,' Single interest groups often use misinformation to propagate particular issues. So we try to put the best, easily ascertainable information out into the public domain, involving a huge consultation process. I personally saw over 9,500 people. Over a two-year period, I got to understand a lot about the surrounding communities.'

Sir Bob Kerslake outlined HCA strategy. 'The HCA is an investment agency which will focus on a place-based approach, with bottom-up issues reconciling national targets with local ambition. Revenue investment will include addressing the skills base as part of a "single conversation", an ongoing dialogue in which challenges are shown "in the round" to reflect their inter-relationships – not their exclusivity.'

Kerslake reflected on where UrbanBuzz can make a contribution. 'The HCA Academy,' he said, 'built on the foundations of the former Academy for Sustainable Communities, will become a key resource for accessing learning and best practice across the housing/regeneration sector. The Academy's resources could improve and raise the game across the country, and be a source of development for the work undertaken by UrbanBuzz.'

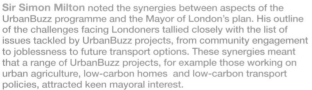

Sir Simon Milton noted the synergies between aspects of the UrbanBuzz programme and the Mayor of London's plan. His outline of the challenges facing Londoners tallied closely with the list of issues tackled by UrbanBuzz projects, from community engagement to joblessness to future transport options. These synergies meant that a range of UrbanBuzz projects, for example those working on urban agriculture, low-carbon homes and low-carbon transport policies, attracted keen mayoral interest.

Milton stressed the importance of cross-sector working. 'We are,' he said, 'going to unify the work done on the next mayoral transport strategy with the revisions to the London plan, so that the two are completely joined up. That may not sound like rocket science, but it will be the first time that that has been done, with both plans developed by teams of people working together in the same place.'

Nick Raynsford MP reminded the audience that place-shaping cannot be done by local authorities alone, stressing that partnerships are essential in order to deliver successful, mixed-use communities. He touched on another issue central to many UrbanBuzz projects – local authority democratic accountability. 'When we come to the creation of sustainable communities,' said Raynsford, 'we cannot operate within traditional silos, let alone replicate the socially divisive patterns of development which created rigid geographical divisions between separate uses and an almost apartheid separation of market from social housing. We now recognise the importance of supporting mixed communities and the importance of mixing different uses.'

'Issues relating to community empowerment also need attention,' he said. 'How do we mediate between the needs of developers, who understandably want faster and less bureaucratic planning procedures, and the concerns of local residents who, naturally and reasonably, want real opportunities for their views to be heard on development proposals?'

Edited highlights from keynote speakers at *The reality of creating sustainable communities* can be viewed online: visit www.urbanbuzz.org

Matthew Taylor addressed delegates on the issue of capacity. 'The prevailing economic downturn,' he suggested, 'means that capacity is going to diminish, both in the public and private sectors.' Indeed, Taylor observed that UrbanBuzz was created in a world looking towards long-term sustainability, and ends at a time in which short-term survival tops many agendas. The need to tap into the 'unused' capacity in civil society was now greater than ever before, he stressed. As communities become more disconnected due to the conflicting strains of demographics, tenure and changing lifestyles, social care needs are not being met and job losses arising from the downturn create 'unused' capacity that could be mobilised. The self-management of support services, in a way that mobilises this 'unused' civic capacity and leads to empowerment, could be an interesting way forward, he suggested.

Programmes such as UrbanBuzz have a role to play, he added, particularly in helping to develop new ways of engaging communities. 'Local authority self-serving opinion-polling and surveys should be replaced with time invested in action research, to find out what people really "do" rather than what they "think",' says Taylor. He noted that policymakers do not normally have the time to probe in this way whereas, as UrbanBuzz has shown via a number of projects, academics do.

When it comes to channelling this capacity effectively, several UrbanBuzz projects, for example ABUNDANCE, an urban agriculture project, have used the concept of a 'timebank'. This is a way of linking together pockets of hidden capacity, in this case, time and willingness on the part of local estate residents to grow food on their premises. Another example would be bringing together pupils 'alienated' from school due to their disruptive influences and learning difficulties, and partnering them with elderly people who cannot manage their gardens.

In generating the right kind of 'space' for these idealistic visions, collaboration is fundamental to progress, says Taylor. 'Bringing specialisms together to increase this kind of capacity is key – one more reason why UrbanBuzz has been so important'.

Peter Bishop noted that increasingly complex sets of variables – environment, energy and security – are facing designers. How do we negotiate decisions based on the growing number of factors in the planning and development mix, and how do we broker between the various interest groups? 'London is very much an urban centre created via brokerage and negotiation, rather than by grand planning,' he said. 'Our cities are, in many ways, shaped by the unintended consequences of policymaking rather than grand decisions.' The smoking ban and its unintended impact on creating a café society is a good example.

'Taking these complex variables into consideration, it's a complex political and social and environmental framework that we operate within,' said Bishop. Land ownership in particular adds complexity to the mix, with various dysfunctional parcels of London owned by different parties, so hindering the implementation of a clear vision across developments. 'The planning system in this country will maintain control and make sure that each of those developments is shaped,' he continued. 'But there's no mechanism at all for making the whole thing hang together.' The solution, he stressed, is yet another aspect of partnership working, including bringing landowners together with local authorities, practitioners and construction industry stakeholders.

Sunand Prasad referred to recent visions for the UK's ecotowns, and captured their essence as being 'not about top-down micro-management and design variety, but about political leadership, integrated investment, planning and delivery, and involvement of urban populations in the co-production of new spaces'. Prasad spoke of community residents embedding the way they want to live in the way they design their homes, streets and neighbourhoods – another theme that has been of great interest to the UrbanBuzz projects.

Prasad also advocated the emergence of carbon as a key sustainability measure. He claimed that carbon 'offers hard, measureable targets and compels new ways of thinking about economics, lower carbon logistics and ways of working'. Delegates agreeing with Prasad will find that several UrbanBuzz projects have made progress on this issue, from VIBAT's transport emissions simulation game to the CARBONBUZZ online carbon emission monitoring tool.

Professor Malcolm Grant
'UrbanBuzz doesn't end. It enters a new phase, a longer process of dissemination and engagement with partners and with the Homes and Communities Agency'

Roger Madelin
'Misinformation is the cancer of democracy. Single interest groups often use misinformation to propagate particular issues. So we try to put the best, easily ascertainable information out into the public domain'

Sir Simon Milton
'We want the London Plan to respond to London's unique character and the identity of its urban villages. People live and raise families in neighbourhoods. What happens in their own communities and the opportunities open to them there matter far more than what might or might not be happening on the other side of London'

Professor Alan Penn
'Sustainability requires that the way we run our government, our cities and our communities is both equitable and empowering. Yet they must also be inspirational. People must want to live in the places that we build. We have to think about culture, heritage, creativity and personal identity. We must support innovation'

Tim Stonor
'UrbanBuzz was an opportunity to explore the relationship between spatial layout and value through the ultimate objective of delivering sustainable communities. Our project, i-VALUL, has been the largest beneficiary of UrbanBuzz funding, led by Space Syntax with 20 partners. The contributions of all partners in the programme have been significant'

Professor Tim Broyd
'The programme's challenge at the outset was not lack of policy but lack of coordination – to get the right knowledge where it can be channelled'

Sir Bob Kerslake
'The HCA is an investment agency that will focus on a place-based approach, with bottom-up issues reconciling national targets with local ambition. Revenue investment will include addressing the skills base as part of a single conversation'

Robin Hickman
'There's a great deal of debate in some sustainability fields, for example transport and urban planning, but very little in others. And there's little action. Within the transport sector, we're still rising in terms of carbon emissions. We need to urgently accelerate our efforts'

Matthew Taylor
'Collaboration is fundamental to progress. Bringing specialists together to increase capacity is key – one more reason why UrbanBuzz has been so incredibly important'

Sunand Prasad
'Carbon offers hard, measureable targets and compels new ways of thinking about economics, lower carbon logistics and ways of working. The true implications of carbon counting have yet to sink in and this is one of the big lessons that needs to be learned'

Julian Hart
'The real value from the UrbanBuzz programme was the bottom-up, grassroots proposal of projects. There are projects that would not normally have been funded. Some projects have broken new ground, and will continue to do so going forward'

Professor Bob Lowe
'UrbanBuzz has given us the opportunity to create partnerships. We have seen through the eyes, and heard the opinions of, people who work in the construction industry. They have things to bring to the table that academics do not have. It takes time and care to construct and maintain these partnerships'

Peter Bishop
'London is very much an urban centre created via brokerage and negotiation, rather than by grand planning. Our cities are, in many ways, shaped by the unintended consequences of policymaking rather than grand decisions'

Professor Allan Brimicombe
'Our project was about evidencing change in sustainable communities, looking at changes in population and the way that feeds into social infrastructure planning. The UrbanBuzz funding allowed us to take a totally new look at estimating populations using local authority administrative data'

Gemma Moore
'The UrbanBuzz programme aimed to bring together individuals and groups that might not normally work together. It takes engagement to a different level and gets people actually working together. It's an active process of learning, for practitioners and for academics, which is quite novel in the research community'

Nick Raynsford MP
'When we come to the creation of sustainable communities, we cannot operate within traditional silos, let alone replicate the socially divisive patterns of development which created rigid geographical divisions between separate uses and an almost apartheid separation of market from social housing'

The UrbanBuzz programme

Delivering education and training material was at the heart of the UrbanBuzz mission. Projects tackled technologically-based challenges relating to building performance and transport emissions, as well behavioural issues relating to the social sciences, such as improving approaches to community consultation and engagement.

Providing an overview of the programme's education and training outputs, however, is challenging, due to the sheer diversity of subject matter. 'Education', in this context, is taken to refer to all outputs delivered in an academic environment, including contributions to formal qualifications. 'Training' relates to all other tangible outputs, for example toolkits and guidance documents, that feed into the wider knowledge base of society. These may be in the form of commercially-driven training courses, continuing professional development (CPD), or presentation of material in accessible formats on the internet, in print or on DVD.

Given the 'back-loaded' character of the programme, the timing for delivering education and training (E&T) outputs has varied. Whilst many projects have delivered E&T within UrbanBuzz's two-year funding period, others will begin to deliver as the project work concludes and dissemination begins.

The real 'legacy' for projects rests in their continuing momentum following completion of the programme. All projects were asked to include provisions for E&T and, where 'gaps' were exposed, UrbanBuzz sought to provide additional financial support. E&T content has ranged from academic courses through to the compilation of good practice guides that move social processes, especially community engagement, forwards. The Programme Office team sought to ensure that all guidance documents produced by projects are disseminated as widely as possible.

UrbanBuzz case studies

At the outset, UrbanBuzz committed to produce 30 case studies. No single definition of a 'case study' suits all projects, and each team has tailored its interpretation to suit targeted end-users. The key element of all case studies is that they contain material of real E&T value, and draw on 'real-world' practical experience. The table on page 48 lists the case studies that have arisen from the programme.

Core to the success of developing E&T material was the project teams' commitment to ensuring that such materials deliver real value to end-users. The projects know their stakeholders and audiences well, and have reflected on which knowledge exchange mechanisms will be most effective. As the projects progressed, it became clear that where commercial or third sector organisations either led, or were engaged with, projects, the dissemination of outputs was more proactive than the projects led by academics.

The Programme Office team fulfilled an important supporting role by creating outlets for project E&T materials – principally through arrangements with other organisations servicing the needs of professional or stakeholder groups. This process is far from complete and forms an important strand of post-programme activity

The outputs from the following projects will be actively used in education and training:

ABUNDANCE a new MSc module has been produced, to be included in the MSc on Urban Agriculture provided at UCL's Development Planning Unit at the Bartlett.

ESP-SIM the UrbanBuzz support for this project enabled the development of YouCanPlan software, which will represent a core part of Slider Studio's business in future. To this end, Slider Studio has the commercial incentive to continue to inform and train potential users and collaborators on the issue of enabled self-procurement.

i-VALUL a key aim of the i-VALUL project focused on effective ways of informing and training different audiences in the use of specific spatial analysis applications.

MCSC a core output from the MCSC project will be a guidance document that can be used to help communities to understand the potential of community mapping and to engage in community mapping initiatives. The success of the MCSC project has led to the creation of a new social enterprise dedicated to working with communities on mapping activities.

RETILE-COMBEEP the project has developed an evaluation tool that is being embedded into the workflows of the charity organisation Groundwork. This will involve the ongoing training of staff and volunteers associated with projects.

SCREAM guidance developed from this project will inform a new Masters module at UCL, exploring digital media in urban environments.

SEDUC has produced a vital resource on the relationship between antisocial behaviour and design and will be used actively for training by the Jill Dando Institute at UCL.

THE ROOTSCAPE PROJECT The project has provided the material to help teachers and youth workers to engage young people in built environment issues, whilst equipping students with multimedia skills.

VIBAT the project team has developed a simulation tool that is being actively employed by Halcrow in cities across the world, to help decision makers understand how to reduce the impact of transport on carbon emissions.

Developing the knowledge base
Many of the 27 UrbanBuzz projects have created education and training material within the programme's two-year funding period. Others will begin to deliver new courses and toolkits as project work concludes and dissemination of outputs begins

The outputs from the following projects provide resources for all with an interest in the subject:

E-POD has produced a series of podcasts relating to low-carbon buildings that are available via a free online resource.

GBE the 'Gendersite' website is informing planners and designers with an interest in inclusive design and promoting equality in the built environment.

LOWCARB4REAL has created an educational website for students and professionals to help them better understand the gap in energy performance between design and construction.

MOBILISING KNOWLEDGE has produced a comprehensive toolkit for those who wish to engage elderly people in regeneration initiatives.

SUSTAINABLE TRAINING has produced two significant outputs, based on the input from a range of academics and planners to a series of design review exercises. The publication *A Planner's Guide to Carbon* will be disseminated by the Good Homes Alliance to planning departments across England. A second good practice guide, *Rules of Thumb for Sustainable Design* will form the basis for new seminar-based workshop material to be used by Urban Design London in a training programme aimed at London's councillors and design champions.

The UrbanBuzz programme: developing the knowledge base

Project name		Reports, documents, papers and case studies	Distribution
ABUNDANCE		A green mapping guide	http://transitiontowns.org/Brixton/TheABUNDANCEPROJECT
CARBONBUZZ		A guidance document on how to use the website, feauturing case studies from live developments	www.carbonbuzz.org
CD-G WORKSHOP		A summary of the experience from various community workshops, setting out what worked and what did not, and providing advice to academic architectural departments on how to involve the public in student and community projects	www.cd-g-workshop.blogspot.com www.urbanbuzz.org (select projects)
CLOVIS		Papers will be submitted to academic journals	Contact j.kelsey@ucl.ac.uk for details
DEI DEMONSTRATION	01) 02) 03)	Academic paper: Leung, C and Gage, S, Dynamic External Insulation, MEADA magazine (2008), 3, 76-80 Conference paper and book chapter: Gage, S and Leung, C, The Mechanical Homunculus, Cybernetics and Systems 2008 (2008), ed. Trappl, R., 1, 103-108 Journal article: Alexander, K and Gage, S and Leung, C, Pavilion tests shuttered external insulation journal, Architects' Journal, 2008, 227, 43	www.deployable.org.uk http://eprints.ucl.ac.uk
EASY		Academic paper describing the EASY model; (pp348 – 353) of conference papers for the GIS Research UK 2008 conference. 'Scenario-based Small Area Population Modelling for Social Infrastructure Planning', Yang Li, Allan J. Brimicombe, UEL. Project papers and reports are available from the project website	www.unigis.org/gisruk_2008/proceedings/proc_GISRUK 2008.pdf www.uel.ac.uk/geo-information/EASY/
E-POD		A wide range of multimedia presentations is available online	www.lowcarbonbuildingsdirectory.org
ESP-SIM	01) 02)	Enabled Self-Procured housing, a case study YouCanPlan software download and user guidance	www.esp-sim.org www.youcanplan.co.uk
FEtUR		Fresh Eyes regeneration toolkit: a multidisciplinary perspective	www.urbanbuzz.org (select projects)
GBE		Series of short case studies provided on Gendersite resource to highlight built environment equality issues	http://www.gendersite.org/pages/case_studies.html
i-VALUL	01) 02)	Summary of experience training space syntax to local communities Summary of experience training space syntax to planning professionals	www.spacesyntax.com/en/valuing-urban-layout.aspx
LEVH		Measured heat loss and air permeability of two exemplar low energy English dwellings Summer overheating in Victorian refurbished houses: Maria Nikolaidou, MSc dissertation; Environmental Design and Engineering, UCL 2008	www.levh.org.uk
LOWCARB4REAL		Project posters and reports are available on the project website	www.lmu.ac.uk/as/cebe/projects/lowcarb4real/index.htm
LSTS		A briefing document, drawing on experience of building a London-based network of students and organisations and working to facilitate knowledge-sharing and networking, is being prepared for careers services, with the aim of harnessing the skills and enthusiasm of the next generation of sustainability professionals	www.lsx.org.uk/whatwedo/lsts_page3067.aspx Contact K.Balmer@lsx.org.uk for details
MCSC	01) 02) 03)	The importance of community mapping in enabling community empowerment, using practical examples: the Royal Geographical Society annual conference, 2008 Method for creating community maps for non-technical users, drawing upon MCSC experience Web GIS tools to empowering community groups and individuals, strengths and weaknesses of the MCSC approach	www.mappingforchange.org.uk
METRICITY		The project's reports are available on the project website	www.metricity.net
MOBILSING KNOWLEDGE		Guide to engaging older people in regeneration projects, drawing on consultation exercises	www.goldsmiths.ac.uk/cucr/pdf/mobilizing-knowledge.pdf
REBOPSE	01) 02)	Job Seekers and Social Networks: Agent Based Modelling Using a Database of Job Seekers in the London Borough of Camden, Amy Heineike and Paul Ormerod (Volterra consulting) December 2008 Weak ties – Strong Job Chances, Susan Batty (CASA) 2009: forthcoming CASA Working Paper	www.urbanbuzz.org (select projects) www.casa.ucl.ac.uk
RETILE-COMBEEP		Three case studies: application of the RETILE methodology to regeneration projects at Camden Goods Yard, Regents Park and Brecknock Estate	www.urbanbuzz.org (select projects)
SCREAM	01) 02)	Project framework document available online Selected academic papers available online or as reprints	Framework: www.vr.ucl.ac.uk/projects/scream/ Papers: www.vr.ucl.ac.uk/people/ava/publications.htm
SEDUC		A comprehensive literature review and briefing document on anti-social behaviour in the built environment: Jill Dando Institute, UCL; various project reports on geo-coding and spatial analysis and and the use of web 2.0 in building social cohesion, plus reports from project case study areas	www.uel.ac.uk/geo-information/SEDUC
SSSP		Project documentation available online	http://aedas.com/Europe/RandD/SmartSolutionsfor SpatialPlanning/
SUSTAINABLE CONSTRUCTION POLICIES		Project final report available online	www.urbanbuzz.org (select projects)
SUSTAINABLE TRAINING		*The Planner's Guide to Carbon*, a training document to help planning officers address energy issues in the planning determination process, is available online from several partner organisations	www.goodhomes.org.uk and www.nbtconsult.co.uk; www.natural-building.co.uk
THE ROOTSCAPE PROJECT		A 'storybook' of the project experience is available, as is a DVD 'toolkit' training built environment professionals in ways of engaging young people in urban design participation	Contact gbutina@brookes.ac.uk for copies
TOWARDS ZERO CARBON SCHOOLS		Multimedia presentations from the project-supported CIBSE Schools Design Group members are available online	www.lowcarbonbuildingsdirectory.org
VIBAT LONDON		A wide range of reports, presentations and academic and conference papers is available on the project website	www.vibat.org/publications/index.shtml

'In future, I don't think undergraduate degrees will be perennially "single discipline". Exposure to a combination of subjects that require both qualitative and quantitative analysis is a better model for the future of undergraduate education in this country, and one that we're currently exploring at UCL. Sustainability is the big challenge for all of the professions associated with land, property and development, and we need interdisciplinary activity to take place'
**Professor Malcolm Grant,
President and Provost, UCL**

City
School
Secondry

CITY HOSPITAL

What does a sustainable community look like?

A sustainable community is designed to be a safe, low-carbon, inclusive democracy where graduate retention is high and agents for economic change thrive. Its residents benefit from integrated transport, housing supply and tenure, along with environmental, educational, societal, ethnic and cultural strategies that generate vibrancy and a sense of proud association.

The challenges tackled by the 27 UrbanBuzz projects impact on every aspect of civil society. The following pages grapple with key thematic issues – urban density, the move to low carbon living, access to information, sustainable design skills, the planning framework and community empowerment – arising from project activities, all of which are experiencing development 'watersheds'. UrbanBuzz has sought to dismantle entrenched stakeholder positions through improved understanding of each others' viewpoints, and has fostered a spirit of collaborative working to deliver practical solutions in these thematic areas.

The progress of many of UrbanBuzz's 27 projects has been contingent on accessing geographic and demographic information held by public bodies and private organisations.

Knowledge-sharing meetings between project teams revealed that several were experiencing problems relating to data accessibility and consistency: conflicting data formats, a lack of understanding or skills at the data provider, poor or non-existent metadata, a lack of standardisation and disaggregated data.

Improvements to data quality and accessibility could, the project teams agreed, be greatly beneficial to researchers and policymakers working in the sustainability field. It could augment innovative technological approaches to interpreting local community geographies, and be useful in directing and assisting future policy development in areas from infrastructure planning to designing out crime to community engagement.

Recently, government has begun to tackle concerns regarding data accessibility. The Power of Information Taskforce, set up by Tom Watson MP in 2008, and the ongoing Power of Information agenda are positive steps forward in this regard.

Power of information

The boom in internet communications and usage in the UK led to the Government commissioning, in January 2007, an independent review to explore new developments in the use and communication of citizen and state-generated public information in the UK, and to present

analysis and recommendations to the Cabinet Office as part of the policy review. The review's recommendations for action related to three interconnected areas: engagement in partnerships with user-led online communities, ensuring that pace is kept with changing demand in the information market, and advising civil servants on how best to participate in 'new media'.

The overall intent of this agenda demonstrates an institutional belief in the need to make local and national data more accessible. Access to data is a key element of local democracy, as several UrbanBuzz projects demonstrated. Those projects involved with spatial analysis and geo-mapping, in particular, were dependent on publicly-held data, much of it in the control of local authorities.

Initially, and perhaps most fundamentally, the project teams found that, although local authority contacts engaged with the project objectives, for example antisocial behaviour mapping or digital masterplanning, they frequently lacked the knowledge and understanding of Geographic Information Systems (GIS) necessary to enable them to provide data in useable formats. Paul Coates, senior lecturer in the School of Architecture at the University of East London (UEL) and principal investigator for SSSP, recalls that requests for GIS data led to the provision of a map in image format.

For several projects, the lack of usable data was resolved by the involvement of Dr Yang Li at UEL who, working closely with the local

The power of information
Improvements to data quality and accessibility could help researchers and policymakers working in the sustainability field to create democratic, evidence-based approaches to social infrastructure planning and community engagement

Generic data access issues from local authorities, experienced by project teams

Data issue	Problem behind this issue
Project teams not aware of which datasets are available that could be used for GIS. i-VALUL coordinator Space Syntax felt stifled by the constraints of commercial access to Ordnance Survey data, knowing that there must be other data sources available.	There is no concerted, complete and up-to-date list of data, use and formats and sources in the UK.
Despite the involvement of local authority departments in projects, many were reluctant to supply data.	Project team not linking with correct part of local authority organisation.
Data in wrong format for project activity, for example being supplied with images rather than map data.	Caution on the part of data suppliers following recent losses of public data. Local authority participants not communicating with colleagues at local authorities regarding the value, purpose or security of the requested data. This can occur when the project team does not clearly communicate its needs and intentions to local authority partners.
	Local authority data collection and management systems are maintained independently.
In cross-authority projects, supplied data can exhibit huge differences in scale and quality.	There may be competition or political tension between boroughs that exacerbates this lack of centrality.

authorities, was able to manipulate the available data into the required formats whilst ensuring that data quality was preserved. Although successful, however, this process took valuable time and project resource.

Christian Schwander, i-VALUL project coordinator, notes that local authority project partners were frequently unaware of what data they held. Allan Brimicombe of UEL, project coordinator for EASY and SEDUC, comments that one of his key assets is a mental data map of the UK – details of dataset availability are not common knowledge.

Privacy and security

The personalised nature of certain data means that public bodies have (frequently misplaced) privacy and security concerns. The SEDUC project team experienced severe delays in accessing data on antisocial behaviour due to its location-specificity; the project progressed only because core project team members already had the necessary Metropolitan Police clearance to view confidential crime data. In order to disseminate the data, however, it had to be de-personalised by assigning individual instances of reported antisocial behaviour to streets rather than addresses. Brimicombe notes that data became profoundly more difficult to access after the widely publicised loss of Child Benefit data in November 2007. In many cases, data simply became unavailable.

Who holds what data?

Knowing who to approach for data was also an issue. The size and complex structure of local authorities meant that project teams were not necessarily talking to the appropriate people about data access. There is no standard approach from local authorities on this matter, inferring a lack of communication or collaboration between departments and between authorities. The SEDUC project team was frustrated by the conflicting messages coming out of local authorities. Community safety departments were very willing to be involved in the project and could see its potential value. Yet the IT departments responsible for the data were reluctant to supply any, being extremely cautious as regards data protection issues.

Similarly, the SSSP team found that required data were not always freely available. Local Land and Property Gazetteer (LLPG) data had to be purchased from one borough, and its existence was denied in another. The MCSC team encountered situations in which communities were keen to know the registered owners of particular land parcels, but were unable to do so due to the expense of land registry data.

Finally, there is a political dimension that threatens the availability of data. Brimicombe notes that local authorities are essentially in competition with each other, the result being that it is often difficult to engage with several authorities: one authority may be reluctant to share data when it could result in another gaining the benefit, or in comparisons being made.

Louise Francis, a participant in the MCSC project, found that getting timely and up-to-date information about ongoing or proposed developments was particularly difficult. The MCSC team worked with Planning Aid for London (PAL) in order to access plans and information from local government planning departments. Francis suggests that the tendency of large projects to evolve over time, coupled with political and economic sensitivity, for example relating to Olympic development in Hackney, meant that the council was very reluctant to provide such data.

Data capture and consistency

Data consistency and quality has also been an issue for project teams. Different ways of recording data, including the scale and level of information capture, was found across London's boroughs. The SEDUC project team found that antisocial behaviour had been recorded in such differing formats across the boroughs that they were forced to make use of three distinct methodologies to derive an end product, once again adding time and expense to the process.

The EASY project team was compelled to move away from local authorities as a source of data. Initially, key stakeholders in the project were local authorities and Primary Care Trusts (PCTs), both of whom receive funding based upon resident populations in their relevant geographies. Thus EASY, which aimed to model population change from local government and Office for National Statistics (ONS) data, had the potential to influence local government and Primary Care Trust (PCT) funding through its findings. As a result, reports Brimicombe, working effectively with local authorities was all but impossible. The team turned instead to nationally available datasets.

Far fewer data access issues were noted when using nationally available data from providers such as the ONS. The primary issue with nationally available data was the scale at which it could be obtained, which was often too ❯

Networks and trust for data access

One overarching factor, noted by all the project teams, that proved key to the data accessibility process was trust. Simply put, all project teams found that if members of the team had 'connections' with data providers, or endeavoured to establish such connections at the outset, then they stood a better chance of getting the data required in a useful format and timely manner.

Louise Francis, participant in the MCSC project, notes that a key factor for the MCSC team was gaining the trust of individuals within the community, and of the community as a whole. Being unable to follow up on the ideas and suggestions that community members make, because the data is inaccessible, hinders effective relationship-building, she says.

The MCSC project is using 'community maps' as a way of representing less visible community members. The kind of data accessibility that concerns the MCSC team involves making sure that those with the power to act, in local government or councils, are aware of the opinions and perspectives of the local communities they govern. Active networks, word-of-mouth and trust in the process are key in spreading 'community mapping' to a wider audience of community participants, and stakeholders.

The project teams also noted that the time budgeted for data acquisition and manipulation activities can often increase far beyond the constraints of the project plan. As such, trust built up in the initial stages of a project can be damaged if established contacts are required to move onto other projects before they have been able to make their agreed project impact.

large for the project's needs, and the fact that national datasets are frequently at least two to three years out of date due to the analysis and dissemination process.

Commercial companies such as Space Syntax, lead organisation on the i-VALUL project, experienced greater difficulties in accessing geographic data than academic project leaders. In academic institutions, when project work remains 'research', the project teams have access to datasets and other access privileges via the 'Athens' service or similar initiatives. The project team for i-VALUL, however, had to set up a research consortium agreement with the Ordnance Survey (OS) in order to access to mapping data.

This initially hinders access to data as it can take time, and specific features of the agreement can place constraints on work. The i-VALUL team, for example, was able to agree only a three-month licence for specific OS data, and was required to apply for an extension as the project progressed, adding time, cost and administrative burden.

The advantage that private companies have in terms of data accessibility is the relative ease with which they can commercialise specific outputs of the projects, based on negotiated data access agreements. Academic project coordinators, on the other hand, would be required to establish new data contracts, funding and operating environments.

So, is data accessible?

The key conclusion is that much has been achieved through collaboration and trust between project teams and data providers. It is questionable, however, to what extent this is a valid methodology; as the process of developing meaningful collaborations can be prohibitively time-consuming, especially for a short-term project. Likewise, relationships are often project-specific and hence have no longevity, or are short-lived simply due to project-based work structures at data providers, with established contacts being frequently moved onto new teams or initiatives.

Does the Government's Power of Information agenda have the scope, in future, to improve access to the kinds of data that UrbanBuzz projects have been working with? The major stalling point for most projects was the local authority, and The Power of Information agenda has several recommendations pertaining to the increasing accessibility of public sector data. However, whether or not such access is realistic comes down to local authority structure, internal communication, local politics and, inevitably, power. If a local authority does not wish to share a dataset then, unless compelled by regulation to do so, it does not have to. This may well adversely affect the general public more than commercial bodies or academic institutions, simply because communities do not have the influence enjoyed by the latter.

Improving access to data

Where data is difficult to access due to security and privacy issues, The Power of Information Agenda has very little scope to improve matters. Accessibility to this kind of data will remain problematic as the Government and local authorities have a duty to protect it. There is not sufficient understanding of data, supply, access and use across different groups within local authorities to allow confident risk management in the supply of data.

Further, the Power of Information Agenda has limited muscle with which to deal with reactionary or prohibitive data initiatives in this area, as they can be seen to be acting in the greater public good in being protective.

The general feeling from the UrbanBuzz teams was, rather than having access to government statistics and similar, communities actually wanted processes in place through which they could create and use their own data. User-created content, mash-ups and wikis are becoming increasingly popular, and The Power of Information Agenda recommendations should encourage a greater appreciation of, and participation in, these new media forums.

Information is a valuable commodity and it is crucial, in both the long and short term, to highlight and critique current practice in data collation, storage and access. To this end the Power of Information Agenda and Taskforce has an important role to play in the overall accessibility of information and future knowledge exchange. The UrbanBuzz projects have done much to illustrate what can be achieved if datasets are available.

The Power of Information Taskforce:
http://powerofinformation.wordpress.com/

'A major challenge faced by many project teams was gaining access to consistent data for GIS and computational analysis. Taking part in UrbanBuzz projects encouraged public bodies to be upfront and honest about the quality of their data and what they realistically can use it for. All these things are programme strengths'
Dr Carol Dair, Oxford Institute for Sustainable Development (OISD), and UrbanBuzz independent evaluator

In its 2008 *Communities in Control* consultation document, CLG states: 'We want to shift power, influence and responsibility away from existing centres of power into the hands of communities and individual citizens. This is because we believe that they can take difficult decisions and solve complex problems for themselves. The state's role should be to set national priorities and minimum standards, while providing support and a fair distribution of resources.'

The original requirement for a developer submitting a planning application of a certain size was to place an advertisement in a local newspaper – the smaller and more hidden the better as far as the planning consultant was concerned. The public sector had no obligation to consult: it was simply assumed that local democracy worked and that elected representatives would provide sufficient protection to the wider community.

No longer do we assume that all local authority policies are in the interests of entire communities. The Environmental Impact Assessment regulations, which the UK was required to adopt from Europe in the late 1980s, opened the regulatory breach, placing much greater emphasis on publication of intent where major projects were concerned.

Then came the road wars. The highly televised battles of Twyford Down versus the M3 planners made it clear that chasms existed between the views of elected representatives and significant minority interests. The communications revolution has helped to spread debate, enabling those with facilities to tune into what is happening across the world, never mind locally.

Notwithstanding the general consensus that consultation with the public and with communities is positive and beneficial, a problem is emerging: some local communities do not seem to be particularly interested. Once engaged and involved, community members taking part in a range of UrbanBuzz projects proved themselves to be motivated, and with valuable insights and knowledge to offer. However, the recent *Disconnected Citizens* report from the Social Market Foundation suggests that 'evidence of concrete outcomes of community empowerment is patchy at best, as is evidence of a huge and unsated public appetite for engagement'.

In part, says the report, this mismatch between evidence and enthusiasm reflects that the concept itself remains ill-defined – in language, aims and ambitions. It further suggests that there is also mismatch between the Government's ambition to reinvigorate local democracy and the community empowerment mechanisms that it hopes will provide the solution, particularly in a context where citizens have only limited time and willingness to participate. A 'false dichotomy' between representative and participatory democracy; a failure of initiatives to transfer power in a meaningful sense, and a lack of clarity and transparency in lines of accountability for decisions all lead to the public's seeming non-interest in engagement activity.

Barbara Gray, Area Initiatives Officer, Lewisham, worked with the MOBILISING KNOWLEDGE project team to engage the participants in a planning summer school. 'It was a challenge to reach people, and in the end we

Community engagement: local democracy in action

The investment in public consultation expected of all developers has increased dramatically over the last 15 years – but more does not necessarily mean better. There is much to learn about effective community engagement

worked with individuals who were already active in the community. Now we have a process in place, we hope this will help to bring in new groups.'

As this and other UrbanBuzz projects have shown, initial contact with communities can take a lot of hard work and effort. 'In my experience, it's actually reaching the people that's the big, big issue,' says Lovelace Poku, former planning policy officer, Lewisham, now at the Royal Borough of Kensington and Chelsea, and a MOBILISING KNOWLEDGE summer school expert participant. 'It's very difficult to engage with people so you can move on to offer different channels and methods of consultation. Getting people's attention is the main sticking point for most councils. We also need to bear in mind that our efforts are measured in results,' says Poku.

Other UrbanBuzz projects tackled similar problems. The CD-G project learnt quickly when a couple of proposed workshops, perhaps badly timetabled, had zero attendance, and instead developed relationships with existing community groups, with more success. THE ROOTSCAPE PROJECT, working with young students, was set up to re-engage with communities that had become numb to consultation initiatives.

Engagement is part and parcel of living in a democratic society. Successful engagement requires a two-way flow of information – real knowledge exchange – and for those organisations leading the engagement process to be willing, and able, to act on the outcomes. 'It is also a matter about which we have much to learn,' says Nick Raynsford MP. 'There can be cases where the local authority may be in conflict between the aspirations for the local authority and the locality. There could also be cases where individual groups from different cultural backgrounds or ethnic backgrounds have a different perception of what is in the interest of the area. There is the familiar problem of NIMBYism.'

Learning from the projects

The learning from these projects suggests that successful engagement lies in the degree of influence that people feel they have on issues under consideration. 'The most successful engagement occurs when you identify what kinds of "stake" different groups have in any project,' says Adeola Dada, Southwark regeneration team, and a participant in the CLOVIS project. 'There are winners and losers in all initiatives, and it's important to manage expectations. Even diverse views can be handled, if the communication is honest and candid.'

If this is the case, then it suggests that requirements simply to 'consult' are short-sighted. As part of its duty to create a Local Development

The future for engagement: The Planning Bill

The 2008 Planning Bill puts effective public consultation and participation at the heart of the planning framework:

01 By creating a clear duty to ensure effective public consultation on National Policy Statements. This consultation should include positive and proactive means of engaging citizens and communities. Where National Policy Statements identify locations or potential locations for development, there will be a duty to consult in those locations.

02 By placing clear legal obligations on developers to consult local communities before submitting a planning application, and ensure that consultation is of high quality.

03 By making planning inquiries accessible and ensuring peoples' rights to be heard are protected. In particular the Bill will make it clear that any person who registers an interest can give oral evidence at relevant stages of the inquiry.

Framework, every council must prepare a Statement of Community Involvement (SCI) and a Sustainable Community Strategy (SCS). 'Our baseline standard is to post letters and put announcements in the local press,' says Poku. 'Yet we often go further in order to communicate with hard-to-reach groups. It's very difficult to engage with certain groups of people.'

It has long been recognised by practitioners that there is no 'one-size-fits-all' engagement strategy. 'The more forward thinking and canny developers have come to understand this, especially when they are working on contentious projects,' says Julian Hart, planning consultant, Lancefield Consulting. 'They engage with, and involve, the local community from an early stage in order to pre-empt problems at a later stage, by which time it would be very expensive to change course and would increase "planning risk". Unfortunately, such developers are few and far between. A great deal of consultation for the purposes of planning determination is still a very cynical affair.'

The public sector suffers from an equally problematic situation in regard to consultation, but for very different reasons. 'Local authorities may be full of good intentions when seeking to consult with local communities,' says Hart, 'but the real issue lies in their ability to follow through and deliver.' A local authority might run out of money for the proposed project, or run into a shift in internal politics. 'Communities need to see action, or they become cynical and uncooperative,' says Georgina Hackett, Southwark regeneration team and CLOVIS participant. 'Engagement approaches should not be top-down, but community engagement teams do need to be led by stakeholders with vision and commitment.'

Speaking at the UrbanBuzz final conference, Sir Bob Kerslake, chief executive of the Homes and Community Agency (HCA), outlined his commitment to community engagement: 'If we think about investment, we don't invest in things where we're not convinced that we're going to get a return, whether that's a social return or a financial return. I think one of the litmus tests for development is whether those seeking investment have good approaches to community engagement. We will develop a standard for community engagement that will apply both to how we do our business, and how we expect others to do it too.' ›

UrbanBuzz projects have outlined engagement tools and processes for the future

The ESP-SIM project represents a revolutionary way for developers to engage with local people and take forward development projects. The MCSC project uses mapping technologies to identify better and easier ways for communities to participate in decisions concerning their locality. CLOVIS brought together teams from two live regeneration projects, the Bath Western Riverside Project and the Aylesbury Estate Programme in Southwark, to create a toolkit for gaining stakeholder support. The

MOBILISING KNOWLEDGE project explored older people's experience of the city and created ways of incorporating their perspectives into the planning and design process. The young students taking part in THE ROOTSCAPE PROJECT in Oxford are getting involved in the planning and design of new homes and schools – and teaching the professionals a thing or two in the process.

For further details on other UrbanBuzz projects involved in community engagement, please see page 76 onwards.

ESP-SIM: enabling participation

The ideas behind the ESP-SIM project are not new to Germany or north America, but they are a radical departure for the UK. 'In the UK we build houses and then flog them,' says project coordinator Michael Kohn. 'There is very little in the way of involvement for those who will live in a newly-created community before it is completed and ready for sale. We are seeking to create an environment where those who are interested in living in a particular location can participate in the development process from the outset.'

The ESP-SIM project has created a virtual environment and interface that would enable those interested in living in a new development to invest in the project, effectively becoming a partner. The developer subtly, but significantly, changes role from housebuilder (designer, constructor and seller of houses) to that of community enabler, helping these customers to

realise a community vision for a new development. Those joining the development late would clearly have less input into its masterplan, but could influence the design code for the terrace of houses in which they wish to live, or at least the internal layout and fit-out of their chosen house. There could still be those who join the community by buying a new house in the normal way at the end of the process.'

ESP-SIM could also work as a percentage of larger development. 'Imagine if five per cent of the homes were offered through ESP-SIM at a major project such as Barking Riverside. That could be good for the Thames Gateway because there's a need for people to plant themselves in these new communities, to invest time and energy, and to seed social sustainability,' says Kohn. See page 120.

'We are seeking to create an environment where those who are interested in living in a particular location can participate in the development process from the outset'
Michael Kohn,
ESP-SIM project

'The most successful engagement occurs when you identify what kinds of "stake" different groups have in any project'
Adeola Dada, Southwark regeneration team and CLOVIS participant

MCSC: community mapping for change

The vision that MCSC has in mind could have a long-term impact on the public sector's role in engaging communities. The MCSC team has harnessed the latest geographic information system technology to help communities create online, locally-owned and managed maps of their local area. Each community chose its own map theme: noise nuisance, antisocial behaviour or historic sites. Many local authorities provide a great deal of information about their administrative areas through online maps.

The maps can include planning policy information as well as the history of planning applications for individual buildings and other items of geographic information. The next obvious step is to bring this information together with the community mapping process in order to re-invigorate local democracy and community involvement. The interactive maps used by the MCSC project could, for instance, be included as a required channel for developers to display planning application proposals.

The maps could be used to consult people on new planning policy proposals, such as the boundaries of a conservation area. They could be used to coordinate voting amongst local residents on a planning policy boundary change, such as a school catchment area. MCSC participants created a map to capture and plot data around noise nuisance relating to a planning application from London City Airport, and to organise a community response (see page 154).

'Community mapping helps to raise awareness. It gives the community an impetus, and a reason to go to the council and say "right, we've got something to show you" '
Colleen Whittaker, MCSC project

CLOVIS: identifying stakeholders

This project brought together teams from two live regeneration projects, the Bath Western Riverside Project and the Aylesbury Estate Programme in Southwark, to outline their approaches to gaining stakeholder and community support. In the case of the Aylesbury Estate community engagement initiative, the team had valuable insights to share. Successful engagement is complex, intensive, resource-heavy and creative work, frequently reliant on the communications skills and strategies of the team leaders rather than rooted in robust policy, practice or process.

'Consultation fatigue can apply to engagement officers as well as communities,' says Aylesbury regeneration officer Georgina Hackett. 'Communication must be honest and candid,' says regeneration assistant director Adeola Dada. 'A key to success is the identification of the different "stakes" that groups of residents may have during any regeneration process. It's important to recognise that there will be winners and losers, and to effectively manage needs and expectations,' says Dada (see page 104). Intensive, hands-on initiatives have proved popular with local communities at Southwark:

01 Local residents have been taken on visits around Europe to better understand regeneration and design. These programmes are designed to broaden residents' minds to showcase what can be achieved. City visits have included Paris, Amsterdam and Dublin. They show what is possible and, once engaged, residents became community design champions and helped to engage others.

02 A hands-on planning game designed by masterplanning practice Urban Initiatives enabled residents to feed back comments in ways they understood.

03 A photography project attempted to engage and empower people. The photos captured the estate as it is now, and encouraged residents to think of change.

04 Identifying and creating young leaders, and the setting up a 'leaders' group, is helping young people to get involved in regeneration activity.

05 A planned engagement strategy is much more effective than one that simply evolves. Both the Bath and Southwark teams recommended keeping control of the engagement process, rather than passing responsibility to development partners, to ensure that communication is candid and expectations honestly managed.

The UrbanBuzz-funded METRICITY project, led by the RCA's Helen Hamlyn Centre, sought to inject a measure of objectivity into the heated density debate by breaking away from the crude, but typically used, dwellings per hectare (dph) or habitable rooms per hectare (hrph) density metrics.

The project created a new density matrix, one closely based on current work-life-leisure-travel patterns. Traditional density measures are useful tools in residential contexts, but are less effective when related to the UK's growing number of mixed use urban areas with relatively low levels of residential accommodation. METRICITY provided some blue-sky thinking on urban intensity, attracting the attention of many major players in the design and planning sector. In due course, these new concepts will prove a useful contribution to the wider density debate.

There are some who believe that the starting point for residential development should move away from density, which is rooted in concern for land, says Dr Nick Gallent, Bartlett School of Planning, speaking at the UrbanBuzz Showcase (see page 36). For the moment, however, planners are stuck with the traditional 'dwellings or habitable rooms per hectare' metric. Placing this

Debating density: a cultural challenge
The word 'density' is emotionally loaded in the planning context, embracing issues of housing, private and public space, transport and the provision of public amenity. Several UrbanBuzz projects are contributing to the development of tools and processes that will help to put new density-related knowledge in the hands of communities, practitioners and policymakers

in context, research carried out internally within Arup by Juan Alayo during the 1990s showed that the urban form supporting the lowest energy consumption through transport (all forms of powered transport, from lifts to cars to trains) arises at density levels of around 250 dwellings per hectare (dph), which equates to at least 600 habitable rooms per hectare (hrph). This is a dense urban form, seen in very few UK urban areas. It correlates more closely to central Paris or Manhattan, and gives rise to average building heights (including open spaces taken as zero building height) of around seven storeys.

Increasing density to achieve higher average building heights, equating to Hong Kong-type urban forms, leads to higher energy consumption through vertical transport, for example via lifts and elevators. Reducing density from the 250 dph energy minimum leads to increased carbon emissions through horizontal transport – public and private combined. Contributing to this knowledge base, the UrbanBuzz VIBAT London project (see page 206), which focused on reducing carbon emissions from transport in London, identified and outlined a significant transport 'policy package' that could make a key difference:

using urban structure to support sustainable transport through higher-density development, clustered around a public transport system.

There is no need for UK planners to adopt Parisian mores and design incredibly dense locations. But there is food for thought here: density levels in UK cities and towns are currently far from the 250 dph level. Moves towards increasing densities will lead to reductions in energy consumption. UK policymakers need to face up to the simple fact that higher-density living is inherently a lower-energy consuming way of life. ❯

The UrbanBuzz programme
Debating density: a cultural challenge

Transport and suburban forms

At 50 dph, which equates to around 200 hrph, comes the transition between suburban versus urban. This is at the upper limit of 'suburban' density. The importance of this key metric in terms of urban form is that it represents the transition point between a car-dependent society and a pedestrian and public transport-oriented society.

The 50 dph threshold is the level at which public transport becomes viable. It is also the level at which district heating systems become technically possible (below this density, heat losses in the distribution network negate benefits). While policymakers may not have any intention of raising general urban densities towards the energy minimum noted above, raising average densities to above 50 dph is not an unrealistic proposition. It certainly would offer significant benefits in terms of reducing carbon emissions, as well as providing scope for reducing social exclusion.

However, the vast majority of our townscape is built to densities that are well below 50 dph, or 200 hrph. Most London suburbs are built to levels that are closer to 20 to 30 dwellings per hectare (50 to 150 hrph). So, from an energy-efficiency perspective, planners should be looking to raise urban densities. But this idea does not necessarily sit comfortably with residents who have become used to large detached houses and sizeable gardens.

Using a density matrix

The METRICITY project created a new density matrix, one based more closely on current lifestyle patterns than existing matrix tools. Although promising, this approach needs further analysis before it will become a useful tool for local authority use. In London, other matrices are already in use. The Greater London Authority's (GLA) 2005 density matrix, based upon public transport accessibility levels (PTALs), represented forward thinking in its day.

The lowest range in the GLA matrix is 30 to 50 dph (150 to 200 hrph) which, in objective terms, was a move in the right direction – towards densification. However, the use of this density

The METRICITY project (see page 160) examined new urban density metrics. When considering a sustainable society, many architects, designers and planners have argued that the UK needs metrics that more accurately reflect today's patterns of life. The METRICITY team explored many possible new density metrics in its initial evidence review, including those below.

● **Energy use**

Looking at individual carbon footprints or credits per hectare to indicate energy usage and management in the community

● **The metropolitan index**

Starbucks per hectare? Frank Duffy, from DEGW architects, suggests a knowledge economy is measured by ideas per cubic metre per minute

● **Cultural complexity**

The number of languages per hectare indicates cultural density, an important factor during the bidding process for the 2012 Olympics

● **Hyperactivity of the city**

Measuring the walking speed of a citizen. The average pace of city dwellers indicates much about the psychology of inhabitants

● **The impact of GDP**

Technology indexes, patent applications per head per hectare, the numbers of gay residents or creatives as a measure of an area's prosperity

● **Health density**

Health consultants map the geographical impact of diabetes in order to track populations that are worst affected as a result of poor living conditions

● **Technological density**

Assessing the number of wireless hotspots per hectare or infra-red signals per hectare can show technology distribution across the city

● **Happiness as a form of density**

The number of ASBOs (Anti-Social Behaviour Orders) as a measure of social unrest, or iPods as a measure of affluence per hectare

● **Demographic growth**

Measuring fertility rates or number of births per hectare to gain insight on varying socio-economic circumstances

● **Noise complaints**

Antisocial behaviour and noise complaints rose five-fold from 1980 to 2005, according to the Office of National Statistics data

matrix created political friction between regional and local policy makers. While the GLA makes it clear that the density matrix should take into consideration local character, there is a growing concern that its application frequently ignores it, especially when developers are seeking to maximise density in order to boost profits.

Such a scenario leads many to worry about increasing densities, fearing that undue pressure to maximise land values will override the importance of local character and community wellbeing. The fear is that local authorities desiring to maximise the uplift from an increase in land values, as well as meeting nationally imposed housing targets, may well find themselves permitting high density developments that service metrics rather than local community and character.

'If we needed any convincing that how we measure urban density has a major influence on urban planning and design, the METRICITY study provides conclusive evidence. It is clear that the old metrics result in single-minded solutions... we badly need urban development that is planned in a more animated and holistic way, especially when dense urban schemes are considered around transport hubs. Only then will the city become more inclusive'
Professor Jeremy Myerson, Helen Hamlyn Centre, Royal College of Art

The UrbanBuzz response: expanding the urban density knowledge base

Knowledge for public benefit
Communities must decide whether the impact from densification is acceptable, and what form any mitigation might take. The inconvenient truth is that we need a more sophisticated planning system to compensate communities for reduced quality of life at the behest of the wider public benefit.

At the heart of UrbanBuzz has been this meeting of local democracy and actual practice, with all 27 projects contributing, in one way or another, to the development of real-world tools and processes that can put power and knowledge in the hands of communities, practitioners and policy makers.

Communicating the benefits
The potential benefits of densification need to be communicated effectively to affected communities – the downside is frequently more loudly voiced. The incidence of crime and antisocial behaviour may be reduced by higher density living, for example, assuming that the design is right, as evidenced by the i-VALUL and SEDUC projects, which have applied complex spatial analysis to correlations between urban layout and behavioural, socio-economic and demographic factors (see pages 134 and 180 respectively).

Moreover, the UK is on the threshold of bringing in the Community Infrastructure Levy (CIL), a levy on the value of land gained by planning permissions. But can such 'planning gain' resolve the complex issue of densification?

The CIL, and its equitable implementation, has been a key focus of attention for the UrbanBuzz EASY project (see page 112). The reality is that this is a brave new world that we are facing and it may be that our current systems simply are not sufficiently sophisticated to deal with it.

In a seminar hosted by UrbanBuzz on 'Securing Successful Densification in our Suburbs' during its six-week Showcase (see page 36), several case studies were presented in which local authorities are seeking to counter density pressures through the use of local characterisation studies, and through retaining a focus on the provision of quality public spaces and services.

When masterplanning a new community at high density, the necessary public space and community amenities can be factored in from the outset. But this is clearly more problematic when dealing with fill-in development such as suburban extensions and the densification of suburbs. The unavoidable fact is that if suburban intensification is not accompanied by public space and amenity improvements, then the extant community may lose out in terms of quality of life. The current planning system, intricately grounded in a system of local and national democracy, struggles to tackle issues of this nature – possibly more so now that community empowerment has been bolstered by the 2008 Planning Bill.

Engaging communities
The CLOVIS project has outlined ways in which stakeholders with a range of views can be accommodated within the engagement process (see page 104). ESP-SIM (see page 120) explores the use of an Enabled Self-Procurement route to housing delivery via a virtual world, and supports the involvement of communities in developing and setting design codes for their development. The MCSC project (see page 154) has developed tools that enable communities to become better informed about spatial planning, and provides a means for them to communicate their views.

Despite promises and good intentions, there is a growing gap between policy, regulation and reality. This gap is apparent at many scales: the urban form, construction, transport, and in the way that we collectively live in and around buildings.

There is one obvious reason why this reality gap has emerged: there is no established system of recording and monitoring the impacts of urban interventions, energy consumption or carbon emissions. The consequence of this lack of performance monitoring is that Government and politicians are formulating policy, and its interpretation into regulation, based on estimated of quantities of oil, gas and coal consumed and electricity produced by nuclear plants.

The UrbanBuzz LOWCARB4REAL project has provided interesting insights on this issue (see page 146). The project focused on closing the gap between design estimates and the actual performance of new housing, a gap that had become apparent during a recent seven-year monitoring programme carried out on a large new housing development at Stamford Brook.

Researchers at Leeds found that an 'energy efficient' development seeking to build at high quality delivered actual energy consumption levels 25 per cent higher than originally predicted by design targets. To put this another way, homes built to Code for Sustainable Homes Level 3 standards would have only just passed minimum Building Regulations requirements. The collective opinion of experts at one LOWCARB4REAL workshop was that the 25 per cent gap at the case study development was most likely one of the narrowest – there is anecdotal evidence that many housing projects are performing even more poorly. But no one knows for sure. The old business management mantra comes readily to mind: 'If you cannot measure it, you cannot manage it.'

Another UrbanBuzz project that highlighted the growing reality gap was the SUSTAINABLE TRAINING project (see page 194). A Sustainable Design Review Panel comprising academic experts from built environment disciplines reviewed live planning applications. Their comments and criticisms were fed back via training workshops to planning teams in five participating local planning authorities.

The project's Sustainable Design Review Panel, perhaps better described as a technical review panel, came to the conclusion that few planning applications make real commitments in terms of sustainable design. In the words of one panel member: 'I have no confidence, in any of these case studies, that the realised projects will deliver good energy performance.'

It is apparent from these examples that our construction industry must raise its game in order

Low-carbon living: closing the reality gaps
Carbon emissions must fall by 80 per cent before 2050, according to Government targets. Achieving such reductions will require political drive and wide-ranging behavioural changes. Several UrbanBuzz projects have demonstrated the extent of the challenges – and ways in which we can begin to meet them

to deliver buildings designed to achieve targeted performance, and our planning system is frequently failing to filter poorly designed projects. These failings are driven largely by a lack of skills, a lack of interdisciplinary working, and the absence of appropriate systems to plan, design and build in the ways that are required to deliver better performance.

It should be relatively straightforward to put in place regulatory requirements covering the effective monitoring of society's carbon emissions. Yet it is a non-government initiative – an UrbanBuzz project driven by the private sector – that is setting standards for collecting and disseminating forecast, and actual, information on building-related carbon emissions. The CARBONBUZZ project (see page 96) has entered design and post-occupancy performance data from buildings into an innovative online database designed to relate forecast and performance data back to best practice benchmarks.

Speaking at the CARBONBUZZ launch, George Stowell, Chair of the RIBA Client Services Task Group, explained that the CARBONBUZZ monitoring platform will do two key things. 'Firstly, it is really important in terms of transparency, and will allow design teams to understand the impact of what they're designing, and how to improve. Secondly, it will communicate to the client that ›

'The Climate Change Bill will go some way towards the monitoring of public sector buildings. We need to go further with measuring, and UrbanBuzz is helping in this respect'
Stephen Timms, MP, then Minister for Construction

there are differences between the way buildings are designed and the way buildings are used. It will allow clients to understand what these differences are, and how they can manage their buildings better.'

CARBONBUZZ project participant Ricardo Moreira, Director of XCO_2 energy consultancy, stresses the importance of both monitoring and collaborative working: 'This tool has the potential to bring carbon emissions thinking and energy thinking into projects from the early stages. It's bringing everybody – architects, engineers and clients – together with the same goal. I think it's the first time this has been done in the UK.'

The recently adopted Climate Change Bill will necessitate implementation of effective monitoring strategies. In the spirit of the CARBONBUZZ project, we need to be assured that this critical performance data will help to inform future designs.

The UrbanBuzz programme has certainly raised some interesting issues. The project teams investigating urban density noted that moving towards a low carbon future may well require some uncomfortable behavioural and cultural changes. Two major challenges are our transport system and our existing building stock, both public and private.

These issues were tackled by several UrbanBuzz projects: the LEVH project (see page 140), which refurbished an existing Victorian house to achieve high-energy performance under typical occupancy patterns; TOWARDS ZERO CARBON SCHOOLS (see page 202), which is informing policy on improving the design and performance of schools; the E-POD project (see page 116), which has established a new alliance of professional organisations, academics and practitioners to share knowledge and experience relating to the design and operational performance of low-carbon buildings; the DEI DEMONSTRATION project (see page 108), which highlighted the importance of building occupancy patterns; and the VIBAT LONDON project (see page 206), which models transport policy interventions to help decision-makers understand the real implications of measures for reducing carbon emissions from public and private transport in the capital.

These projects have exposed the scale of the challenges ahead. The Victorian house did indeed achieve an 80 per cent reduction in carbon emissions, and a Code for Sustainable Homes rating of Level 4, but it also raised serious issues relating to costs and conservation. The reduction in carbon emissions cost more than £300,000 – close to the total value of the house. In the case

of the VIBAT LONDON project, players of the project's online game, devised to explore transport policy options, quickly discover just how difficult it is to deliver the necessary carbon savings despite embracing the suggested policy interventions. If airline emissions are taken into account, the carbon reduction target, based on actual policy predictions, is unobtainable.

The UK's European counterparts are making headway towards closing their own reality gaps. In Germany, for instance, all buildings must be monitored for two years post-completion, and their performance reported and recorded for society's benefit. UK policymakers have no excuse for not following suit. If the CARBONBUZZ project achieves critical mass, then it may well prove to be one of the most immediate legacies arising from the UrbanBuzz programme.

Professor Bob Lowe, coordinator of UrbanBuzz projects exploring energy performance in new and period homes says: 'We were looking at gapology: the gap that exists between what we think buildings should do and what they actually do. These projects suggest that there is a very, very deep-seated problem of energy underperformance in buildings.'

Lowe stresses that the key to progress is to bring people together to work out solutions to the problems we face. 'To understand even something as apparently simple as a house takes a great deal of time and effort. We have seen through the eyes and heard the opinions of people who work in the construction industry. They have things to bring to the table that academics do not have. Active partnerships are essential to tackling both the need for new technologies, and their deployment. It's a very complex issue, which is essentially societal in nature.'

'We need to re-think the way we heat and light our spaces. Technology provides options, but it's people that come up with solutions'
Professor Stephen Gage, DEI DEMONSTRATION project

'There is a very, very deep-seated problem of energy underperformance in buildings. We must deploy new technology in order to drive down CO_2 emissions. But it is not sufficient to develop technologies; partnerships are essential to tackling the challenges of technology deployment.

The UrbanBuzz experience has shown us that need for partnership comes from all sides, from academia, from builders, from designers, from those using buildings. To understand something as apparently simple as a house takes a great deal of time and effort. It's a bigger job than one sector can handle'
Professor Bob Lowe,
Complex Built Environment Systems, UCL

With half the world's population living in urban areas – up to 85 per cent in developed countries – the problems and opportunities offered by city living need our greatest attention. Around the world, many individuals and organisations are exploring creative new technologies as part of their urban and spatial analysis. These 'next-generation' technologies and ideas are not to be found in the local planning department – yet.

Where they *are* found is in research labs such as UCL's Centre for Advanced Spatial Analysis (CASA), MIT's Senseable Cities Lab, and the HumanSpace lab in Milan. In these labs, and in pioneering private practices, technology is being used in innovative and exciting ways to describe and communicate 'place': 3D Geographic Information Systems (GIS), Global Positioning Systems (GPS), digital imaging techniques, GSM, Bluetooth and Web 2.0 'mash-ups'. These new techniques are having a growing influence on the way we analyse space, monitor activity, share ideas and ultimately create places for people. They are also at the forefront of the 'evidence-based' approaches to community-building that underpin several UrbanBuzz projects.

Town planners have had a strained relationship with new technologies and spatial analysis since the original town planning act of 1947 set out a planning framework for the UK. This framework involved planners, in the guise of 2D-focused architects, drawing maps that recreated post-war, bomb-damaged city centres. Through the 1950s and 1960s, the focus changed to engineering, infrastructure and ease of movement for traffic. By the mid-1960s, most of our new towns were 'engineered' on this basis, using computer simulations that turned towns into complex interlinked systems. By the 1980s, these programmes had become incredibly expensive and complex affairs. Several economic booms and busts, sadly not predicted by the computers, proved to be their downfall. The love affair was over, and the cultural hangover is still apparent 30 years later.

Re-engaging with the computer

Today, local authorities are still wary of over-reliance on costly technology. But things are changing. 'Through research originated at UCL, we understand space and its role in determining patterns of movements in cities,' says Tim Stonor from Space Syntax, lead organisation on the UrbanBuzz i-VALUL project (see page 134). 'The technology already existed to simply, but cleverly, analyse spatial layout and forecast movement patterns. Such analysis comes down to measures of spatial accessibility. The more accessible you are, the more movement you get.'

'Movement,' explains Stonor, 'relates to added sustainability in land use terms for commercial and retail space, and impacts on security and value for residential areas. We had a clear understanding that spatial layout shapes basic human interaction. Everyday activity is

Spatial analysis: next-generation ideas
Geographical Information Systems (GIS), 3D virtual-reality applications, web-based maps and powerful new computing tools are changing the way that professionals and the public understand, describe and communicate about place

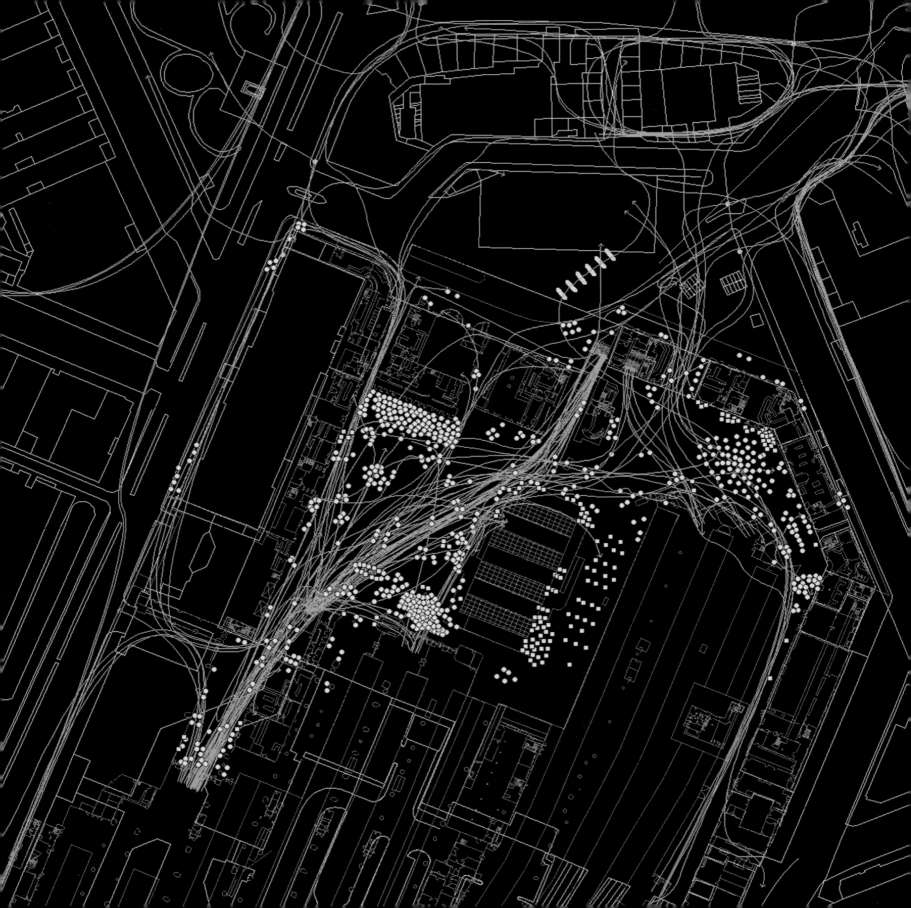

influenced by the way the layout makes it easier, or more difficult, for people to move around. Those interactions are both social and economic.'

The i-VALUL project has generated processes and tools that can help practitioners, academics and the community sectors to communicate about social and economic value. The new tools can help to measure previously intangible aspects of spatial design such as the quality of a street, or the vitality of a town centre. 'When it comes to property value,' says Stonor, 'which is easier to measure, we've been able to show that there is a clear, demonstrable connection back to layout, and that the work of planners actively influences value.'

Through active partnerships such as UrbanBuzz, planners are beginning to re-engage with spatial analysis tools. A new generation of computational modellers, for example those working on the UrbanBuzz SSSP project (see page 184), aims to bring masterplanning into the digital age in an efficient and cost-effective way. SSSP project partner Jennifer Currier works on Newham's regeneration team. 'Initially, we had questions as to how we could use some SSSP tools,' she says, 'but the value of others was immediately apparent. For example, one tool can predict and visualise on a map how far people can actually walk in a given time, according to actual site conditions. Another can assess site permeability, specifying and visualising specific points on the map where an "intervention", such as a bridge or a new crossing, needs to be placed.'

Whilst Geographic Information Systems (GIS) have been used by analysts for many years, GIS rarely helped town planners with understanding socio-economic relationships or identifying efficiencies in service delivery. Today, things are changing, and it is in this area that other UrbanBuzz projects are breaking new ground. It is now possible to link and connect different types of spatial data in GIS, and to understand issues such as the relationship between antisocial behaviour and urban layout, and between foot traffic on the street and the rental value of adjacent buildings.

'Local authorities hold increasing amounts of information in GIS,' says UCL's Professor Alan Penn, UrbanBuzz's lead academic. 'It is now possible to use datasets and a GIS system to answer questions that policymakers are very interested in.' Online tools, for example the community maps created by the MCSC project (see page 154), will also impact on the local authority role, says Penn: 'Planners are in an interesting intermediary role between lobby groups, political masters and the public. It's all part of e-government.'

The rise of geo-mapping

From crime maps to green zones, local authorities are using GIS to record and visualise city data that everyone can understand. 'The key to GIS is being able to integrate diverse datasets on small area geographies,' says Professor Allan Brimicombe, Centre for Geo-Information Studies at the University of East London, and coordinator of the EASY and SEDUC projects.

'GIS can help to integrate social, economic, physical and environmental data for detailed analysis. We analysts provide a kind of meso to macro view of the context in which any sort of development is going to sit,' says Brimicombe.

The EASY project (see page 112), has interpreted a variety of different administrative datasets in order to generate accurate estimates of populations at very localised levels. 'There are some fundamental differences across official population statistics,' says Brimicombe. 'Our purpose is not to say that any source of official statistics is inadequate, but simply to say that we have a new view.'

What's hanging in the balance, he adds, is accurate population estimates on which to base social infrastructure planning. The Community Infrastructure Levy (CIL) comes into play in 2009,

'Local authorities hold increasing amounts of information in GIS. It is now possible to use your data and your GIS system to answer questions that policymakers are very interested in'
UCL's Professor Alan Penn, UrbanBuzz's lead academic

'I like to think about landscapes. There's a landscape of poverty out there. There's a landscape of accessibility to a GP or to a park. These landscapes may be social, cultural or physical. We bring these out into the open and map them. Policy makers and designers can then base their strategies on our data'
Professor Allan Brimicombe, UEL, EASY and SEDUC project coordinator

alongside current Section 106 arrangements (planning gain agreements that encourage developers to provide community benefits), and revenue for boroughs is best accessed via a social infrastructure plan based on evidence-based population projections.

The SEDUC project (see page 180) has collected and interrogated data from council reporting systems in order to realise useful information about local townscapes, in this case identifying locations that suffer high levels of anti-social behaviour – and explaining which urban layout factors may be contributing factors.

Facilitating active participation

Combining the potential of these new computer techniques with the interactive geographic information interfaces used by the MCSC project, it is possible to imagine a future in which everyone could actively participate in the planning process. Yet putting technology tools aside, we will still need expert planners and designers. For Mandar Puranik, SSSP project partner and an urban designer from Tower Hamlets, the SSSP case study, which has 'test-driven' the new tools on a live site, has been the focal point. 'The case study showed how

designers' experiential skills and expertise, plus information gained from physical mapping, can be factored in, and how SSSP could work with our current tools,' he says.

As they develop, these new tools and processes could have a variety of applications, particularly in the private sector. SSSP could be useful for developers seeking investors to get a scheme up and running. The i–VALUL tools will inform wide-ranging masterplanning decisions. MCSC has provided a process for actively engaging communities in collective decisions about the future of the places they live in.

Collaborative working is increasingly recognised as the only practical approach to the complex social, economic, environmental and physical forces that impact upon the creation of successful communities. And, as UrbanBuzz has clearly demonstrated, moves supporting data access and systems interoperability will greatly support the exchange and use of data amongst collaborating project teams and the public. 'The recent rise in the availability of data has driven the new interest in GIS-based analysis,' says Brimicombe. 'The challenge, one that UrbanBuzz is helping to meet, is to be able to analyse that data into what we'd call actionable insights.'

The SSSP project is developing a set of tools and processes for digital masterplanning. Digital links, supporting efficient data exchange, would enable the widespread use of efficient computer-based analysis. Such scenario testing capability could quickly answer complex 'what if' questions, allowing the development of well-informed design options

While the concepts of sustainability and sustainable development have been with us since the *Brundtland Report* in 1987, it was only at the end of the 1990s that 'sustainable design' began to rise up the planning agenda. The 1999 *Urban Task Force* report, with its focus on design quality, and the first UK Sustainable Development Strategy of the same year, marked a significant turning point. Sustainability criteria are now central to the design of new buildings and the built environment, resulting in an increasing number of considerations that need to be taken into account within the design process.

Issues that were once the domain of major developments requiring Environmental Impact Assessments (EIAs) have become pertinent at much smaller scales. Knowledge of renewable energies, hydrology, lighting, thermal design and waste management is increasingly important. Alongside this, the growing acceptance of advanced spatial analysis as a determinant for accessibility, connectivity and mobility means that urban design is becoming an increasingly technical discipline, based on scientific methodology rather than architectural intuition.

The response by government to these changes was initially slow, but has accelerated in recent years. In 2005, Planning Policy Statement (PPS)1 was adopted, placing sustainable development and design quality as the foremost objectives of the planning system. In 2006, the Building Regulations relating to energy were substantively revised and ramped up in terms of performance expectations. In 2007, the Code for Sustainable Homes (CSH) was adopted, requiring that all new homes are zero-carbon rated by 2016.

During the same period, each planning authority across the country has sought to develop its own supplementary guidance relating to sustainable design. At first this was rather loosely written, avoiding performance expectations and simply asking planning applicants to think about ecology or waste management during the preparation of a planning application. This began to change post-2006: the Greater London Authority (GLA) adopted guidance on sustainable design and construction in 2006, with a focus on precise performance expectations, and the London Borough of Merton adopted its pioneering planning policy regarding the use of onsite renewable energy technologies (the Merton Rule).

The consequence of these refinements is that, in the space of less than 10 years, the number of issues that need to be addressed within planning applications has ballooned. Every six months or so, a new technical issue is added to the list. Presently, the focus is on life cycle analysis, life cycle costing and materials usage. In the near future, within major metropolitan areas, more formal analysis of urban heat island effects ›

Skills for sustainable design
Sustainability criteria are now central to built environment design. Knowledge of renewable energy, hydrology, thermal design and waste management – along with inclusive design principles – is now increasingly necessary for planners and designers

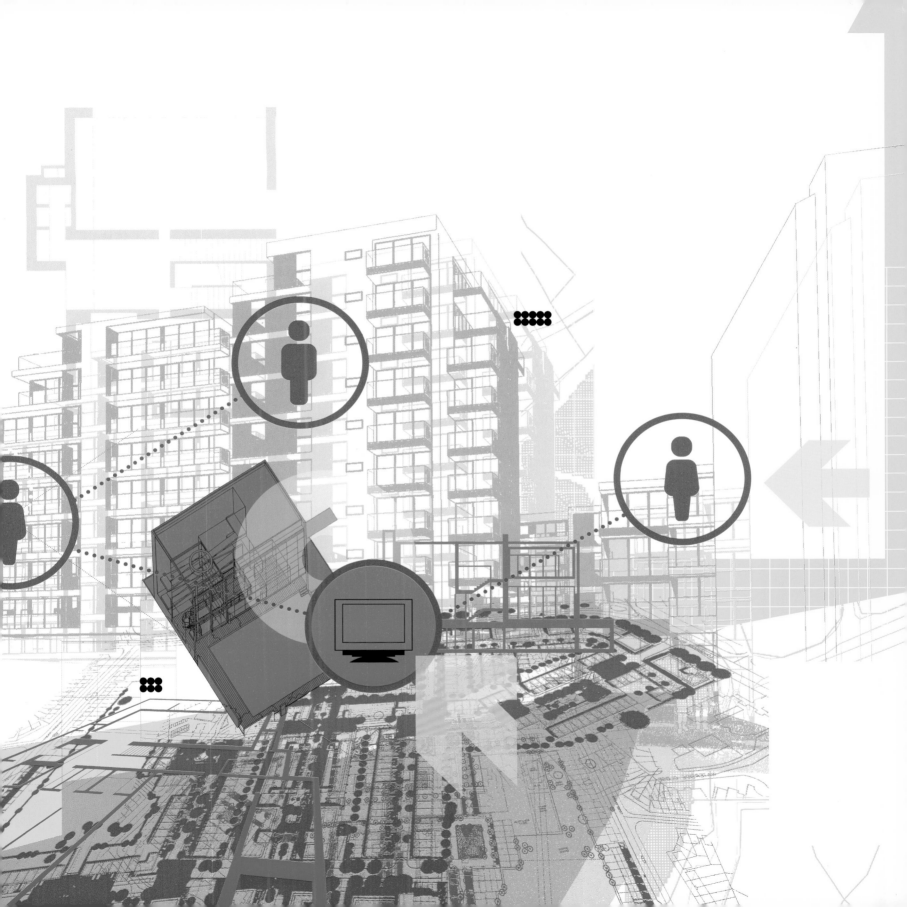

can be expected. Not to mention, of course, the expectations for climate adaptation should the UK warm up faster than expected.

In the context of all these recent rapid changes to the practice of planning, the UrbanBuzz SUSTAINABLE TRAINING project (see page 194) was established to critique live planning applications. Project coordinator Julian Hart, a planing consultant, established a Sustainable Design Review Panel comprised of academic experts on urban lighting, hydrology, noise, energy performance and other disciplines. The panel met to consider planning applications, and feedback was taken back to planning teams across London. The aim was to help train planning policy and development control officers in aspects of sustainable urban design.

'In the average planning department, relatively under-paid planning officers, often with social science degrees, are working hard to assimilate highly technical subjects,' says Hart. The result is that many design and development issues are not being addressed, he suggests. It is simply beyond the resource and skills capacity of planning officers across the UK.

To make matters worse, there is continuing uncertainty about the use of the Code for Sustainable Homes (CSH) within the planning process: can local authorities set conditions requiring the performance of new developments to meet specific CSH levels? Many planning authorities are now doing so, but there has been no formal position from government or the planning inspectorate on the legitimacy of such interventions. 'Where such conditions are being used, they are often badly worded, providing plenty of scope for developers to wriggle out of them,' says Hart.

There is evidence that this lack of development control is keenly felt by concerned communities. 'Every time a neighbourhood sees that an area next to them being proposed for development, there's a negative reaction,' says Professor Alan Penn, lead academic for the UrbanBuzz programme. 'This perception is something that has grown over the last 50-70 years, as the planning system has developed. We have realised that the planners, architects, developers and builders involved in constructing our built environment frequently make mistakes.

'The UrbanBuzz response has been to use academic knowledge about how things can go wrong as a starting point for changing these negative perceptions,' says Penn. The LOWCARB4REAL project, for example, (see page 146) set out to disseminate the results of research into the energy performance of new buildings, and revealed that energy performance forecasts are not being met by recent housing developments. The i-VALUL project (page 134) is seeking to ensure that developers recognise the value of good urban design, and plan to higher standards. The MCSC project (page 154) aims to involve communities in local decision-making.

Closing the skills gap

The findings from the UrbanBuzz SUSTAINABLE TRAINING project and recent research projects are striking. The report *Mind the Skills* gap, commissioned by the Academy for Sustainable Communities (now the Homes and Communities Agency Academy) and undertaken by Arup in 2007, provided the first cross-sector assessment of the skills required to deliver sustainable communities. This wide-ranging

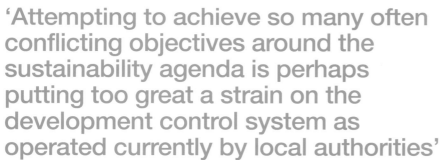

'Attempting to achieve so many often conflicting objectives around the sustainability agenda is perhaps putting too great a strain on the development control system as operated currently by local authorities'
Nick Bailey, University of Westminster

report acknowledged an acute skills gap within the public sector planning profession. Since then, new initiatives such as 'Capacitycheck', a method of appraising urban design skills, have been set up to address this urgent issue. Alongside these moves, the UrbanBuzz programme provided the kind of specific examples that planning teams needed in order to improve their understanding of sustainable design.

At the beginning of 2009, as UrbanBuzz drew to a close, a new 'expert support network' of renewable energy experts was being set up to offer advice and support to planning professionals across England. The network, managed by Centre for Sustainable Energy (CSE), will be run in association with the Department of Energy and Climate Change (DECC) and the Department for Communities and Local Government (CLG).

Design review

The Commission for Architecture and the Built Environment (CABE) is a champion of Design Review Panels. These are now enthusiastically adopted across the country at regional and local levels. 'Originally, CABE's Design Review Panels comprised architects, but CABE now aims to include sustainability experts, usually one per panel,' says Hart. 'Often, at the local level, panels are unable to have such representation, and sometimes do not even extend to urban design expertise, relying entirely on architects.'

While all panel members selected by Hart for his review panel were technical experts in their disciplines, and knowledgeable on the impact of their technologies on the built environment, in general they were not familiar with the planning application and determination process.

They were therefore reviewing the submitted planning applications with fresh eyes, with no preconceptions arising from familiarity as to how the planning system 'works'. They focused specifically on how their technical subject area was dealt with by the applications they reviewed.

The challenges to good design

One sample planning application stood out from the rest in terms of highlighting the issues. For confidentiality reasons, the project cannot be identified. It was for a 250-unit residential development with a mix of uses at ground floor, designed to a density of 330 dwellings per hectare. The location was central London; the value was well in excess of £50 million (pre-credit crunch). The problems associated with the development raised by the panel were alarming.

01 The planning application made frequent references to the wrong project, indicating that material on several subject areas simply had been cut and pasted. The design was not locally specific. This alone should have provided grounds to reject the planning application.

02 The energy statement had been resubmitted half way through the determination process in order to claim that higher renewable energy targets could be met. The resubmitted energy statement showed no attempt to consider the implications of these very significant design changes. The energy experts on the panel concluded that even meeting energy building control requirements would be questionable.

03 Other issues included poor urban design, with affordable housing tenants excluded from communal gardens, and poor provision for daylighting, with significant overshadowing of adjacent buildings. The glossy graphics indicated a green lawn for the roofscape, but the text of the planning application contained no reference to the provision of green or brown roofs.

This particular development had been given planning permission before the panel response could be made available to the planning officers. The planning officers did not appreciate the panel's criticisms concerning energy and ecology. They had sought to address the daylighting issue, but lacked the resources to challenge the developer at appeal.

While this particular project encapsulated problems on almost every front, these and other issues appeared across many other projects, which were also given consent, suggesting that the planning application system is not delivering as we would like on the sustainable design agenda. 'As the panel process proceeded, it became clear,' said Hart, 'that there is a large and growing credibility gap between aspirations, planning guidance, and delivery.'

The project experience confirmed that planning applications are very loosely written so as to provide developers with as much flexibility as possible, and to limit the degree to which they are committed to delivering on the sustainable design agenda. 'Planning officers are in a difficult position on receiving planning applications because these documents simply do not spell out what new development projects will actually provide,' says Hart. For instance, the extent to which Design and Access Statements commit to CABE's 'By Design' expectations, which are essentially rules of thumb principles in urban design, is frequently to paraphrase the CABE documentation with no explanation as to how the design of a scheme actually meets the principles.

'What urgently needs to happen,' says Hart, 'is a review of the whole framework for controlling the quality of new buildings and urban areas. As sustainable design, taken in its widest sense, becomes an important objective for new development, the once-clear boundary between planning and building control is now confused.

'We need to look at the entire process, from pre-application through to final occupation of buildings, and decide what issues should be addressed, as well as when and how,' continues Hart. 'Planning is, at its heart, a local political issue about the acceptability of new development in its context, whether new development works successfully at an urban level and whether the impact of the development on neighbours and the public is acceptable.'

The wider solution will certainly encompass a greater division of labour, or more accurately division of competence, within the regulatory system. The planning and building control systems need to be able to draw on a range of skills and expertise matching that available to developers. This already happens to a degree in London for larger developments, where the Greater London Authority provides a central core of expertise for local planning authorities to rely on.

In Germany, and soon in Sweden, the owners of newly-built homes have the legal right to sue a developer if the energy performance of a dwelling, once occupied and measured over the first two years of occupation, does not meet exacting standards.

If applied in the UK, such regulation would remove worries at both planning and building control stages regarding energy performance, and such radical approaches possibly could be extended to other technical areas such as daylighting or water management.

Whatever the solution, sustainable design represents a major challenge to all parties in the community-building process. It requires us to find new and better ways to work together, rather than against each other, to secure better places to live for ourselves and for our children.

THE URBANBUZ PROJECTS

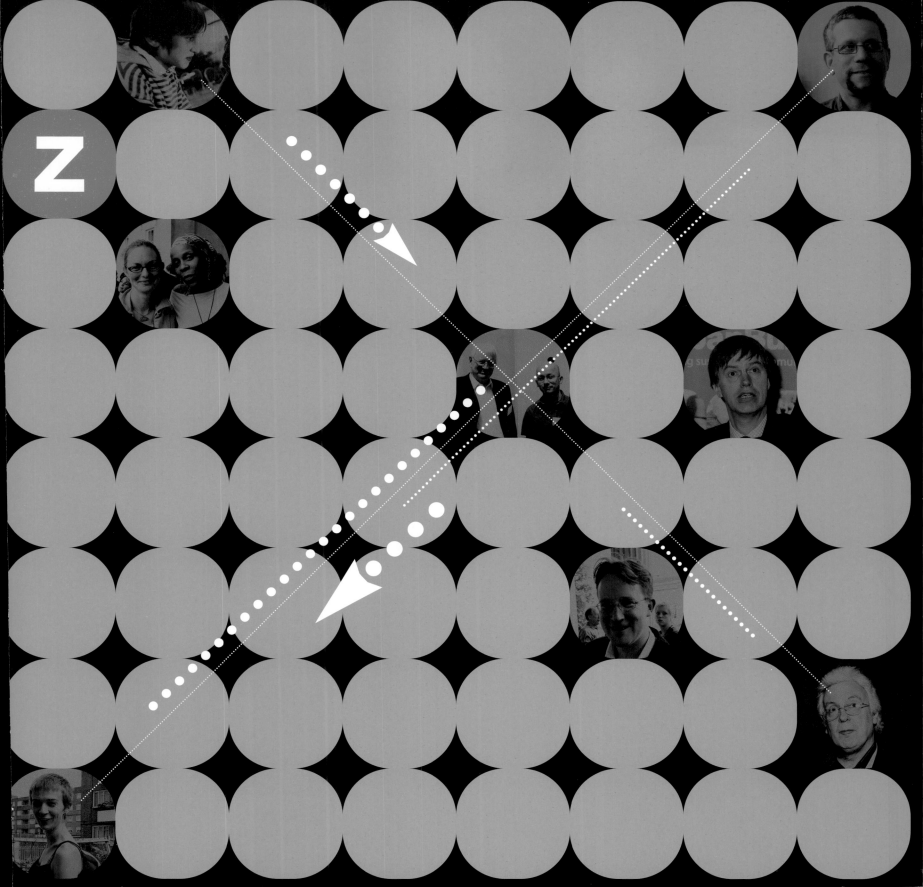

'The 21st century will be shaped by some very profound forces,' says Peter Bishop, Design Director in the office of the Mayor of London, speaking at the UrbanBuzz conference in December 2008. 'Oil, energy, population growth and food shortages will be the factors shaping the cities that we are designing.'

This short statement highlights the key issues tackled by the 27 UrbanBuzz projects. From food production capacity in cities to social cohesion and low-carbon lifestyles, each project is rooted in the need to create innovative tools and processes that support sustainable living.

Although they may have addressed very different issues, the project teams share a view on what sustainability means in practice. Sustainable communities use resources effectively and efficiently. They are low-carbon, low-crime, inclusive democracies in which agents for economic change thrive. Residents benefit from integrated transport, housing supply and tenure. As Bishop noted, there is much work to be done: 'There's no simple solution, due to the complexity and the diversity of our environments. Looking at the placemaking agenda, we have to answer some simple questions.' Do we want dysfunctional, failing cities, or thriving cities designed around human beings that provide a sound foundation for 21st century life? 'There is,' says Bishop, 'a compelling need to equip "placemakers" with evidence-based tools to help them create the public and private realms of the future, generating activity, vibrancy and a sense of proud association.'

With this in mind, each project has tackled one or more aspects of the complex interaction between the physical, social, environmental and economic processes that underpin sustainable communities. Key outcomes are new and effective processes and practical tools that can be used by public, private, community and third sector partners. More than 150 organisations have been involved in the programme, and most projects involved local communities where, ultimately, the benefits of UrbanBuzz will be most strongly felt and appreciated.

The wide-ranging sharing of knowledge is key to involving, and engaging, professionals and communities in a collective future. 'That is what the UrbanBuzz projects are all about,' says Jean Venables, President of the Institution of Civil Engineers (ICE). 'We need to use the best science available to make considered judgments, and then use these skills and judgments to design communities for the future. Many practitioners don't necessarily know where knowledge lies. Often they rely on central organisation research facilities to inform them of the latest thinking and processes. UrbanBuzz has been different. It has been proactive in promoting the benefits that new tools and processes can offer.'

This proactive approach has seen a wide range of project participants working together. The 27 projects, which ran for between six and 20 months, were led by academics (17), private sector organisations (7), a local authority (1) and voluntary sector organisations (2). UrbanBuzz support ranged from just £7,000 to £383,000 per project. 'Contributions in kind' added £2.75 million to the total value of the programme.

Changing the way we think
The 27 UrbanBuzz-funded projects, so varied at first glance in terms of partners, objectives and outcomes, shared an overarching theme of knowledge exchange. All projects were innovative and multi-disciplinary, as befits a programme designed to produce tools and processes that will change the way we think about sustainable communities

The projects: outputs and outcomes

At a practical level, the approach taken by UrbanBuzz to maximise ongoing knowledge transfer and dissemination of project outputs and outcomes was threefold:

01   Education **Ensuring that academic partners incorporated outcomes of projects into university courses and, wherever possible, created discrete educational and/or e-learning modules.**

02   Training **Ensuring that outcomes of projects have appropriate linkages with existing training delivery agencies and, in particular, making sure that outputs from projects are made available on web portals and existing communication channels, and so accessible to a wide range of audiences.**

03   Case studies **Journal articles and academic papers are being generated by project leaders to ensure that knowledge and understanding is disseminated effectively to interested parties (see page 48).**

Classifying the projects

Knowledge is not an easy concept to define or evaluate. It can be distributed (only certain people can do/know certain things), ambiguous (it may or may not fit with a pre-existing mental view of the world) or disruptive (it could change practice). Each project has confronted these challenges, and the initial evaluations are presented here in graphic form.

There are inherent limitations with any classification process, especially for projects that are complex in both their nature and approach. Nevertheless, to communicate and understand the projects, their relation to each other and how they fit into the programme, classification is a necessary process. Three key classification themes are outlined on the following pages:

01   facets of sustainability;
02   broader contributions to sustainability;
03   collaboration and end users – organisations (project collaborators and end users); physical, information, social outputs and outcomes.

01

Facets of sustainability

The typology of projects being funded is illustrated here. The top radar diagram (below) illustrates the average scores against 19 key facets of sustainability, whilst the bottom diagram illustrates average scores against primary sustainability indicators. Both diagrams are based on feedback scores from the project originators.

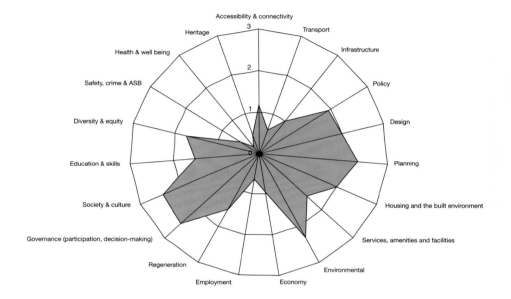

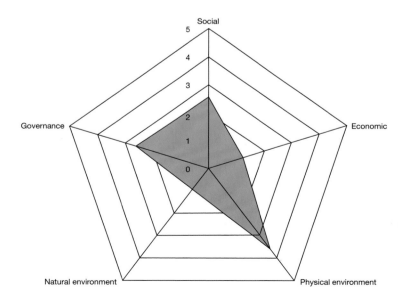

02

**Broader contributions
to sustainability**
During the course of the programme,
projects were analysed in terms of
sustainability sectors. The pie charts
illustrate the distribution of these that each
project sought to address. The sectors have
been aggregated into seven facets.

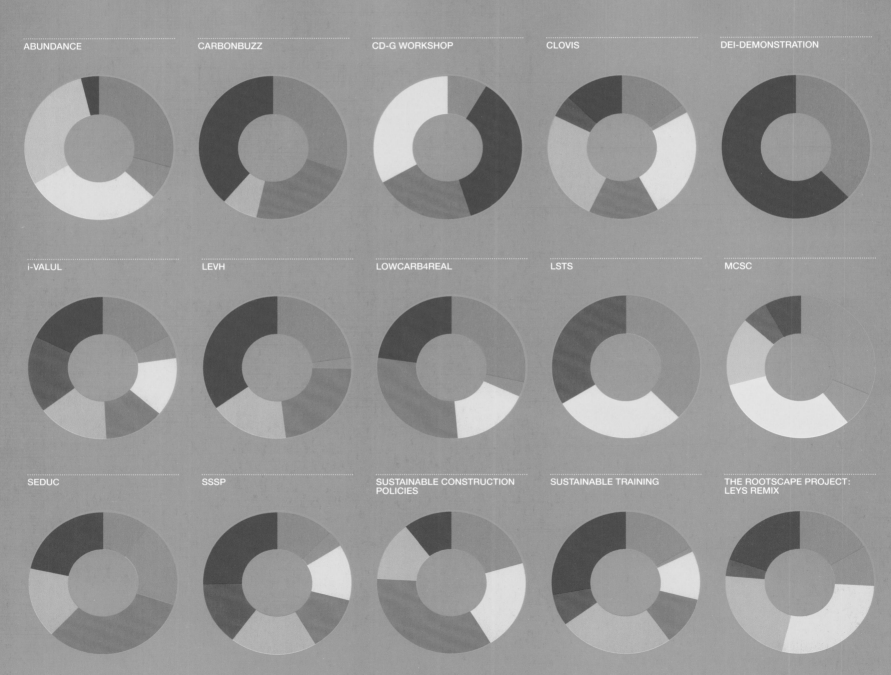

ABUNDANCE

CARBONBUZZ

CD-G WORKSHOP

CLOVIS

DEI-DEMONSTRATION

i-VALUL

LEVH

LOWCARB4REAL

LSTS

MCSC

SEDUC

SSSP

SUSTAINABLE CONSTRUCTION
POLICIES

SUSTAINABLE TRAINING

THE ROOTSCAPE PROJECT:
LEYS REMIX

Proportion of each project's contribution to the following sustainability facets:

- Environment
- Policy
- Design/housing
- Society
- Planning
- Governance
- Infrastructure

The following groupings apply:

Environment	Natural environment, and reduction of CO_2 from buildings and transport
Policy	Government and local government policy on sustainability
Design/housing	Design, housing and the built environment
Society	Society, economy, employment, diversity, safety/crime
Planning	Planning and regeneration
Governance	Participation and decision making
Infrastructure	Accessibility, connectivity, transport and infrastructure

EASY

E-POD

ESP-SIM

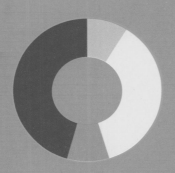

FEfUR

GBE

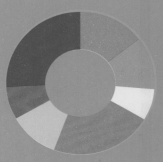

METRICITY

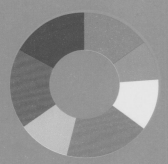

MOBILISING KNOWLEDGE

REBOPSE

RETILE COMBEEP

SCREAM

TOWARDS ZERO CARBON SCHOOLS

VIBAT LONDON

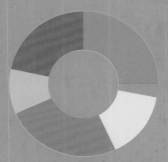

The UrbanBuzz projects
Changing the way we think

All projects aimed to contribute to between two and seven of these defined sustainability facets, and their relative proportions are shown in the charts on pages 80 and 81, and on the individual project pages.

An example of this relative proportionality is provided (below) for the i-VALUL project. Within these categories, which are explained on page 81, the distributions within each project can be illustrated as shown.

Please note that absolute values are not shown, but merely expressed as a percentage of each project's total contribution to each of the sustainability categories.

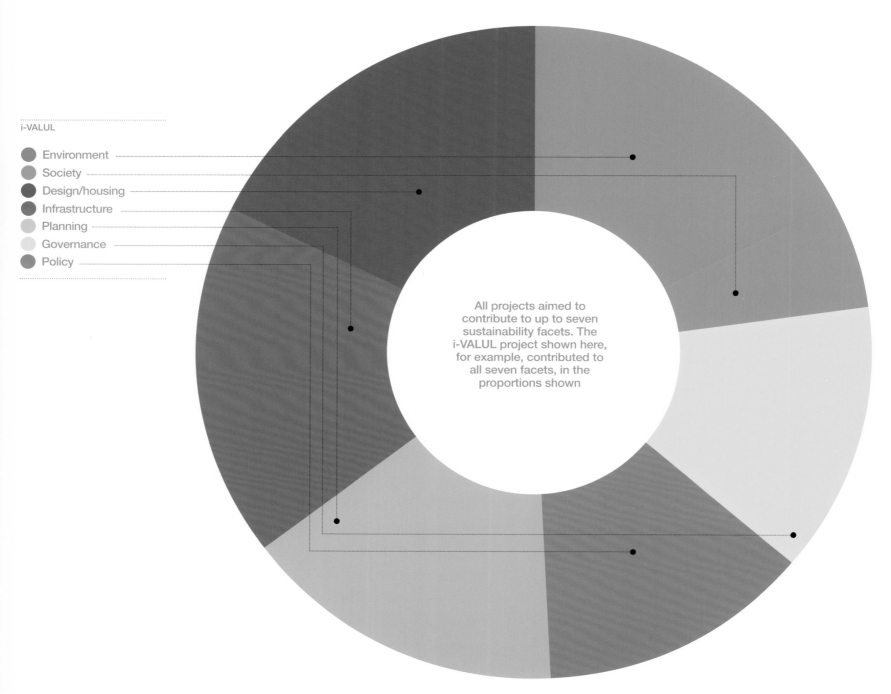

i-VALUL

- Environment
- Society
- Design/housing
- Infrastructure
- Planning
- Governance
- Policy

All projects aimed to contribute to up to seven sustainability facets. The i-VALUL project shown here, for example, contributed to all seven facets, in the proportions shown

03

Collaboration and end-users
As the projects developed, it
became apparent that natural 'clusters'
were forming, as outlined below.

Cluster	Projects
Spatial planning	EASY, i-VALUL, SEDUC, SSSP, METRICITY
Community and stakeholder engagement	ABUNDANCE, CD-G WORKSHOP, CLOVIS, MCSC, ESP-SIM, LSTS MOBILISING KNOWLEDGE, THE ROOTSCAPE PROJECT, GBE, FEFUR, REBOPSE, SCREAM, RETILE
Low carbon living	CARBONBUZZ, DEI DEMONSTRATION, E-POD, LEVH, LOWCARB4REAL, SUSTAINABLE CONSTRUCTION POLICIES, TOWARDS ZERO CARBON SCHOOLS, VIBAT LONDON, SUSTAINABLE TRAINING

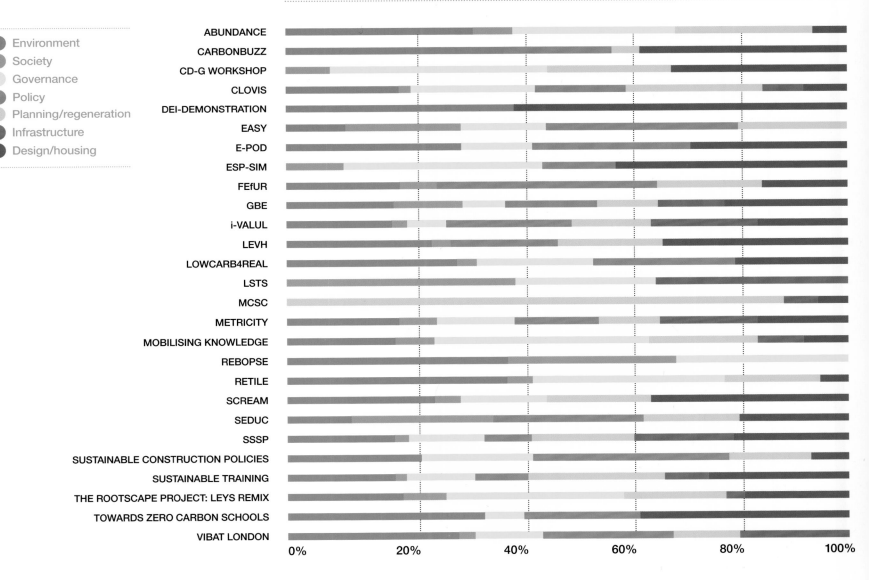

- Environment
- Society
- Governance
- Policy
- Planning/regeneration
- Infrastructure
- Design/housing

Division of each project's contribution to sustainability categories

The UrbanBuzz projects
Changing the way we think

Many (18 or 66.67 per cent) of the UrbanBuzz projects aimed to exchange knowledge with, and influence the activity of, local government. Nearly as many were targeting the private sector. There is considerable overlap between the projects.

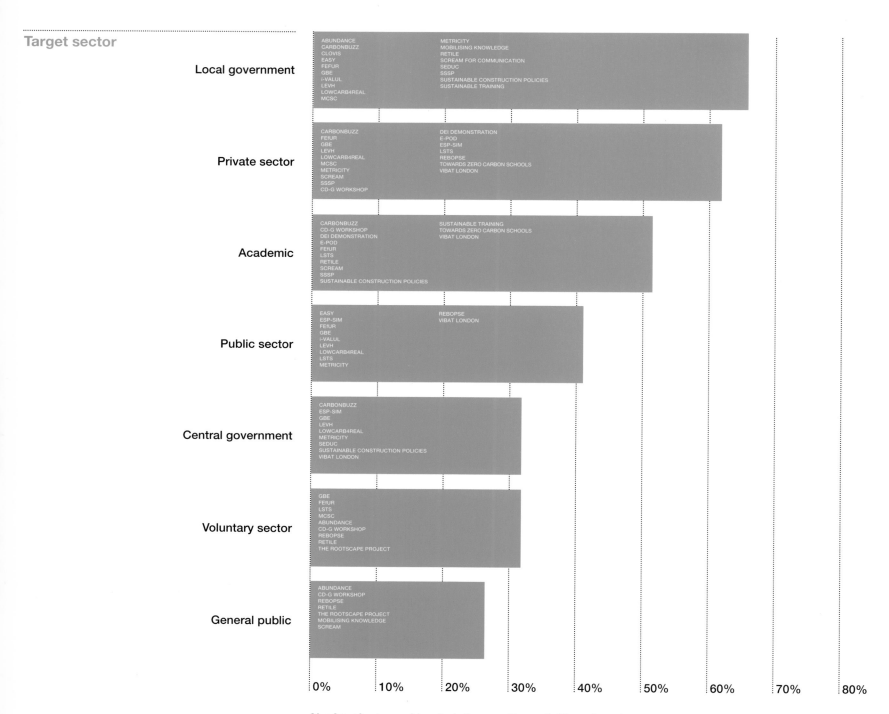

Target sector

Local government
ABUNDANCE
CARBONBUZZ
CLOVIS
EASY
FEFUR
GBE
i-VALUL
LEVH
LOWCARB4REAL
MCSC
METRICITY
MOBILISING KNOWLEDGE
RETILE
SCREAM FOR COMMUNICATION
SEDUC
SSSP
SUSTAINABLE CONSTRUCTION POLICIES
SUSTAINABLE TRAINING

Private sector
CARBONBUZZ
FEFUR
GBE
LEVH
LOWCARB4REAL
MCSC
METRICITY
SCREAM
SSSP
CD-G WORKSHOP
DEI DEMONSTRATION
E-POD
ESP-SIM
LSTS
REBOPSE
TOWARDS ZERO CARBON SCHOOLS
VIBAT LONDON

Academic
CARBONBUZZ
CD-G WORKSHOP
DEI DEMONSTRATION
E-POD
FEFUR
LSTS
RETILE
SCREAM
SSSP
SUSTAINABLE CONSTRUCTION POLICIES
SUSTAINABLE TRAINING
TOWARDS ZERO CARBON SCHOOLS
VIBAT LONDON

Public sector
EASY
ESP-SIM
FEFUR
GBE
i-VALUL
LEVH
LOWCARB4REAL
LSTS
METRICITY
REBOPSE
VIBAT LONDON

Central government
CARBONBUZZ
ESP-SIM
GBE
LEVH
LOWCARB4REAL
METRICITY
SEDUC
SUSTAINABLE CONSTRUCTION POLICIES
VIBAT LONDON

Voluntary sector
GBE
FEFUR
LSTS
MCSC
ABUNDANCE
CD-G WORKSHOP
REBOPSE
RETILE
THE ROOTSCAPE PROJECT

General public
ABUNDANCE
CD-G WORKSHOP
REBOPSE
RETILE
THE ROOTSCAPE PROJECT
MOBILISING KNOWLEDGE
SCREAM

0%   10%   20%   30%   40%   50%   60%   70%   80%

% of projects seeking to influence the activities of each sector

Knowledge exchange: collaboration, not competition

'UrbanBuzz has been a really successful example of an unusual collaboration,' says John Lock, Development Director at the University of East London. 'Ten years ago, you might have had individual academics partnering each other, but you wouldn't have had the kind of institutional collaboration that has happened here, where we've played to each other's strengths. We've "grown" projects that wouldn't otherwise have happened because they've been constructed not around doing research, but around knowledge exchange, and have focused on making things happen for people.'

Knowledge exchange within UrbanBuzz was encouraged from the programme's outset. Proposers had to share their ideas openly on the UrbanBuzz website, encouraging collaboration. Project consortia were required to have at least one 'fellow' from both academic and non-academic organisations (see page 30 for more on fellows and networks). Knowledge could thus flow within projects, between projects and between project teams and their target audiences, using a range of knowledge exchange mechanisms.

Professor Stephen Gage, Professor of Innovative Technology at the Bartlett School of Architecture, UCL, led the DEI DEMONSTRATION project. 'The value of UrbanBuzz lay in the transmission of knowledge,' he says. 'It allowed us to progress an innovative project, with students, without having to construct a complete research argument from the outset. Some of the ideas that we've worked with have been in place since the 1960s, but nobody has really explored their potential. Combined with this, there has been truly innovative thinking. Our team has invented things together, things that haven't been made before, and we're still inventing.'

Gemma Moore is a PhD student at UCL and an UrbanBuzz project monitor. 'The challenge,' says Moore, 'is to communicate what has happened during the UrbanBuzz programme to the stakeholders that shape communities. There's a lot that can be learned from this experience and shared with parties that haven't been involved in the programme.'

For effective knowledge exchange to take place, critical 'stakeholders' were assembled to join project teams. Where necessary, these were complemented by directions from an expert advisory group. Most project teams noted that success was more likely if end-users were engaged early on, to help ensure adoption of the new tools and processes when ready.

The CD-G WORKSHOP project clearly demonstrated such engagement in action. The team tackled 'consultation fatigue' in communities across the Thames Gateway by investigating ways in which active community collaboration and dialogue can be stimulated. Urban designers, planners and developers met with communities in hands-on sessions to discuss student designs for public spaces in North Greenwich and Beckton.

'The plan was to encourage interaction and scenario-testing with community members. We have all collaborated in knowledge exchange; a mutual learning that opened processes and discussions about the social and spatial future of the Thames Gateway. The ability to take part in the system, and to invest in and contribute to change, is what matters to people,' says Christoph Hadrys, UEL, the CD-G WORKSHOP project coordinator.

'Ten years ago, you wouldn't have had the kind of institutional collaborations that have happened here. Projects have been constructed not around research, but around knowledge exchange, and have focused on making things happen for people'
John Lock, UEL Development Director

Knowledge exchange mechanisms
The knowledge exchange mechanisms selected by projects generally addressed in-project collaboration, with perhaps less consideration being given to post-project dissemination. Where there was a shortfall in planning,

UrbanBuzz stepped in to provide further support in order to harness project value and increase outreach dissemination activities. The project chapters provide further details on the level (between whom) and types (mechanisms) of knowledge exchange.

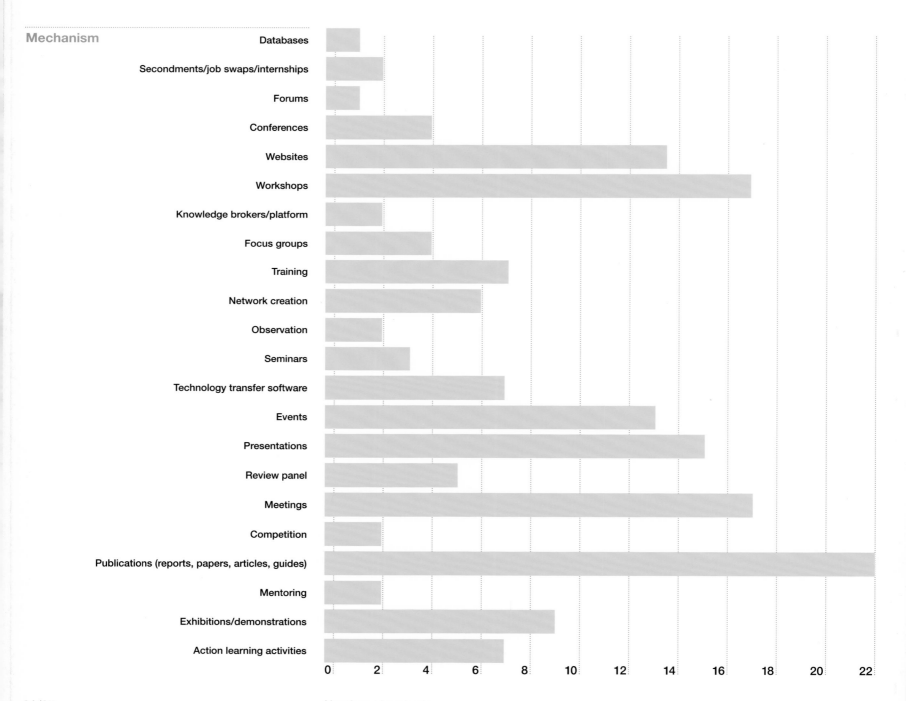

Mechanism

Databases
Secondments/job swaps/internships
Forums
Conferences
Websites
Workshops
Knowledge brokers/platform
Focus groups
Training
Network creation
Observation
Seminars
Technology transfer software
Events
Presentations
Review panel
Meetings
Competition
Publications (reports, papers, articles, guides)
Mentoring
Exhibitions/demonstrations
Action learning activities

0   2   4   6   8   10   12   14   16   18   20   22

Number of projects

'There's a great deal of debate in some sustainability fields, for example transport and urban planning, but very little in others. And there's little action. We are underestimating the scale of change required to hit recently adopted targets. Within the transport sector, we're still rising in terms of carbon emissions. We need to urgently accelerate our efforts' **Dr Robin Hickman, associate director and transport planner, Halcrow**

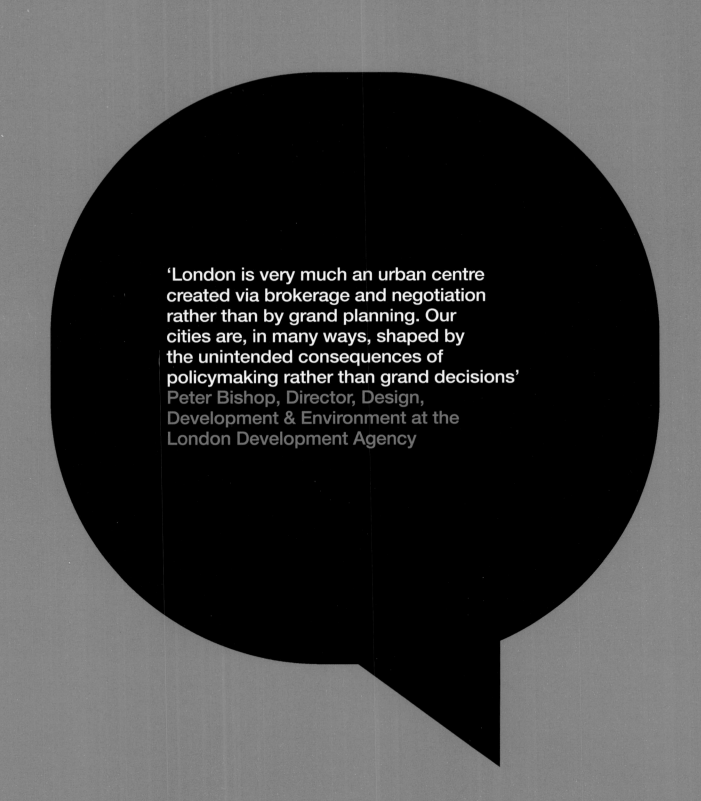

'London is very much an urban centre created via brokerage and negotiation rather than by grand planning. Our cities are, in many ways, shaped by the unintended consequences of policymaking rather than grand decisions'
Peter Bishop, Director, Design, Development & Environment at the London Development Agency

E-POD	ESP-SIM	FEfUR	GBE	i-VALUL	LEVH	LOWCARB4REAL
At this one-day event, key presentations on energy performance and environmental design were recorded and then converted into educational podcasts.	Promote an alternative, proactive method of building housing developments and provide an online tool to support this process.	Workshops brought academics from a diverse range of disciplines and other representatives together to consider a live development site.	An online database called Gendersite was constructed. It contains titles and links for English-language resources that consider gender and the built environment.	Development of an evidence-based urban layout evaluation tool to overcome barriers that prevent layout factors from being considered in economic appraisals.	Complete refurbishment of a Victorian house in Camden to reduce carbon emissions by over 80 per cent.	Synthesising and disseminating learning on sustainable residential energy design, construction, fabric and process aspects from Stamford Brook field trials.
Disseminated the principles behind built environment engineering – particularly energy and ventilation – to a wider audience, and offered practical guidance through international case studies.	Offers citizens and organisations an alternative route to satisfy housing needs through a framework and tool for Enabled Self Procurement.	Urban regeneration is increasingly collaborative and involves more specialist disciplines. This project sought to identify any other areas of expertise that might contribute.	For those seeking to deliver greater accessibility and equality in development, Gendersite provides access to knowledge, learning and research results.	To ensure that there is greater incentive to deliver best practice in urban design, i-VALUL sought to make its economic value more tangible.	This project demonstrated the contribution of different CO_2-reducing measures and associated cost benefits.	Addresses energy-efficient building designs, and the gap between design and actual energy performance, through workshops involving those responsible for site practices.
Focused on design and construction, and improving knowledge on how to achieve best practice.	This new information technology tool helps to merge the processes of planning and design.	Primarily, this project focused on the planning stage. The management stage was also relevant, but to a lesser degree.	The database covers all steps of the process, from policy through to regulation, by providing a knowledge-base for practitioners in each area.	Design was initially the project's main focus. However, in due course it may have a strong influence on policy, planning and regulation.	Monitoring the project's outcome will inform future regulation relating to energy performance of existing building stock.	Aims to bridge this gap between design and construction, to ensure that new buildings perform as they have been designed and/or revisit the design bases.
A new website featuring the podcasts has been created to help people learn quickly from experts in relevant fields of learning.	Comprehensive guidance to the new approach was provided for professionals and lay people. In the future, this new approach is inherently a KE mechanism.	The workshops and site visits included a range of non-urbanist disciplines that brought fresh insights to the development challenge faced.	The majority of the KE will be ongoing, as people access the database to learn about accessibility and equality issues.	Achieved by making a Space Syntax map of the south-east widely available, and developing new tools and trainig courses for use in the public sector.	Collaborative effort between building contractors, suppliers, engineers and academics.	Publicised the outputs of an extended research project. Workshops increased understanding of on-site practice and improved knowledge exchange materials and styles.
A new website hosts a series of podcasts and other relevant information on best practice.	The significant output of the ESP-SIM project is an innovative software called YouCanPlan.	A toolkit/guidebook on urban regeneration. It comprises a series of questions, methods, observations and processes that any potential scheme should address.	An online searchable database bibliography of all research literature in the area of equality in the built environment.	A layout value map of the Greater South East, and a suite of layout valuation tools, was created. Projects with Local Authorities tested the map and tools.	The house was refurbished to a high standard for energy efficiency. Monitoring will inform a simulation model to encourage wider application.	The Low Carbon Housing Learning Zone, a website hosted by Leeds Metropolitan University, has the project's outputs in the form of learning and guidance modules.
he website and podcasts are available o all and will remain relevant for some time to come.	If this alternative technique were to become widely practiced, it would revolutionise development activity in the UK and build new communities.	Guidance on how to apply these novel insights to the regeneration process in other areas will be available from BURA.	The website will be kept up-to-date, providing a valuable resource for any researchers and practitioners in gender and equality issues.	Part of the ongoing process of learning about the use of Space Syntax methodologies to inform urban planning and to deliver better quality urban environments.	The learning from this project will inform Government strategy for a larger refurbishment programme of existing housing stock.	Knowledge from the original Stamford Brook field trials is now available in an easy to access format, enabling fast learning of methods to improve design.
One-hundred-and-sixty-five people attended the one-day event, and 56 of the attendees signed up to IBPSA-England within 72 hours of the event.	A competition to find 10 architectural pattern book house designs to initially populate YouCanPlan attracted 539 online votes between the 38 entries	Seventy-seven people attended the two Fresh Eyes events, including 52 academics.	The database lists 1,600 books, bibliographies, broadcasts, case studies, conference papers, journals and reports.	To create the greater southeast layout valuation map, 2.4million street segments were used.	Through the 'Old Home – Super Home' scheme, 1,800 people have visited the house.	Five workshops were held, and each group listed 'key imperatives' that will form the basis for discussion and recommendations to academia, industry and government
Visit www.lowcarbon buildingsdirectory.org	Visit www.esp-sim.org and www.youcanplan.co.uk to try out the software	Visit www.urbanbuzz.org	Visit www.gendersite.org	Visit www.spacesyntax.com /en/valuing-urban-layout.aspx	Visit www.levh.org.uk	Visit www.lmu.ac.uk/as/ cebe/projects/lowcarb4real /index.htm
See page 116	See page 120	See page 126	See page 130	See page 134	See page 140	See page 146

UrbanBuzz project description For further information: www.urbanbuzz.org	ABUNDANCE A living example of community agriculture, this project applied learning from South America to turn an unused green space into a high-yield urban plot.	CARBONBUZZ A platform to benchmark and track building energy-use from design to operation.	CD-G WORKSHOP The experimental project explores the potential for collaborative urban and architectural designs through academic, expert and community engagements.	CLOVIS Very different live regeneration projects in Bath and Southwark were compared in order to improve communication between stakeholders.	DEI DEMONSTRATION A technology demonstration project using phase changing wax (driven by temperature and building occupancy) in pistons to open and close shutters.	EASY Two-part project: provided a new approach to accurate local population estimates; and explored the use of estimates for the Community Infrastructure Levy.
Contribution towards sustainable development *Level 7*	Helps to reduce the food miles and carbon emissions associated with food production, while simultaneously involving communities in challenging public ownership of space.	Creation of a live system to capture data on design performance of new buildings against accredited benchmarks. This will help to generate better future designs.	Helped communities to envision the potential of their local area, and provided students with training about the importance of communication and engagement.	Live projects were used to improve processes for identifying stakeholders, applying appropriate engagement practices and learning from mistakes.	This project incorporated new technology that significantly improved energy performance – which was modified according to occupancy – in buildings.	More accurate and up-to-date information about populations enabled planning authorities to plan social and physical infrastructure requirements.
From policy to regulation, where does the project have most impact? *Level 6*	Aimed principally at social infrastructure policies, this project demonstrates the potential of using idle, publicly owned, green urban space to grow food.	The platform is a visual template for communicating energy-use during design and post completion, with a view to informing low-carbon design and influencing policy and regulation.	The principal focus of the project was at the planning and design interface, where new designs were tested out in a social context.	The main focus was planning, on the premise that it is during planning that consultation is most important.	Design technology to complement other approaches that optimise building performance.	This innovative way of deriving data on population from a range of sources is a social infrastructure planning tool.
Knowledge Exchange (KE) mechanism *Level 5*	Took learning from South America, combined it with academic understanding in the UK, and secured the engagement of local communities during the demonstration project.	A growing, active network of participants – primarily architects and service engineers – populate the database and learn from it.	Primarily architecture students explaining their projects, and what they'd learnt during them, to a lay, but interested, audience.	KE took place during the workshop and meetings. Key points included the need to identify all stakeholders and to manage their expectations.	The key KE occurred between architects and engineers during construction. The installation was also seen by 9,000 visitors to the UCL summer exhibition.	Local authorities trialled the new tool, and its potential benefits were disseminated to local councils across the UK. Several have expressed an interest in future usage.
Principal outputs/ outcomes *Level 4*	'Introduction to urban agriculture', a new module in UCL's Environment and Sustainable Development MSc. Integral to the first city Transition Town launch – Transition Town Brixton.	In the future, this website for inputting new information will provide a comprehensive dataset of the design and performance of new buildings.	Guidance, concerning how to engage communities through student projects, has been produced for dissemination across architectural schools.	A final report will summarise the lessons learnt and provide the means to disseminate the learning to a wider audience.	A test passive drive system is being monitored at Trinity Buoy Wharf. Commercial backing will be sought for the patented technology.	This new tool will be supplemented by a discussion report on its use in assisting infrastructure planning.
Legacy *Level 3*	New understanding of the practicalities and viability of urban agriculture within the UK policy and regulatory environment.	Will help to ascertain how current regulations may need to be revised. A collaboration between architects, it shows the way for future activity.	This guidance is a new piece of learning within the education environment – forming, for example, part of the material within UEL's Alternative Urbanisms MA.	This is part of the continuing debate to help advance our collective knowledge of best practice in community engagement and ultimately community empowerment.	This technology means that large windows are still an option architecturally. Such windows make good use of natural light, while retaining comfort and modern energy performance standards.	Local authorities, PCTs and the Healthy Urban Development Unit of the NHS will use this method to assist more focused infrastructure planning within shifting populations.
Quantitative information *Level 2*	Two-hundred-and-fifty people attended the launch of Transition Town Brixton on 2 October 2008, which featured ABUNDANCE and its locally produced food.	By 25 November 2008, 80 users had provided 83 projects on the platform.	A series of hands-on workshops, involving local communities, discussed the students' design projects and decided which would be most usefully implemented in Beckton.	There are clear principles involved in stakeholder management and engagement; there may be issues in the way these are managed in the education of future planners.	Over 9,000 visitors viewed the installation during the Bartlett School of Architecture Summer Exhibition, and more than 3,000 have visited the project website so far.	Eleven Thames Gateway Boroughs were modelled using the new method to estimate population change.
Additional information on all projects www.urbanbuzz.org (select projects) *Level 1*	Visit http://transitiontowns.org/Brixton/TheABUNDANCE PROJECT See page 92	Visit www.carbonbuzz.org See page 96	Visit www.cd-g-workshop.blogspot.com/ See page 100	Visit www.urbanbuzz.org See page 104	Visit www.pachube.com/feeds/1044 and www.deployable.org.uk See page 108	Visit www.uel.ac.uk/geo-information/EASY See page 112

The UrbanBuzz projects:
At-a-glance guide

open

The UrbanBuzz portfolio of projects tackled a range of sustainability issues, from low carbon living to community engagement.

This fold-out table provides an at-a-glance reference guide to each of the 27 projects, outlining the objectives, contribution to sustainable development, knowledge exchange mechanisms, impact and outcomes/outputs for each one.

References to further reading within this book are also included.

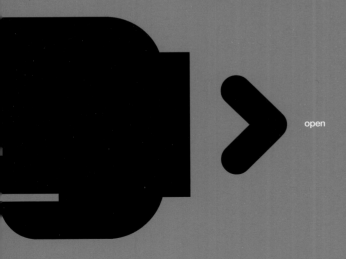

open

SEDUC	SSSP	SUSTAINABLE CONSTRUCTION POLICIES	SUSTAINABLE TRAINING	THE ROOTSCAPE PROJECT: LEYS REMIX	TOWARDS ZERO CARBON SCHOOLS	VIBAT LONDON
Mapped local-authority held, anti-social behaviour records to identify 'hot spots' and then developed guidance on urban design to help 'design out' anti-social behaviour.	Provided two local planning authorities with 3D digital design simulation software.	Seminars identified problems in the political and regulatory framework, and suggested how to address them.	A Sustainable Design Review Panel assessed live planning applications in training workshops for local authority planning teams.	Engaged young people in Oxford in design projects and provided training.	Launch of the CIBSE School Design Group, at a time when the Government plans to invest £45bn over 15 years in low-carbon schools.	The creation of a computer simulation tool that can help people understand the implications of different transport policy interventions in reducing CO$_2$ emissions.
Little in the way of scientific research has been done to understand the correlation between urban design and anti-social behaviour. This project found layout-based patterns for ASB activity.	The software is capable of giving immediate feedback on the sustainability of differing urban design options in relation to local spatial planning and development control.	Shortfalls and failures in policy and regulation were best understood by those involved in implementation. These were collated and documented to enable changes to be made.	Design expectations at the planning determination stage were increasing without a sufficient and corresponding up-skilling of planning teams.	Through urban-design-focused workshops the project enabled young people to develop a range of career-related and practical skills.	The multidisciplinary CIBSE School Design Group challenged silo mentality, which characterised the decision-making process for school design and operation.	There is a need to reduce carbon emissions from transport, but there was a lack of understanding about the impact of potential policy interventions or combinations of them.
This was a planning project, researching ASB geo-location issues and considering how and where design interventions should be focused.	The main impact areas of this project were a combination of planning and large-scale design (masterplanning).	The intent of this project was to influence policy, regulation, academic teaching, training, professional practice and future research.	This project facilitated the planning process by teaching planning teams rules of thumb to quickly ascertain whether development proposals were acceptable.	The project's key focus was urban design and will feed into the area regeneration work within Oxford.	The main area of impact was in relation to design, but will also help to draw more learning from monitoring and feed this through to designers.	The project simulated planning scenarios with the intention of identifying possible options for regulation in order to implement over-arching policy.
Most of the KE related to this project took place after project completion, when the guidance document was rolled out to inform urban planning teams.	KE was achieved through a combination of working with the planning teams in the case study area and then disseminating examples in various workshops.	KE took place during workshops and subsequent dissemination of the report findings within government departments, including a final major consultation with ministerial presence.	The Review Panel delivered KE by involving 13 different experts. Thereafter, KE was achieved through workshop training.	A number of activities were used to engage the young people. In the future, the KE will relate to the teaching of design and planning engagement processes to a wider audience.	A network of experts interested in school design has been created and a central internet resource has been provided through which they can communicate.	An active publications and presentations programme publicised VIBAT to policymakers in the UK and abroad.
Developed a learning guide setting out how and why urban design influences anti-social behaviour, and what can be done in design terms to mitigate this.	The prototype simulation tool, as applied to a region in Tower Hamlets/Newham, demonstrated the potential of this technology. A report has been produced.	A report that summarised discussions from the workshops. This was widely disseminated and will influence the design of a new UCL programme in sustainable construction.	Two documents – 'A planner's guide to carbon' and 'Rules of thumb in sustainable design' – were produced, and the latter will be turned into seminar material.	A guide shows a selection of case studies on how the teaching of urban design can be delivered and how best to engage young people.	The main output is an ongoing network with a central information resource on the internet.	VIBAT London has created an online simulation tool to better understand the performance of a range of policy interventions. This was supplemented by reports and papers.
The project contributes to ongoing learning on what makes good places and best practice in urban design.	As with several other projects, this is part of ongoing learning about how to design places better.	An ongoing process of seeking to identify which policies and regulations are working, and how to improve the regulatory environment.	The project distilled technical details into more accessible and digestible forms to help planning professionals do their work more effectively.	Guidance for decisionmakers on how to involve a range of communities in urban design processes and issues.	This network of people, all heavily involved in school design, should enable ongoing improvements in understanding about best practice in design of schools.	The VIBAT tool is a resource to help transport planners and policymakers understand how to minimise carbon emissions in the transport sector.
The ASB geocoding success rate can be lower than 50% using standard methods. The team's enhanced geocoding methods can deliver a 90 per cent success rate.	The project has created evidence-based, quantifiable digital processes that can improve the speed and flexibility of masterplanning at the urban block scale.	Seven regional seminars concluded with an event with ministerial presence in January 2008.	There were 13 academics on the Sustainable Review Panel. Seventy-five people, from 21 London Boroughs and three Government organisations attended the final project workshops.	Forty-eight young people were involved in the project.	The CIBSE School Design Group bulletin was sent to 1,000 professionals. Over 200 people became members of the CIBSE SDG during the lifetime of the project.	The online tool allows users to make decisions on 12 different policy packages.
Visit www.uel.ac.uk/geo-information/SEDUC	Visit http://aedas.com/Europe/RandD/SmartSolutionsforSpatialPlanning	Visit www.urbanbuzz.org	Visit www.urbanbuzz.org	Visit www.brookes.ac.uk/schools/be/research/jcud/urbanbuzz/rootscape.html	Visit www.cibse-sdg.org www.lowcarbonbuildingsdirectory.org	Visit www.vibat.org
See page 180	See page 184	See page 190	See page 194	See page 198	See page 202	See page 206

LSTS	MCSC	METRICITY	MOBILISING KNOWLEDGE	REBOPSE	RETILE COMBEEP	SCREAM
Created a network of employers and students; placing interns into sustainability related internships.	Produced interactive, internet-accessible maps of locations – having engaged communities to provide content for them.	New approach to density within the urban environment, applied to a real site and tested among specialists.	Workshops focused on the way older people view and interact with the urban environment, and making use of this information.	The creation of an online network aimed to bring together businesses and socially excluded people looking for employment in the 'green' economy.	Devised an effective way for regeneration organisations, such as the environmental charity Groundwork, to evaluate their projects.	A series of workshops aiming to develop guidance on the use and application of large urban digital screens.
Harnessed the resources of the London student population to actively contribute towards sustainable development in a work environment.	Represented the coming together of technology and communities. In the long term, interactive maps may influence local democracy.	Urban density is a critical measurement, but existing assessment of density, as dwellings per hectare, left out much of the real experience of urban environments.	The growing ageing population must not be marginalised. This project explored ways in which to enhance social inclusion and tap into a rich source of knowledge and experience.	Investigated the use of information technology to connect socially isolated people with others, and provided volunteering/ work opportunities.	Provides the means for Groundwork to measure, understand the impacts and learn from the projects with which it is involved.	Extensive deployment of public information screen is being contemplated for the 2012 London Games it is, therefore, vital to harness the latest technology.
Touched on all areas – from policy through to regulation. In each case, impact depended on the nature of the internships and students involved.	Currently informs planning. In the future, however, it may help to frame the development of local policy.	At first glance this project is primarily of planning interest. However, its impact could be far wider, influencing policy and design.	Greatest in the area of planning, and, to a degree, design.	Touched on all areas – from policy through to regulation – depending, in each case, on the nature of the placements.	The evaluation framework developed is designed to gather evidence relating to local authority target indicators.	The correct use of digital screens is primaril a design issue, with important impacts on planning and management.
Eight-hundred students and employers were linked into the network and received a regular bulletin on sustainability issues. Organised events promoted human networking.	The principal KE took place during workshops, where participants discussed what they considered to be important about their local area.	The project included a variety of stakeholders who all learnt from their involvement. Outputs have been captured in a book: 'Metricity: exploring new measures of urban density'.	Workshops with the elderly produced guidance on how to engage with them. In December 2008, practice was embedded at Lewisham council via involvement in equality training.	Networking brought diverse people together. It gave them opportunities to improve their skills and knowledge. The project team learnt the limitations of active networking IT.	The team learnt how to ensure uptake of the methodology at all levels of organisation. Most KE will take place in the future, when Groundwork staff are taught the methodology.	KE has been achieved through a series of workshops, involving those in the advertising profession, architects and town planners.
Seventy-five per cent of first year LSTS student placements have subsequently gained employment in sustainability linked jobs.	The interactive web-based community maps enable ongoing input from local people, thus offering a mechanism through which people can engage in local place making.	The book tells a series of stories about the urban environment, to show how different interpretations of density lead to very different perspectives and design decisions within it.	A booklet and DVD documentary provide step-by-step guidance on how to optimise the engagement and involvement of elderly people in planning and design.	One-hundred-and-forty-eight businesses have signed up to the website. Volunteers have taken part in activities across Camden and 15 jobs have arisen.	A comprehensive toolkit and supporting documentation has been produced for training Groundwork staff in project evaluation.	A guidance document to advise planning authorities on the use of digital screens. The project is also feeding into new education courses.
This novel approach to brokered intern placement now offers a proven business model for application in any technical domain.	A social enterprise, 'Mapping for Change' is being created to follow this project.	Project participants will take the debate and thinking arising from the project's density consultations forward.	As part of equalities training, a follow-up workshop embedded inclusive thinking and methodology in Lewisham council's regeneration departments.	A new way of engaging with jobless and otherwise excluded people. Improved local economic competitiveness.	There is great potential to role out the methodology to other organisations, to help them appraise and learn from their own activities.	The guidance document will most likely feed into new policy in the UK, focusing on the use of digital screens in public environments.
Network has 800 members and 32 placements were completed.	Five interactive local community maps. The final MCSC event was attended by 117 people from various government agencies, academic institutes and community organisations.	Four design scenarios for 2018 were created, each representing a new way of exploring measures of urban density.	Twenty-two local residents took part in a series of six interactive sessions together with planners, councillors and community workers during a three-week summer school.	Fifteen jobs arose through REBOPSE networking and activity.	Two evaluation methodologies – GPE and GPE + – have been developed through this project.	Sixteen people, from backgrounds such as academic research, art, screen management, scree curation, funders and scree technologists, attended two project workshops.
Visit www.lsx.org.uk/ whatwedo/LSTS_page30 67.aspx	Visit www.communitymaps. london21.org	Visit www.metricity.net/	Visit www.goldsmiths. ac.uk/cucr/pdf/mobilizing-knowledge.pdf	Visit www.greenmaniac.com	Visit www.bartlett.ucl.ac.uk/ web/ben/ede/Intro.htm www.urbanbuzz.org	Visit www.vr.ucl.ac.uk/ projects/scream
See page 150	See page 154	See page 160	See page 164	See page 168	See page 172	See page 176

Contents
The 27
UrbanBuzz
projects

Project categorisation table

- ● Target sectors
- ● Collaborators (including target sectors)

		ABUNDANCE	CARBONBUZZ	CD-G WORKSHOP	CLOVIS	DEI DEMONSTRATION	EASY	E-POD	ESP-SIM	FEFUR
Organisation	**Target sectors and collaborators**									
	Public sector - central government	●	●		●		●	●		
	Public sector - regional / local government	●			●		●		●	
	Public sector - quangos / public services			●	●		●		●	
	Private sector		●		●	●		●	●	●
	Professional institutions / trade associations		●							●
	Voluntary sector									
	Academia	●	●	●	●	●	●	●	●	●
	General public	●		●					●	●
Physical	**Outputs and outcomes**									
	Physical / environmental improvement	●								
	Technique or technology demonstration	●				●			●	
	Carbon reduction strategies	●	●			●		●		
	Advance in urban design or urban planning									
	New policy, planning or design tool						●		●	
Information	Process improvement								●	
	Improvement in information capture		●			●	●			
	Data interpretation / modelling						●			
	Good practice creation / dissemination				●					●
	Improved education or training material	●		●				●	●	
Social	Involving new or diverse stakeholders	●	●	●					●	●
	Improving social inclusion				●					
	Enabling professionals		●		●		●	●		
	New social network		●							
	Learning from engagement			●	●					●

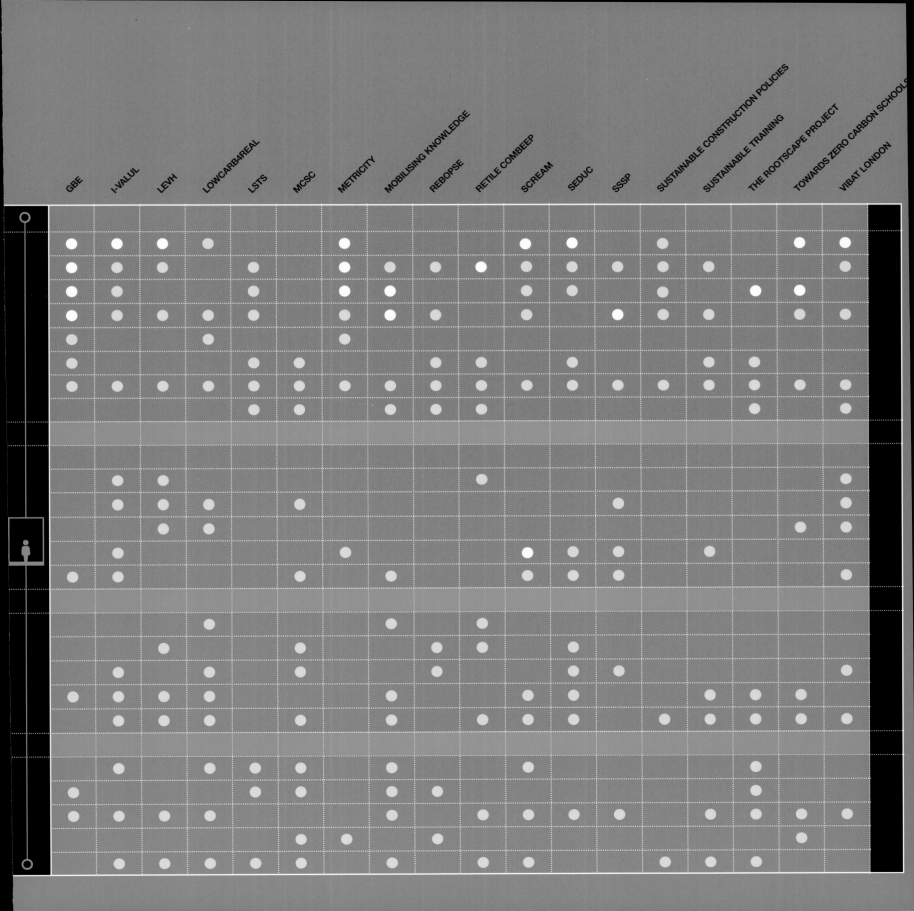

ABUNDANCE: Activating Blighted Urban
Niches for Daring Agricultural Networks of
Creativity and Endeavour

Lead organisation
UCL

Project coordinators
Yves Cabannes, Robert Biel

Project start and end dates
November 2007 to November 2008

Total UrbanBuzz funding
£17,063.25

Total CIK
£11,513

Contact details
r.biel@ucl.ac.uk

- ● Environment
- ● Society
- ● Governance
- ● Planning/regeneration
- ● Design/housing

The context: sustainable food cultivation

'Surveys suggest that a significant amount, as high as 60 per cent, of food needs could be met within cities if all available space were to be cultivated, including rooftops, balconies, allotments and urban green space,' says project coordinator Robert Biel.

A key driver for ABUNDANCE is the emerging global food crisis and the desire to reduce food miles, with food and fuel prices soaring and global urban populations outstripping rural ones for the first time. This project brings in extensive experience from countries that have been forced by circumstance to cultivate all available land – Cuba and Argentina, for example.

In Argentina, community gardens were created to mitigate the effects of the 2001 economic collapse. As the economy recovered, the popular concept was reworked into government-run urban agriculture programmes providing unemployed workers with food and an income. It would seem that adversity breeds sustainability, as many London plots, parks and gardens were last cultivated during the food shortages of wartime Britain.

Another key aspect of the project is the need to explore the policy and planning arrangements that lie behind land cultivation. The UK policy context is complex: do residents have the right to cultivate land on social housing estates? How can we create common property management criteria to manage the space and distribute food? 'These issues have been investigated in some detail in the Latin American context, but they're completely new here,' says Biel.

Key project objectives

The project team wished to demonstrate the potential of currently unused urban green space within London by creating a community-managed agricultural garden on vacant land belonging to a London social housing estate. The key aims were:

01 to demonstrate the effectiveness of a high-yield, low-input style of urban agriculture that has been delivering good results in Argentina, Cuba and several Latin American countries;

02 to develop guidance for managing the institutional process of developing an urban agriculture plot, including managing land ownership, permissions, community engagement and access rights;

03 to engage local residents, as well as communities across London, in the process of designing, creating and managing urban agriculture plots;

04 to create training and educational modules using the plots developed by the project partners as exemplars;

05 to feed good practice from the project experiences into the urban planning situation, and inform future policy on urban agriculture; and

06 to promote knowledge exchange between the global south and north.

Urban agriculture for all
The ABUNDANCE project is rooted in the potential of cities to produce food. A community in Brixton, South London, has created a flourishing urban agriculture demonstration plot and is working through the issues involved to create and sustain such plots across the city

The project response

The project team, partners and local residents have created a sizeable urban agriculture plot on a social housing estate in Brixton. The plot's yields so far have been impressive, and the harvested food has been shared among project participants and local residents.

A guidance document has been developed, outlining the process for identifying, mapping and developing small urban agricultural plots of less than two acres (5,000 square meters). This is focused on determining the accessibility, suitability, current usage and feasibility of a particular land parcel for urban agricultural use, including the necessary processes for identifying local stakeholders and landowners, and for engaging them in the project aims.

'The institutional issues involved in surveying the land and understanding how to resolve ownership problems is a very important part of this project, along with exploring potential links and policy opportunities in regard to urban planning and land use planning,' says Biel.

'What's needed is to build up a body of experience in the London context.'

The team has examined these institutional issues in relation to several south London sites, including a social housing estate in Tulse Hill, as well as the experiences of Latin American countries with established urban agriculture plots. A working group including academics, residents and local council officers has informed the development of the guidance, and will be involved in its future development as additional growing plots are established across the capital. ❯

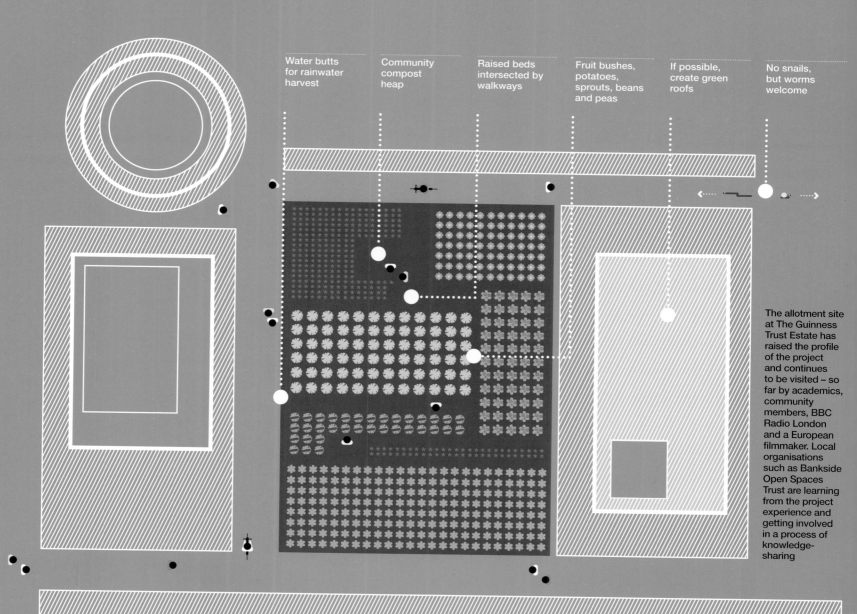

Water butts for rainwater harvest

Community compost heap

Raised beds intersected by walkways

Fruit bushes, potatoes, sprouts, beans and peas

If possible, create green roofs

No snails, but worms welcome

The allotment site at The Guinness Trust Estate has raised the profile of the project and continues to be visited – so far by academics, community members, BBC Radio London and a European filmmaker. Local organisations such as Bankside Open Spaces Trust are learning from the project experience and getting involved in a process of knowledge-sharing

Project partner Transition Towns Brixton has
brought the idea of local food cultivation to the fore
of local authority thinking. A recent report
states: 'The council should promote and
expand food growing groups and
networks across the borough.'
A ward councillor attended the
project networking meeting
and has offered seed funding
for a growing project
on neighbouring
Loughborough Estate

Robert Biel a
Sarah Canno
**Community
engagement**

Yves Cabannes
**Chair of Development Planning,
UCL Development Planning
Unit (DPU)**

**Project coordinator and
development of guidance
on mapping cultivable
green space**

Transition Towns
**The Transition Towns Initiative
involves a community in the
creation of low-impact, low-carbon,
sustainable futures. The Transition
Towns team has been giving
permaculture training courses on
the Brixton plot, and Brixton has
become the first Transition site in
London. Transition Towns Brixton
will lead local initiatives to develop
more local growing plots**

Robert Biel
Senior lecturer,
Development Planning
Unit (DPU), UCL

Project management
and coordination

'We will get a significant yield
from the Brixton plot. We're
employing a no-dig method,
meaning that you don't turn
over the soil. The input in
labour is very low. We pile
compost on top and the
worms will do the job.
This is a crucial element
of the model that
we're developing'
Robert Biel, project
coordinator

The Guinness Trust
**Landlord, involved in
developing resident-
landlord land use
and policy guidance.
Fundraising for the future
support and management
of the community plot**

Expertise and methodology
exported to other sites
**TATE Modern
Royal Parks
Coram's Field, with UCL
SUSTAIN**

Planning and design, and planting and
care of the community plot using high-
yield, low-input agricultural methods

'I'm often here and the kids come up to me and ask: "Who is going to eat all this stuff?" "Can I have my own patch?" "Can I grow what I like?" There's a lot of interest in the plot' Louise, estate resident, who will be helping to develop the plot in future, and has appeared on BBC Radio London to promote community growing

Project impact

ABUNDANCE has delivered a successful example of how housing estates can be transformed and revitalised by cultivating the barren and desolate green spaces that frequently surround blocks of flats. Its key impact has been to stimulate a process of community knowledge-building and action. It has also begun the process of convincing local authorities that they should be just as imaginative as the Guinness Trust Housing Association in welcoming community growing projects on other housing estates.

The project team has held several workshops on the themes of high-yield, low-input urban agriculture and permaculture. Education, and introducing people to the radical new kind of thinking required by the approach of peak oil and climate change, is a key driver for urban sustainability. This education and training has been delivered at several levels: for the public and for social landlords, planners and planning policymakers.

The Brixton plot is well-established, and is being managed by the Guinness Trust and participating residents. This group will be also be supported by project partner Transition Towns – in October 2008, based on the work of this project and the involvement of project participants, Brixton became the first Transition Town in London. The Transition Towns network brings together motivated individuals within a community to tackle shared issues such as sustainability, and the challenges and opportunities of climate change.

Knowledge exchange

The ABUNDANCE project brought together a wide community of academics, practitioners and local residents interested in growing food across London. This wider group, together with Transition Towns Brixton, will continue to explore new opportunities and sites for developing urban agriculture projects. A database of individuals and organisations with a stake in urban food growing in Brixton and beyond has been established, and this group is acting as a catalyst for the community-forming process. The project experience features as a case study in a recent report on food growing and social housing from London Food Link at Sustain and the Women's Environmental Network (WEN), explaining how social housing providers and their tenants can work together to grow food.

Education and training

Experience from this project and the Brixton site will be a key component for the UCL Development Planning Unit's education of future urban planners, adding value to its existing programme of urban agriculture education, field visits in London and distance learning. A new module on urban agriculture has been developed as part of the MSc programme in Environment and Sustainable Development.

The future: a growing network

The project team is currently engaged in discussions, with both UCL and several charitable organisations across London, about applying lessons learned from the ABUNDANCE project to new, unused green plots across the city. Once under way, these new sites will add to the body of London-focused urban agriculture knowledge being developed by UCL and fed back into its educational and training courses.

Across the capital, new initiatives inspired by the success of this project, and the support of the network it has helped to grow, are in development. Capital Growth, for example, is a new 'growing places' project that aims to establish 2,012 new urban agriculture plots by 2012. A web-based green map of Brixton is being developed by project participants to map a range of ecological initiatives, many of them food-related, supported by e-groups and blogs.

The Capital Growth project, supported by food campaign group *Sustain* and funded by the London Development Agency (LDA), aims to create 2,012 new growing spaces by 2012. Projects supported by the ABUNDANCE team will be supported by Capital Growth

A set of community mapping guidelines has been produced, along with a web-based green map of Brixton

Project resources
http://transitiontowns.org/Brixton/TheABUNDANCE
PROJECT (contact the project team for copies of
mapping guidance: r.biel@ucl.ac.uk)
http://www.projectdirt.com/group/ttbfood/forum/topics/
fruit-and-nut-tree-map-green
http://www.sustainweb.org/projectsandcampaigns/
http://www.youtube.com/user/uclurbanbuzz (video clips)
www.capitalgrowth.org

Lead organisation
Aedas

Project coordinator
Judit Kimpian

Project start and end dates
December 2007 to November 2008

Total UrbanBuzz funding
£73,530.67

Total CIK
£63,189

Contact details
info@carbonbuzz.org

● Environment
● Policy
● Planning/regeneration
● Design/housing

The context: performance in use

Buildings are responsible for more than 40 per cent of carbon emissions in the UK. 'The starting point for our project is that architects don't really understand what carbon emissions mean,' says project coordinator Judit Kimpian, Head of Advanced Modelling Group and Sustainability at Aedas. 'It's a major concern for the industry that so few people collect data on how their "product" performs in use. This would be unthinkable in other design-related industries.'

Key project objectives

The CARBONBUZZ online database enables architects and engineers to contrast design forecasts with actual energy use and performance data. It also helps them to understand the causes of discrepancies between total energy use and forecast energy use, and enables them to reference their buildings' performance against other projects and established benchmarks. The database will:

01 enable practices to close the gap between forecast and actual energy consumption by highlighting 'unregulated' energy use (such as plug load, for example) during the design phase;

02 align forecast and actual energy use data, enabling architects and engineers to compare 'like for like' from design to completion, regardless of the type of certification gained; and

03 enable practices to communicate better with engineers and clients on energy use, so contributing to lower energy designs.

An initial survey undertaken by the project team concluded that few, if any, tools are currently used by architects for benchmarking building energy performance. In general, the project team noted poor awareness of existing benchmarks set by The Chartered Institution of Building Services Engineers (CIBSE), which provides sector-by-sector evaluations to benchmark how efficient a building should be.

There was also poor awareness of the relevance of existing benchmarks to recently introduced energy performance measures. Display Energy Certificates (DECs) must be displayed in public buildings larger than 1,000 square metres, and Energy Performance Certificates (EPCs) are required for all properties when bought, sold, built or rented, providing A-G efficiency ratings.

DECs and EPCs are the most important legislation introduced since Part L, yet remain poorly understood by architects. The project team aimed to improve the understanding of building-related carbon emissions amongst built environment professionals, and to bring insight and clarity to current and future legislation.

From forecast to performance data
The CARBONBUZZ team is creating a key evidence base for the management of carbon emissions. Architects, engineers and designers are invited to share anonymous forecast and actual energy use data via an online platform

In particular, the CARBONBUZZ team wished to highlight, and so clarify, the discrepancies between the Part L and EPC versus DEC energy efficiency assessment methods, which are currently a source of confusion in the industry, and to provide easy access to accredited building performance data. A significant proportion of performance data derived from this new legislation was placed in the public domain in 2008, yet much of it is fragmented and inaccessible.

The project response

The online platform is now operational, with 70 projects from a total of 40 practices entered into the database. This generates a breakdown of design parameters that tracks energy consumption, both predicted and post-construction, classifying it under different building types. It also provides the option of a breakdown for different energy types and sources of use in the building.

Project information is entered anonymously, ensuring project and practice confidentiality. Every practice using the tool is able to set in-house targets, track projects and benchmark outcomes against the industry standard CIBSE's benchmarks and CARBONBUZZ sector-weighted averages. The tool offers quick sector filters and a direct route to the CIBSE benchmarks. These provide the reference base for the DEC assessment framework. By tying this into the ❯

Case study

Architectural practice: Aedas
Project: Stockley Academy
Sector: Education
Completion date: September 2006
Gross internal floor area: 12,800m²
Value: £21,474,836
Location: Urban, London

Stockley Academy had been occupied for two years in January 2008, at the time of the post occupancy evaluation. Energy bills for the year commencing December 2007 were used to calculate actual carbon emissions. These were higher than those forecast at the design stage, primarily due to a higher than predicted unregulated energy use. A large number of computers per classroom and issues with the building management systems were identified as the main causes

'CARBONBUZZ is all about trying to get architects to take carbon seriously. We are trying to say to architects: "How can we help reduce the emissions of your buildings?" '
Hywel Davies, CIBSE Technical Director

Aedas Project coordination and management, initial consultation process with launch group of architects on future use of CIBSE tools, analysis and benchmarks. Development of data structure, and storyboard for web interface, and coordinating implementation of the online platform with RIBA/BRE

CIBSE Ensuring that CARBONBUZZ addresses new trends in legislation and services design, ensuring data fields comply with CIBSE sector categories for benchmarking and support links to their benchmarking data, providing input into the development of the database, exploration of user scenarios and resolving implementation challenges

BRE Establishing and hosting the database, and providing the legal framework for data protection and privacy, and contributing to dissemination through internal and external events

UCL Contributing to the development of the data structure and analysis protocols. Reviewing the brief, the storyboard and working documents and reports

RIBA Coordinating the CARBONBUZZ platform with existing RIBA initiatives. Coordinating a 'launch group' of architects, setting up the protocols for the RIBA Carbon Conscious Practice Scheme, developing proposals for the future maintenance of the site, and promoting CARBONBUZZ to engage the profession

XCO2, engineering and sustainability consultant Ensuring that relevant data inputs can be obtained during the engineering design process

'We contributed data to the database. We found obtaining the data from our client, and analysing the data ourselves, a really useful process. It started a conversation with the client that will hopefully lead to further work on the management of the building to improve the performance and reduce energy use'
Natasha Richardson, architect

'We need to bring energy thinking into the design process. We hear about sustainability and the urgency of tackling climate change. Architects are familiar with the tools and strategies to use, but rarely understand the impact of those strategies'
Ricardo Moreira, XCO2

A range of pilot practices, including architects and engineers

design process upfront, CARBONBUZZ will help designers gain an understanding of actual building CO_2 emissions, including the impact of unregulated energy use such as plug load or special functions (cafeterias and swimming pools), along with occupancy patterns, operating hours and building management issues.

To encourage practices to contribute quality data to the database, a scheme that recognises commitment to carbon management – the RIBA Carbon Conscious Practice accreditation scheme – is being set up. This initiative wishes to encourage participating practices to consider the value of publishing data on a 'full disclosure' basis. From 2010, participating RIBA Chartered Practices that elect to publish projects with both design and in-use data will be recognised with the RIBA Carbon Conscious Practice accreditation.

It is intended that this scheme, essentially a framework for the recognition of a practice's commitment to carbon management, will help practices to grow carbon-awareness within their organisations.

Project impact

The anonymous data hosted by the CARBONBUZZ platform, currently standing at data from more than 70 projects, will be used to generate statistical trends and feedback on current practice.

Key building features contributing to carbon emissions such as sector, region, occupancy, sustainability ratings, energy demand, ventilation strategy and renewable technologies are recorded in a format that allows architects to evaluate their projects against CIBSE benchmarks. A high priority will be given to ensuring the credibility of the data, database and subsequent analyses.

'I think for us, one of the most valuable things is being able to benchmark what we're doing against other projects. The process will become more valuable the more projects there are,' says architect Natasha Richardson. 'The

other way that we will use the tool is to improve the way that we work with clients. Using it gives us a route to communicate with clients about the kind of building they're getting, how it will perform in terms of energy and how they can help it to perform better through their participation.'

The project has highlighted the fact that post occupancy evaluations are essential if an understanding of the relationship between design, and performance in use, is to be gained.

George Stowell, a project partner, architect and an RIBA client design advisor, believes that CARBONBUZZ will enable designers, design teams and clients to make informed decisions about energy and carbon targets and how buildings are used and designed: 'It will make this information transparent. As well as being at the leading edge of sharing information, this will also be a very useful platform for engaging with government. Policymakers, especially in the European Union, are already focusing on energy performance certificates. Having access to the information that relates to these, we can keep going with continual improvements.'

Knowledge exchange

In developing the platform, engineers and architects have come together for the first time to discuss how carbon emissions work in practice. The project has initiated a discussion between project teams and clients about the use and management of buildings.

'The challenges were about all sides understanding the kind of data that was needed. This means energy information about the building, and the user's input so we know how that building is used, and how this is affecting its energy consumption,' says project partner Ricardo Moreira, XCO2. The knowledge exchange process led to an understanding of the carbon-assessment procedures followed during the design process.

A summary of project information is available to a wider audience via the project

website and via a printed booklet, available online (see resources). A series of workshops and seminars, attracting built environment professionals from all disciplines, has supported the development of the tool.

Education and training

The Bartlett School of Graduate Studies, UCL is a key partner in this project. Case studies and lessons learned from the project will feature in courses and teaching material within the Bartlett. Presentations and teaching material will be compiled on an ongoing basis as the database grows.

The future: from benchmarks to legislation

Energy performance data is needed urgently to raise the construction industry's understanding of carbon impacts. CARBONBUZZ provides a great opportunity to contrast design with operation, and to build up evidence for what works, and what does not, in low-energy design.

Data from DECs and EPCs will update CIBSE benchmarks. 'We're looking at tens of thousands of buildings needing certificates,' says Hywel Davies, CIBSE. 'Once we get the data back from those, it's going to enable us to look again at the benchmarks and see where we can improve. DCLG is open to exploring the differences between building use and design. This information can be used in the future to improve policymaking through research and better relationships with government.'

UCL will be acting as the auditor of the CARBONBUZZ database, providing regulatory and quality assurance functions for the project team and ensuring that the practice of anonymising data provided by users is maintained.

Project resources
www.carbonbuzz.org
email: info@carbonbuzz.org

'It's a win-win situation: practices have the incentive of using a sophisticated carbon management tool, and collated data will inform the industry about how various sectors are performing' Judit Kimpian, Aedas

All other architects contributing to the database, which currently holds data from 70 projects

CARBONBUZZ is 'a massive step forward because it enables a direct comparison between building energy use projections and reality' Bill Gething, Feilden Clegg Bradley Studios (FCBS)

CD-G WORKSHOP: Collaborative
Design Gateway Workshop

Lead organisation
University of East London

Project coordinator
Christoph Hadrys

Project start and end dates
July 2008 to November 2008

Total UrbanBuzz funding
£10,817.51

Total CIK
£8,000.00

Contact details
C.hadrys@uel.ac.uk

- Society
- Design/housing
- Policy
- Governance

The context: making better connections

Planning and regeneration consultations often fail to make connections with communities, especially those living within the Thames Gateway development zone – the term 'consultation fatigue' commonly recurs in Government and practitioner reports. There is no established method of employing collaborative design practices that 'build in' community participation. The practice of sticking to established negotiation and decision-making processes means that, all too frequently, community workshops are merely 'tick box' exercises that don't offer participants the opportunities to ask 'how' or 'why'.

With a new focus on community engagement mandated in the 2008 Planning Bill, which became law in December 2008 (see page 56), the CD-G WORKSHOP project is investigating ways in which active community collaboration and dialogue can be stimulated and supported.

Key project objectives

Most consultations are designed to collect information or to gauge community acceptance of pre-determined ideas, and are not regarded as key sources of design information. As a result, research shows that many local communities have lost trust in consultation processes. Established design processes 'lock in' knowledge exchange gaps between planners, designers and communities. The team wished to explore different approaches to 'doing' design, and to seek new design frameworks that will enable communities to participate fully in the creative process.

By using specially prepared design scenarios created by students working in participatory design workshops, along with hands-on tools and expert guidance, the CD-G WORKSHOP aimed to engage community members in the development of designs for public and private space improvements in their areas. The project aimed to:

01 encourage local communities to engage in collaborative knowledge exchange mechanisms with design professionals; and

02 enhance knowledge exchange by enabling a series of community workshops to test and demonstrate methods of designing with community participation, through collaborative designs, critical expert guidance and community engagement.

The project response

The CD-G WORKSHOP project rationale is rooted in learning from South America. Project coordinator Christoph Hadrys had been impressed by an innovative approach to placemaking and housing through community engagement in Chile. The Chilean project demonstrated the value of collaborative and participatory design mechanisms, in which communities helped to describe and determine development layouts at an urban scale, according to urban design principles. At the home scale, individual extensions and customisation by community members was possible, again in line with existing guidelines.

The project team selected six student architectural and urban design projects from the ❯

A process for inclusive design and placemaking
The CD-G project is tackling 'consultation fatigue' in communities across the Thames Gateway. The team is developing new ways to stimulate and support active local involvement in the planning process

Canning Town and Custom House Regeneration Project Team
Zahira Nazer Expert on local planning and active member of the community workshop team; helped with access to local communities and local authorities in the Canning Town and Newham areas

Eike Sindlinger
Arup Urban Design
Specialist expertise in sustainable urban design and architecture, integrating social, economic and environmental aspects, and urban infrastructure and technology. Identification of local risks and potentials in the Thames Gateway

Dominic Church
CABE
Experience of design workshops, design criteria and workshop mechanisms

University of East London
Christoph Hadrys

Project preparation, coordination and implementation of academic, professional and community input. Expertise in technology, architecture and urban design

University of East London
Students from the School of Architecture and the Visual Arts (AVA)

Signy Svalastoga
As former subject director in UEL Architecture, Svalastoga gave advice on teaching and learning in practice

Roger Zogolovich, AZ Urban Studio, planning consultants, property and development services
Input on design and community engagement in relation to current development practice; experience of the market potentials of bottom-up developments, including development economics

'Current planning legislation tends to forbid or limit freedom of action for the individual. This restriction has, strangely, not brought with it the benefit that was imagined. We do not seem to have a richer, or more beautiful, environment because of it. I am concerned that this tight policymaking excludes innovation and has led to design of the lowest common denominator, sadly with little character or distinction'
Roger Zogolovich, AZ Urban Studio

'Both public and private space considerations were regarded as important to the community. The ability to take part in the system, and to invest in and contribute to change, is what really matters to people'

Christoph Hadrys, UEL

School of Architecture and the Visual Arts (AVA) at UEL. The designs were selected for their potential in challenging 'traditional' design scenarios, and are a key element in the development of participatory processes. All the designs had proved popular with local residents in previous workshop sessions.

Project coordinator Christoph Hadrys brought together academics, urban designers, planners, developers and members of the community to discuss these student projects, all of which focused on improving areas of public and private space in Stratford, North Greenwich and Beckton. The plan was to encourage interaction and scenario-testing involving academics, practitioners and community members. Hands-on tools were created: 2D design plans were laminated so that community members could add their comments, and 3D blocks were built to allow hands-on manipulation of design elements.

Despite extensive recruitment effort involving posters, leaflets, and contacts with local newspapers and local radio, there were very few community attendees at the first scheduled workshop in August 2008. The project team used the time to discuss projects and ideas in detail. It was decided that as the community hadn't come to the workshop, the project team would instead take the workshop to the community.

In October, after extensive outreach work, a community-based workshop with 20 attendees was held in Beckton. During the event, passers-by were invited to join the proceedings, and around five additional people joined the workshop.

Project impact

Project participant Roger Zogolovich, AZ Urban Studio, notes that the students' proposals asked occupiers how they would like to live, enabling them to express themselves in personal ways. The response suggested that the residents sought flexibility, above all, within a planning framework that would allow living environments to evolve with the changing life of local inhabitants.

The workshop discussions continued on the theme of flexibility: focusing on the negotiation of priorities within the limitations of the existing system. A framework or tool is needed that can handle two priorities: enabling the community to explore ideas and come up with proposals that can be taken on board during design development; and clarifying for the community the relationship between proposals and decisions. This would enable workshop participants to engage in future discussions in a more informed way.

The simple hands-on models representing the student concepts proved popular with participants, and merit further exploration. The design scenarios, along with feedback and analysis from project partners, have been published in a guidance document disseminated to project participants, including the Commission for Architecture and the Built Environment (CABE) and Design for London (see resources). Feedback has been positive, and the issues addressed (enabling, frameworks and participation) are subject to ongoing discussions. As work progresses, project outcomes will be also introduced to local authorities by student participants and a range of project partners.

'The contributions to the workshop were diverse and rich, and locals could easily place themselves within the design schemes. Certain issues can be only judged by local communities, and their optimism was encouraging,' says Hadrys. 'Both public and private space considerations were regarded as important to the community. The ability to take part in the system, and to invest in and contribute to change, is what really matters.'

The team found that the current planning framework, and the non-inclusive manner in which designs are typically created and presented, are key barriers to effective community engagement. Members of the local community showed very little confidence in recent changes in planning policy designed to enable more open and inclusive local decision-making and design processes. Nevertheless, people could see a shift in recent years towards a greater emphasis on engagement for local communities, although they did not feel that most engagement practices were successful.

Knowledge exchange

It was commonly agreed that these kinds of participatory workshops should not be thought of as 'consultations', but rather as opportunities for exploration, interaction and the recording of knowledge exchange. The current planning regime seems, at times, to pose serious hurdles to the idea of inclusive design and development, yet the workshops enabled participants to explore ways in which planning could be enabling rather than restricting. They addressed the inflexibility of current planning, and ways in which the proposed enabling design frameworks would build more flexibility into the system, resulting in better understanding of what people are allowed to do – and what they're not. The result could be faster planning approvals and less bureaucracy, leading to an active city-building community being involved in the long-term vision for a place.

The project team now aims to continue work on establishing a framework and methodology to deliver processes of collaborative and participatory design; remaining within current planning frameworks but also understanding how extensions to the system could be positive.

Education and training

AVA students and staff at UEL will continue to investigate collaborative design scenarios via diploma units and masters modules. The MA Alternative Urbanisms course has begun to build methodology and feedback from the CD-G WORKSHOP into its curriculum, and design scenarios are being refined before approaches are made to local authorities.

The future: towards inclusivity

The project has shown that building sustainable communities works best when it involves a diverse range of people, combining vision, expertise and desire in an open process. Based on contacts established within local communities, the team plans to extend local collaboration. Architect Roger Zogolovich has shown interest in furthering the collaboration, and setting up a more permanent basis for inclusive working.

The team is working towards communicating the project findings to local authorities, many of which are currently reviewing their planning processes as they move towards introducing Local Development Frameworks into planning policy.

Project resources
http://www.cd-g-workshop.blogspot.com/
The guidance document is available from www.urbanbuzz.org (select projects)
The Chilean project; Iquique by Elemental www.elementalchile.cl

CLOVIS: Closing the gap between Vision and
Implementing Sustainable communities

Lead organisation
UCL

Project coordinator
John Kelsey

Project start and end dates
February 2008 to December 2008

Total UrbanBuzz funding
£15,000

Total CIK
£3,000

Contact details
j.kelsey@ucl.ac.uk

- ● Environment
- ● Society
- ● Governance
- ● Policy
- ● Planning/regeneration
- ● Infrastructure
- ● Design/housing

Identifying and connecting regeneration stakeholders
The increasingly complex nature of urban regeneration processes requires professional stakeholders to engage with each other, and with all potential stakeholders, much more effectively

The context: stakeholder engagement

The project focused on the teams behind two live regeneration projects, the Bath Western Riverside Project and the Aylesbury Estate programme in Southwark, London. The former seeks to redevelop a struggling city centre area outside of Bath's historic tourist zone; the latter to establish a sustainable community through the redevelopment of the deprived Aylesbury Estate.

'Research shows that failure to engage with stakeholders at the "front end" of a project is a major cause of later failure,' says John Kelsey, CLOVIS project coordinator. There are currently more than 100 urban renewal projects taking place in the UK, with total estimated build costs of more than £87 billion. Despite the credit crunch, further regeneration growth is forecast for 2009-2010. Yet 'few regeneration models comprehensively address sustainability issues from the outset', says Kelsey.

The two project teams are facing a range of stakeholder engagement challenges as they attempt to create, and gain acceptance of, new visions for their respective areas. At face value, the two projects have very different site constraints and engagement priorities. The Bath and North East Somerset Council (BANES) team, working within a UNESCO World Heritage Site, is facing resistance to development from wealthy residents and heritage professionals. The Aylesbury Estate regeneration team from Southwark Council is engaging with resident stakeholders who will see their homes demolished and rebuilt over the next 15 years. Initial planning began more than 10 years ago, and it has proved a challenge to keep residents 'on board' throughout many policy revisions.

Each team is meeting its challenges in different ways, learning valuable lessons in the process. Each is also demonstrating that key priorities can guide the engagement process despite the apparent differences in the scale and scope of site-specific regeneration challenges.

Key project objectives

Both the Bath Western Riverside project and the Aylesbury Estate programme in Southwark are at the vision-building and masterplanning stages, and as such have practical lessons to offer each other and a wider audience, says Kelsey.

The project aimed to explore the value of 'reflective practitioner' time for busy professionals, Kelsey adds. 'Successful processes of stakeholder engagement have to be able to deal with politicians, financiers, property developers, planners, heritage groups, the rich, the middle class and the poor. A key problem is identifying and attempting to resolve the priorities of different stakeholders, sometimes from within the same organisation or type of organisation, for example, public sector planning bodies.' The project sought to bring together practitioners, policymakers and academics in a one-day workshop to outline approaches to gaining stakeholder support. The project aimed to:

01 explore stakeholder indentification: many projects (not just urban regeneration projects) fail because the vision, objectives and priorities for the project are not properly defined at the outset in consultation with those stakeholders that should be consulted – yet frequently are not;

02 focus on initial priorities. There are relatively few communities where sustainable community models have been effectively taken into account at the design stage; and

03 facilitate a fruitful exchange between practitioners involved with different projects and the academic community. ❯

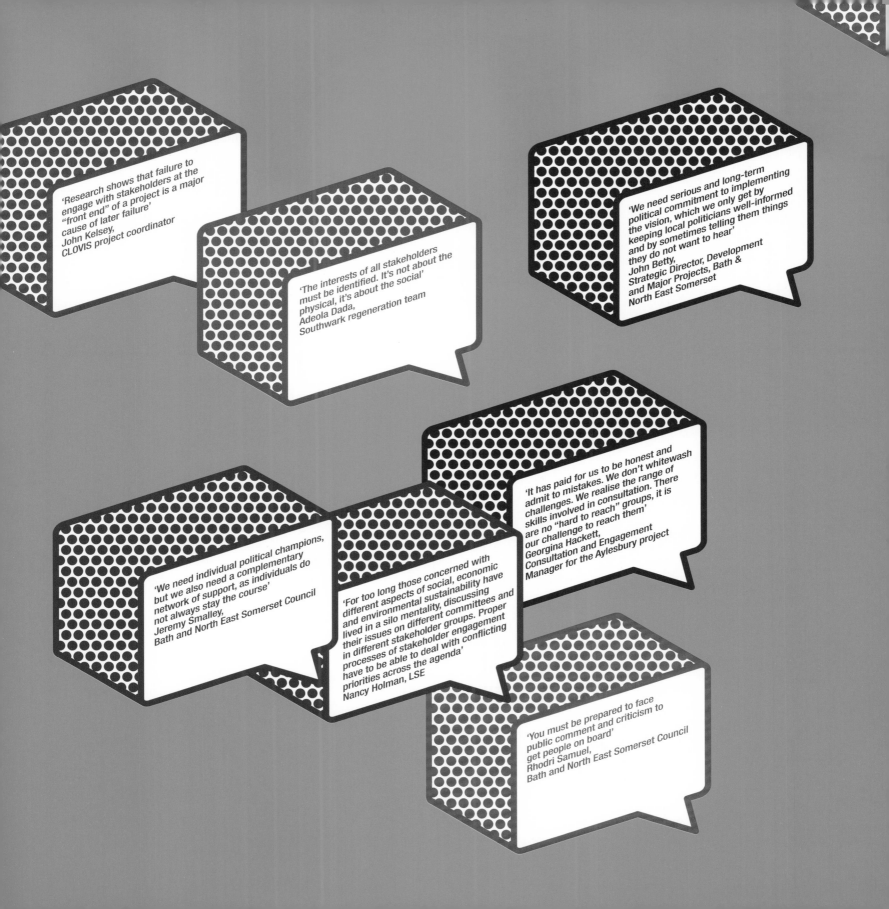

The project response

Twelve people attended a one-day workshop that explored the stakeholder engagement challenges faced by both teams. Each team outlined its key approaches and successes to date, followed by group discussion. All workshop participants felt that it would be useful for their experiences to be 'captured' and documented for the benefit of regeneration teams across the UK.

Unfortunately, due to illness, planned follow-up workshops could not take place.

Discussing the issues raised, the teams charged with the delivery of two seemingly very different programmes found that there was a surprising degree of commonality in problems and solutions. The BANES team engaged well with major public sector stakeholders, realising they needed firm political support. The Bath Western Riverside development proposals are unpopular with many wealthier residents who see the city as a historic site, rather than a potentially sustainable economic centre for the wider region. The Aylesbury team focused on successful community and resident engagement, leaving wider scale policy planning to a range of political leaders.

Each group was successful in engaging the stakeholders it targeted most effectively and resourcefully. In Bath, for example, the 'hard-to-reach' residents in the development zone that have not been engaged remain silent, while wealthier conservationists living elsewhere in the city become increasingly vocal. 'You must be prepared to face public comment and criticism to get people on board,' says Rhodri Samuel, Regeneration Manager of the BANES team.

In the BANES case, however, the consultation process was led by the developer, and the Bath team felt that, in future, control over public consultation should remain with the local authority team. A planned engagement strategy is much more effective than one that simply evolves, noted John Betty, Strategic Director, Development and Major Projects at BANES. Both the BANES and Southwark teams recommended keeping control of the engagement process, rather than passing responsibility to development partners, to ensure that communication is candid and expectations are effectively managed.

Project impact

All participants found the knowledge-sharing event useful, suggesting that it had legitimised and enabled 'reflective practitioner' time. The increasingly complex nature of urban regeneration processes, suggested participants, requires

'Regeneration is not about the physical, it's about the social. Communication and learning has to be two-way. There will be winners and losers from each stage of the development, and we need to identify these and work with them to clarify their personal stake in the project' Adeola Dada, Southwark

Consultation fatigue can be overcome with creative forms of engagement such as roadshows and community events, as happened at Southwark

UCL
John Kelsey
project management

Advisory panel
Peter Morris, Yvonne Rydin

Bath and North East Somerset Council (BANES)
John Betty, Strategic Director Development and Major Projects
Jeremy Smalley
Divisional Director of Development and Regeneration
Rhodri Samuel and Katharine Westcar

Aylesbury Estate regeneration team
Adeola Dada
London Borough of Southwark, Assistant Director, Aylesbury regeneration
Georgina Hackett
London Borough of Southwark, consultation and engagement manager, Aylesbury regeneration

Workshop participants
Aeli Roberts, UCL, lecturer in law, materials and sustainability
Sarah Earl, former team member of Aylesbury regeneration project, now working with UCL
Nancy Holman, London School of Economics, programme director, MSc Housing and Regeneration

Masterplanner Urban Initiatives developed a hands-on planning board game for residents to play at workshops in Southwark

'There is a critical issue in defining the boundaries for identifying stakeholders. Many who are physically outside the formal geographical boundaries of a programme may still be legitimately regarded as stakeholders. Old fashioned ideas such as focusing only within the red line of the planning application area needed to be re-assessed' John Betty, BANES

professional stakeholders to exit their 'silos' and engage with each other to a much greater extent.

Feedback suggested that the need to promote social sustainability among stakeholders should be seen as a key objective alongside economic and environmental sustainability, which are more often than not given greater consideration. Participants also noted that successful engagement is complex, intensive, resource-heavy and creative work, frequently reliant on the communications skills and strategies of the team leaders rather than rooted in robust policy, practice or process.

While there is useful generic understanding of stakeholder management, context is critical. The attempt to spark a fruitful exchange between practitioners and academics, and to move towards providing guidelines on effective stakeholder

engagement, was welcome. The workshop concluded that key public and private stakeholders need to be convinced that a coherent and consistent area vision has, or is, being formed and is backed with a clear political commitment for at least the medium-term.

The teams from both Bath and London felt that clumsy engagement has resulted in 'consultation fatigue'. This can, however, be overcome with creative forms of engagement. Roadshows, 'hands-on' scale models and community events have been used to energise and enthuse a surprisingly wide number of 'ordinary' people – young people and the over-60s showed a particularly strong interest in the Southwark case.

There is a critical issue in defining the boundaries for identifying stakeholders. Many who are physically outside the formal geographical boundaries of a programme may still be legitimately regarded as stakeholders because of the impact of a scheme upon them. Similarly, 'missing' stakeholders who are potentially desirable entrants to a programme area (residents, businesses, financiers) are groups with whom engagement has to be sought, through market research if necessary.

Knowledge exchange
Each team has learned some key lessons about the identification and management of different stakeholder groups. The BANES team engaged well with government agencies and was

well-connected regarding heritage issues and opposition. However, Betty and his colleagues recognised that they had not connected with local populations effectively, nor identified many 'hard to reach' stakeholders. The team concluded that the council should have retained a community leadership role, and not handed the consultation role over to developers.

The Southwark team is justifiably proud of its success in changing residents' attitudes to change and perceptions of redevelopment. Engagement approaches have been thorough and thoughtful. The Southwark team was keen to learn from the Bath team about public sector partnership and intra-public sector communication.

Whilst context is important, 'generic' lessons learned from the project are being disseminated via UCL: many of its postgraduates are part-time students employed by local authorities and other programme-managing bodies and, as such, are valuable knowledge-sharing assets. Educational processes at this level are definitely bi-directional, taking place between teachers and students as well as between students, says Kelsey.

Education and training
Issues arising from the workshop will inform teaching on MSc programmes at UCL, particularly on the MSc Urban Regeneration programme and the MSc Project and Enterprise Management Sustainability module.

The future: qualitative knowledge capture
Both teams felt that there were useful lessons to be learned from one another, and wished conversations started during the event to continue afterwards through similar events. All workshop participants felt that it would be useful for their experiences to be 'captured' and documented for the benefit of regeneration teams across the UK in dedicated knowledge-sharing portals. Bringing engagement professionals together can greatly enhance the way knowledge is shared – forming an active 'Community of Practice'. A system based on secondment to other local authorities and site visits to other schemes would be useful: although e-learning and online resources can be used for disseminating good practice, project members felt that specific issues are much better handled face-to-face.

Project resources
www.urbanbuzz.org (select projects)

'All problems are solvable. The wider the partnership, the more answers there are. The key thing is to make all the connections – up, down and around'
John Betty, BANES

'It's important for the residents to see action, as it's proved a challenge to keep them on board'
Adeola Dada, Aylesbury Regeneration

DEI DEMONSTRATION: Deployable External
Insulation Demonstration

Lead organisation
UCL

Project coordinator
Professor Stephen Gage

Project start and end dates
November 2007 to June 2008

Total UrbanBuzz funding
£19,946

Total CIK
£59,924.50

Contact details
s.gage@ucl.ac.uk

● Environment
● Design/housing

Window on the future
The DEI DEMONSTRATION project aims to give us back our windows – when we need them. A key driver behind this project is to think about sustainable ways for living in and using buildings

The context: avoiding heat loss

Heat energy can be lost through windows five to 20 times faster than through well-insulated walls. The practice of using windows to flood spaces with natural light is being lost, and people find themselves living under artificial lighting. The project aims to bring the possibility of large windows back to buildings in an energy-efficient context.

The building industry's typical response to heat-loss reduction through windows is to reduce the glazed area, or to introduce composite glazed panels of increasing technical sophistication. New building designs frequently show substantial reductions in glazed areas when compared with similar buildings from 10 years ago, and many façades now contain smaller windows than their 19th-century equivalents.

Many buildings, such as schools, colleges and offices, are unoccupied for most of the time. How can the energy consumed by empty buildings be controlled and reduced? It is usually coldest at night, when windows are not needed and are often obscured by curtains and blinds. Can we minimise energy loss at such times?

There is a need to further explore the potential of demountable systems and their control mechanisms. To date, some buildings have been fitted with insulated roller shutters, which are of limited effectiveness because the insulation is relatively thin. Other small domestic buildings have been fitted with demountable insulation, especially in ad hoc settlements in the colder parts of the western USA.

Key project objectives

To explore the possibilities of Deployable External Insulation (DEI: externally mounted insulating window shutters) in order to minimise heat loss from windows. This involved:

01 the design and build of prototype carbon mechanisms for automatically opening and closing the shutters as necessary;

02 the design and production of a demonstration pavilion to develop, test and monitor the concepts; and

03 the stimulation of debate on building use and building occupancy patterns as the world recognises the need to move towards low-carbon living.

The project response

A 6m shipping container has been reworked and turned into the demonstration pavilion; glazed and fitted with automated deployable highly insulated panels (thermal shutters).

A zero-carbon wax piston technology has been developed to drive opening and closing mechanisms for the thermal shutters. The mechanism operates using the phase-change of wax, which responds to the outside temperature, melting and expanding during the day and solidifying and contracting as the temperature drops. This is a solution that has not been previously attempted in this context, although is well-known for its use in greenhouses, in radiator valve systems and in the automotive industry. A manual override, using very little energy, allows users to control the shutters.

This prototype has been constructed using fixed glazing, but shutters could also be fixed over ventilators to help mitigate the occupancy heat gain typical in highly insulated buildings – there are three roof ventilators with shutters, driven by external temperatures, on the prototype's roof.

The prototype is undergoing further testing and monitoring on a rooftop at Trinity Buoy Wharf, east London. Specifically, it has been the subject of continued passive performance monitoring, with the focus on observational studies of daylighting performance. The passive operating performance of the drive mechanism is being monitored and developed with the support of the Bartlett's Thermal Studies Laboratory.

Project impact

The creation of an operational prototype has demonstrated that DEI is a viable option when considering the challenges of low-carbon living, offering potential solutions to the problems of retrofitting existing buildings, the ❯

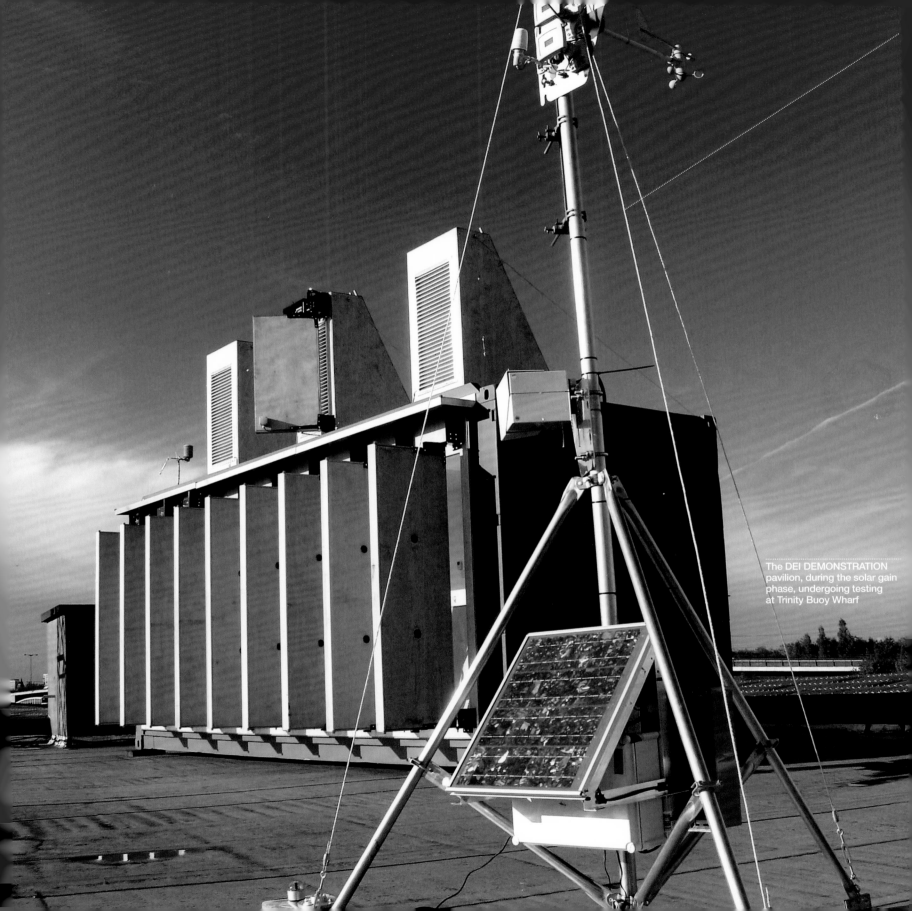

The DEI DEMONSTRATION pavilion, during the solar gain phase, undergoing testing at Trinity Buoy Wharf

design of new buildings, ventilation in highly insulated buildings and building occupancy and use patterns.

The project has resulted in a provisional patent that shows how the use of different waxes can result in an actuator capable of driving a thermal shutter. The patent is being taken forward by a team at UCL Business.

The DEI test cell has attracted active industry interest, and one Government department is potentially interested in using the DEI concept to develop a sustainable coastal tourism project in the UK. The team is also actively involved with a potential industry partner who is keen to develop the DEI concept using electro-mechanical actuators. The target market for this new product will be building refurbishment in the commercial and domestic sectors. A Knowledge Transfer Partnership (KTP) bid is being prepared.

'Gage and doctoral student Chris Leung's test pavilion – a converted shipping container with insulated shutters that open and shut automatically depending on weather conditions – is… a dryly convincing model of the future' *Architects' Journal*, 3 July 2008

Chris Leung
Architect and EngD student at the Bartlett, UCL, studying low energy building technology and vision-based monitoring of drive systems for the environmental control of buildings. Detailed design of the DEI drive mechanism and ongoing performance monitoring

Stephen Gage
Professor of Innovative Technology at the Bartlett School of Architecture, University College London Project coordination and supporting research

Steering group
Matthew Bugg (Make Architects), Bill Watts (Max Fordham Consulting Engineers), Fred Guttfield and Joe Moorhouse (DSP Architecture), Nick Browne (UCL)

Bob Leung, Make Architects
Design review

Bill Watts, Max Fordham
Data review

Haque Design + Research Ltd
'PachuBox' device and 'Pachube' web-service for remote monitoring of the pavilion (see project resources)

UCL students
Site fabrication and erection of the pavilion at Trinity Buoy Wharf and the UCL Quadrangle

Fred Gutfield and Joe Moorhouse and Geraldine Walder, Douglas Stephen Partnership
Design management, design of glazed enclosure, review of project, erection of the pavilion

Prototype piston assembly
Components by Ehlert Stahlbau, a German steelwork company, managed by Bartlett Architecture alumnae Nick Callicott and Kristina Ehlert. Assembly and testing of the drive mechanism at the Bartlett, UCL

Knowledge exchange

The diverse expertise of the project team led to the successful creation of a functional DEI test cell. The fact that a physical prototype was built, and is undergoing sustained monitoring, has had a positive impact on dissemination of the findings, with details of the project outcomes the subject of much industry interest. For example, the test pavilion was a key feature of the Bartlett School of Architecture Summer Exhibition, which attracted more than 9,000 visitors; typically architects, architectural students, academics, structural and environmental engineers, specialist contractors and subcontractors and interested members of the public.

The manned pavilion was included in the Trinity Buoy Wharf London Architecture Open House 2008, and will remain on show at future events connected with the wharf's creative arts community.

Through outreach activity – such as presentations, academic papers and media coverage – a wide range of architects, engineers and manufacturers have been inspired to examine this new approach to low-carbon living. By demonstrating the possibilities of DEI in a very practical manner, and in a public forum, the project has stimulated debate on topical and urgent issues of building occupancy patterns as well as on energy reduction initiatives.

The project team has created a website featuring computer simulation, thermal images, time-lapse video and an image gallery.

Activity and results from the DEI test cell are published online and updated daily (for details, see the project resources section). The performance monitoring feeds sensor data to the 'Pachube' web-service using an autonomous solar-powered 'PachuBox' device. This reads sensors embedded in the pavilion and transmits them by SMS text messages to 'Pachube'.

Education and training

The DEI concept will form part of the UCL MSc in Environmental Design and Engineering, with case studies contributing to an ongoing UCL effort to model scenarios for presentation to building control policy reviewers, specifically part L of the Building Regulations.

The future: towards a commercial product

The team is working on developing a marketable product, and expects to be 60 per cent of the way towards this objective in 12 months' time. There are legislative implications for energy reduction prototypes of this type, and a UCL-wide initiative will be taking planning and building regulation issues forward. The planning acts do not expressly exclude energy demand reduction measures from control by local authorities. Perhaps they should – further debate is needed.

Deployable insulation, along with many energy-reduction initiatives, can have a major impact on a building's appearance. The project has raised awareness of the fact that local authority planners, councillors and planning committees need to be educated to understand that there are visual, aesthetic, conservation and heritage implications to energy reduction.

Building occupancy and use patterns may affect the uptake of deployable insulation. This must be recognised by building control officers, and occupancy scenarios need to be monitored, recorded and incorporated in part L thermal models. Part L of the Building Regulations is currently under review, and a consultation document was issued in January 2009. Project coordinator Stephen Gage will feed experience from the project to Professor Robert Lowe, who is leading the Bartlett response.

Project resources
www.deployable.org.uk

The project team has created an informative website, www.deployable.org.uk, featuring detailed information on the project's partners and design/development phases, illustrated with computer simulation, thermal images, time-lapse video and an image gallery

The prototype pavilion is currently undergoing further tests and monitoring at Trinity Buoy Wharf, east London, where it will remain until summer 2009

Live monitoring activity is available online: www.pachube.com/feeds/1044

Project information is available on: www.urbanbuzz.org (select projects)

'We're turning windows into well-insulated walls when the space behind them isn't in use, or when it's dark. There is little point, as we move towards a low-energy future, in windows that lose heat in winter and gain excess heat in summer'
Professor Stephen Gage

Far left: A zero-carbon wax piston technology has been developed to drive opening and closing mechanisms for the thermal shutters

Left: The DEI DEMONSTRATION pavilion, in UCL's main quad, during the Bartlett School of Architecture Summer Exhibition, 2008

EASY: Evidencing Adaptable Sustainability

Lead organisation
UEL

Project coordinator
Professor Allan Brimicombe

Project start and end dates
June 2007 to November 2008

Total UrbanBuzz funding
£172,311

Total CIK
£90,823

Contact details
a.j.brimicombe@uel.ac.uk

- Environment
- Society
- Governance
- Policy
- Planning/regeneration

An evidence base for social infrastructure planning

A new model is delivering accurate and up to the moment estimates of demographic change across the London Thames Gateway, based on small area geographies and locally accessed datasets

The context: social infrastructure planning

In May 2008, MPs called on the Government to 'improve the population count as a matter of urgency'. According to Sir Michael Fallon MP, chairman of the Commons Treasury Select Committee: 'It is now impossible to accurately estimate the UK population.'

The Community Infrastructure Levy comes into play after 2009, alongside the current Section 106 arrangements (planning agreements that encourage developers to provide community benefits). Borough revenue is best accessed via a social infrastructure plan based on evidence-based population projections.

Much of the Thames Gateway is experiencing uncertainty in demographic composition. Data on population change is crucial to the boroughs and Primary Care Trusts (PCTs) because funding relates to population. Every individual unaccounted for equates to approximately £1,700 per annum, according to one PCT manager. Roughly speaking, if Office of National Statistics (ONS) projections are around 15,000 people short, a PCT could lose more than £25 million a year.

Key project objectives

Sustainable communities must have an appropriate and fair provision of infrastructure for its population, so the need for robust and accessible data is critical. There are issues of accuracy and consistency over time that stop existing population data sources such as the census being the 'gold standard' that we might like, says Professor Allan Brimicombe, project coordinator. 'There are fundamental differences across official statistics. Our purpose is not to say that any particular source of official statistics is inadequate, but simply to say that we have a new view.' The project aimed to:

01 develop a new approach to modelling populations, and create demographic models for 11 east London boroughs;

02 enable local authority staff to access the models to promote information-sharing and evidence-based decision-making;

03 develop models for use in social infrastructure planning, and refine them for use with the tools typically used by borough staff;

04 assess support for social infrastructure planning using the London Profiler and the TGLP Knowledge Platform: web-based online data services portals for London and for the Thames Gateway;

05 make the modelling approach available to organisations involved in social infrastructure planning, for example the NHS London Healthy Urban Development Unit (HUDU); and

06 integrate the models into NHS and Department of Health tools supporting strategic health planning.

The project response

The team has developed a robust multi-stage multiple regression model to obtain population estimates from locally held data at small area geographies. This is a new approach to estimating populations, being model-based rather than count-based. Each borough's model is fine-tuned, using significant variables that relate to context.

The second phase of the project involved bringing project participants and stakeholders together in order to discuss the potential impact of the Community Infrastructure Levy (CIL). Participants also explored existing and future channels for the sharing, dissemination and visualisation of fine-scale data, such as that delivered by the EASY model, across borough boundaries, so facilitating more robust social infrastructure planning across the Thames Gateway region.

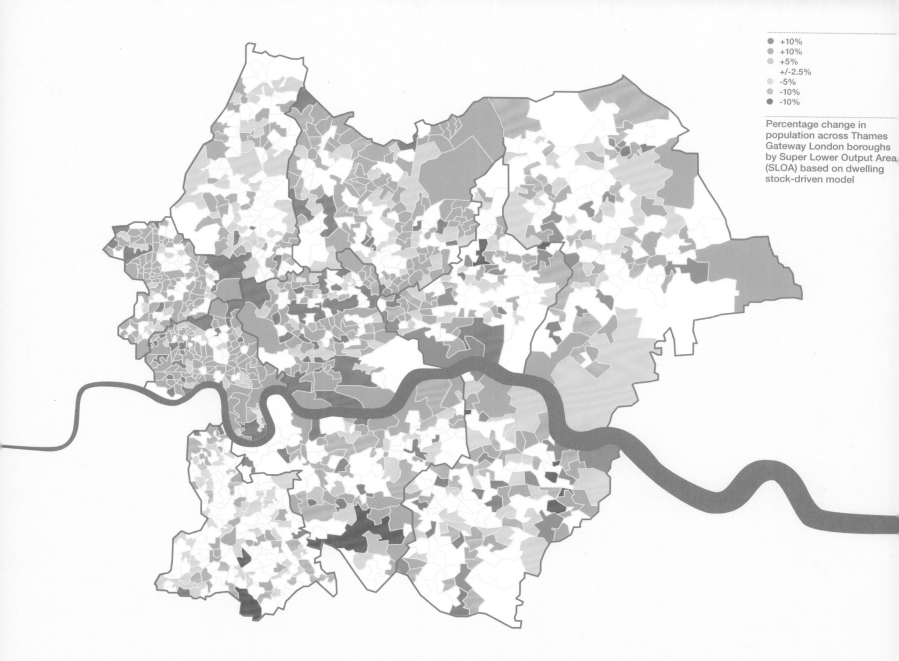

Project impact

Building sustainable communities means making tough decisions about infrastructure planning and provision; negotiating who should bear the costs and reap the benefits. These decisions must rest on robust evidence that allows stakeholders and communities to share a common understanding of facts and values. EASY provides a new approach to modelling populations within London boroughs, addressing issues faced by local authority planners and other areas of local service delivery. 'We believe that in the medium-term, as part of the UrbanBuzz legacy, the project

is changing thinking at all levels on how to approach population estimates from administrative data sources,' says Brimicombe.

EASY offers estimates of populations based on routinely collected local data sources such as school registrations as an improvement on extrapolation from ONS census data. This allows projections at a finer scale, and with more detail than usually provided. The outputs from the model give clear examples of how public data can be used in an appropriate manner without compromising data protection concerns, whilst still addressing political concerns about the

equitable provision of services. The results of the modelling have generated considerable interest amongst local authorities, Primary Care Trusts, the Office for National Statistics (ONS), NHS Healthy Urban Development Unit (HUDU) and the Department for Communities and Local Government (CLG), London Development Agency (LDA) and Thames Gateway London Partnership (TGLP). HUDU, for example, has commissioned the team to map accessibility to specific local amenities, for example dentists and GPs, against borough demographics and the needs of specific patient groups. ❯

Difference between EASY population estimation and ONS mid-year estimates (2001) by Lower Super Output Area: red equals negative change, blue equals positive change

UEL
Centre for Geo-Information Studies

Professor Allan Brimicombe
Project coordinator, stakeholder liaison, modelling

Dr Yang Li
Data collection, quality and microsimulation modelling; data integration

Establishing Knowledge Platform functionality and EASY data integration

Terra Cognita
Dr Chao Li
Data modelling and analysis

Workshops
**Local authorities, PCTs, ONS, GLA, CLG
Data supply, feeding back ideas and comment on model use and social infrastructure planning data support**

Chris Horton
Thames Gateway London Partnership
Outreach and connection to local authorities

'We're very interested in exploring the benefits of this model. We work closely with Tower Hamlets Partnership, our Local Strategic Partnership, on population projections and composition. We're especially interested in the changing nature of our population, how fast it's growing, and where it's growing. We'd like some insurance against current processes' **Clare Wall, strategic planner, Tower Hamlets Council**

UCL

Dr Sue Batty
Advisor on social infrastructure planning

Professor Paul Longley
Advisor on modelling and data dissemination

Thames Gateway London Partnership (TGLP)
Gary Tindell establishing the integration of EASY into the TGLP knowledge platform

All boroughs from within the London Thames Gateway were represented at the project workshops, taking away a new, informed view of population estimates. Also present were representatives from the GLA, ONS and CLG – which used EASY data to help develop a status report on the Thames Gateway. The new population models have been set alongside accessibility models additionally commissioned by the NHS HUDU. By way of a number of invited presentations with Primary Care Trusts and the Department of Health, the modelling process is beginning to impact on thinking on social infrastructure planning for health services.

The EASY model delivers interesting data alongside population estimates. The Pupil Level Annual School Census (PLASC) data records ethnicity and English language usage, enabling the examination of ethnic mix and language use patterns within boroughs. The project team was approached by a political candidate for North Ilford who is interested in using population and demographic data for political research purposes.

The EASY team is advising the Department of Health (DH) on its online Strategic Health Asset Planning and Evaluation (SHAPE) application. The project team has also worked with partner initiatives, each involved in social infrastructure planning, with the aim of improving access to a wide range of local data: the Thames

The EASY model is a multi-stage, multiple regression model. The broad aim of the project has been to use quality administrative datasets to evidence demographic, social and cultural change by small area geographies, and to promote the use of such evidence in the planning of social infrastructure.

The study area for building and testing the models has been the 11 boroughs of the London Thames Gateway region.

The unit of modelling is the Lower Super Output Area (LSOA). The purpose of the models is not to replace, or compete with, either the ONS mid-year estimates (MYE) or with the GLA estimates for wards. The new models provide a different view with which to triangulate population change and should be able to provide up-to-the-moment estimates, using the latest datasets.

There is a separate model for each borough. The data sets used are: dwelling counts by council tax bands, multiple occupancy, child benefit records and school census data (PLASC). The data sets have been sourced from central agencies such as the ONS rather than from individual boroughs in order to ensure consistency in data robustness across the study area.

'We're taking sets of variables, fixing their relationship to the 2001 census, and working out how we move them forward each year,' says Brimicombe. 'If data exposes major new trends, for example an explosion in single parent families in one borough, then the model would require adjustment. Following each census, models need to be recalculated based on available data.'

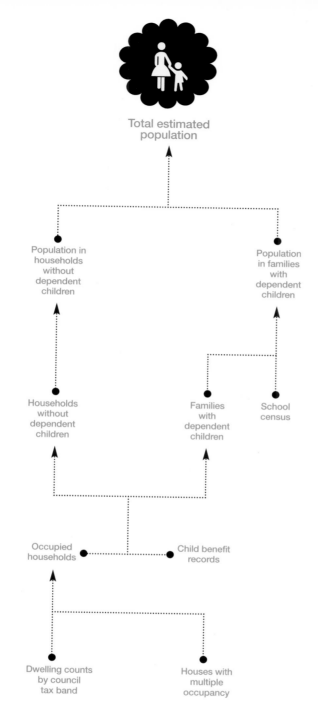

Total estimated population

Population in households without dependent children

Population in families with dependent children

Households without dependent children

Families with dependent children

School census

Occupied households

Child benefit records

Dwelling counts by council tax band

Houses with multiple occupancy

Gateway Knowledge Platform (TGLP) and the London Profiler (CASA, UCL). At a series of workshops and presentations, the team brought together local authority and PCT partners to demonstrate the potential of such online routes for the dissemination, sharing and visualisation of fine-scale data. Such platforms could support knowledge and decision-making, with a focus on the integration of existing tools that facilitate social infrastructure planning.

Knowledge exchange

A range of project partners has been involved in exploring new dissemination routes that can add value to routinely collected local data sources. 'A key further development for the Thames Gateway Knowledge Platform will be to enable locally-gathered data to be entered and displayed,' says Gary Tindall, TGLP. 'As we – local residents, public agencies, voluntary and community groups and private businesses – strive to shape the future of the Thames Gateway, we will need to work in partnership.'

Project participants from CASA, UCL, took the idea of data-sharing and dissemination, using online databases and Web 2.0 platforms, much further, outlining the future impact of a region-wide interrogative database hosting mapping, transport, building detail, land use, business class, rental and sale values, density, amenity, green space and accessibility data, available at fine scales, currently in development at UCL.

Combined with existing and future web-based technologies, such applications could revolutionise data provision for social infrastructure planning. 'Users of web-based services can take on the role of producers as well as consumers of information,' says Dr Hudson Smith, CASA, 'with sharing becoming a dominant mode of adding value to such data. These developments are growing Web 2.0 from the ground up, enabling users to derive hitherto unknown, hidden and even new patterns and correlations in data that imply various kinds of social networking.' The project team will continue to investigate new ways of collating, displaying and disseminating fine-scale data that could be of great benefit to those involved in social infrastructure planning.

Education and training

Learning from the project will be feeding into a new module on social sustainability within UCL's MSc Environmental Design and Engineering.

The future: demographic change

There is considerable interest from local authorities and PCTs in using the new models. Whilst EASY models are already informing decisions around social infrastructure planning, their drawback is that they are not, as yet, 'official statistics' and this will limit their use to support local planning policy and Local Area Agreements (LAA) and funding formulae. Population estimates are politically loaded and, in London, with a choice of ONS and GLA estimates at borough level, local authorities will naturally opt for the highest estimate. 'Where our figures appear to reinforce a lower ONS estimate (compared with the GLA estimate) our models are less welcome than where they support higher estimates,' says Brimicombe.

Project resources
www.uel.ac.uk/geo-information/EASY

A range of project presentations, reports, academic papers, references and links can be found on the project website

E-POD: Energy Performance of Dwellings and
non-domestic buildings

Lead organisation
UCL

Project coordinator
Dr Dejan Mumovic

Project start and end dates
December 2007 to August 2008

Total UrbanBuzz funding
£19,000.50

Total CIK
£22,700.50

Contact details
d.mumovic@ucl.ac.uk

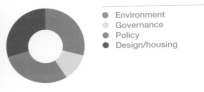

- Environment
- Governance
- Policy
- Design/housing

The context: energy-efficient buildings

The need to respond to climate change has highlighted challenges of energy use and adaptation in both residential and non-residential buildings. The Government has set a national carbon emissions reduction target of 80 per cent by 2050, relative to 1990 levels. Estimates suggest that 50 per cent of UK carbon emissions come from built environment construction and operation, with almost 20 per cent of this total from non-residential buildings.

In October 2008, it became law for any public building larger than 1,000 square metres to show a Display Energy Certificate (DEC). As the law came into effect, more than 18,000 such buildings, including town halls, museums, schools and job centres, were tested to determine their energy efficiency – E-POD project partner CIBSE carried out many of the surveys.

Initial results were not encouraging, with many buildings performing poorly. Environmental campaigners responded that the Government – which has already pledged to make all new public buildings zero carbon by 2018 – must launch an urgent refurbishment programme to reduce carbon emissions.

Key project objectives

The project aimed to raise awareness of the problems related to the design and operational performance of low-carbon buildings, and to instigate a cross-disciplinary dialogue regarding the reduction of building-related emissions.

The project team brought together players from key industry organisations such as the International Building Performance Simulation Association (IBPSA) and the Chartered Institution of Building Services Engineers (CIBSE) with academics, students and practitioners from design and engineering practices. Many participants were engaging in an industry-wide knowledge-sharing initiative for the first time. Several long-term aims were set in motion:

01 to establish a knowledge exchange and learning process focusing on challenges inherent in creating energy efficient, well-ventilated and user-friendly buildings;

02 through the project's partner organisations, to ensure that knowledge exchange will continue, informing professional practice, teaching and learning, training and policy-making. The team also hoped to strengthen the group of volunteers contributing to IBPSA-England activities.

The project response

The team organised a one-day symposium, held at UCL in July 2008. A total of 165 people attended, more than twice the number of attendees originally anticipated. The event has created a model for future cross-cutting events on this theme, acting as a catalyst for the engagement of the non-academic community in university research work and supporting the development of a new community of practice.

The symposium has greatly increased the awareness of IBPSA-England's aims and objectives. Following the symposium, 40 per cent of attendees became members of IBPSA-England. This served to highlight the potentially valuable role of advanced simulation in building design.

Project impact

The presentations and discussion forum held during the symposium were recorded, and 18 multimedia webcasts have been created and are hosted on the Low Carbon Buildings Directory website, which also features news and information on low carbon buildings and sustainable building design. Since its launch in November 2008, the lectures have been viewed more then 600 times. ❯

Energy performance in buildings
A new alliance of professional organisations, academics and practitioners is sharing knowledge and experience relating to the design and operational performance of low-carbon buildings

Natural ventilation stacks at the Frederick Lanchester Library, Coventry

'If the number of new projects on the drawing board which use advanced simulation in the design process was doubled, then the energy saved would be enough to meet the Government's predicted energy gap'
Joe Clarke, Strathclyde University

The symposium raised some key issues to head the agenda in the coming months and years:

01   energy thinking needs to be embedded at the forefront of the design process;

02   a heat and human comfort vulnerability index that includes building effects is needed. More work needs to be done on ventilation and natural ventilation;

03   heat emissions from buildings must be estimated so that we can understand the implications of building adaptation options;

04   GIS-based decision support tools are needed to explore adaptation options for urban planning and design;

05   performance issues are critical and must be taken much more seriously. There is a lack of data on post occupancy energy use;

06   the practice of performance data collation and comparison needs to be embedded into design practice;

07   effective management of a building after construction and commissioning is crucial. The ways in which buildings are used is a key issue. More than 20 per cent of the energy used in buildings could be saved by doing relatively straightforward things such as switching off lights and PCs.

Knowledge exchange

The E-POD team is working with the CIBSE School Design Group, the formation of which was supported by the TOWARDS ZERO CARBON SCHOOLS project (see page 202). In February 2009, a second event, A Roadmap to Zero Carbon Schools, was organised by members of the E-POD team, and the presentations filmed and added to the Low Carbon Buildings Directory resource. The CIBSE School Design Group will host a further session on Low Carbon School Buildings and Building Simulation at the 11th International Building Simulation Conference 2009, to be held in July in Glasgow, Scotland.

The CIBSE School Design Group has prepared a response to a public consultation on Zero Carbon School Buildings, followed by a meeting between CIBSE representatives and Department for Culture, Media and Sport's Task Force on Zero Carbon Buildings.

The delegation at the Symposium included architects, building service engineers, urban planners and local government representatives, students, senior academics and senior civil servants. A wide range of people from different disciplines and backgrounds was able to discuss energy-efficiency challenges for the first time in a multi-disciplinary arena.

Key outcomes are insights into effective design techniques and engineering technologies for low-carbon buildings that can be used by students, architects and building services engineers. The free online resource, Low Carbon Buildings Directory, created to showcase multimedia versions of the presentations and discussions (see project resources), is supporting the delivery of Continuing Professional Development (CPD) across the design and building professions.

CIBSE Home Counties (London) and Complex Built Environment Systems (CBES) at UCL has reached a preliminary agreement to launch the UCL-CIBSE Knowledge Exchange Club in London. This club will organise regular monthly events related to low carbon buildings. All lectures will be filmed and offered to CIBSE Home Counties members a online CPD seminars.

Education and training

Material from the symposium is feeding into UCL graduate programmes on environmental design and engineering. Modules will be developed on the natural and mechanical ventilation of buildings and energy efficient building services.

Lectures from the Low Carbon Buildings Directory have been incorporated as training material within the MSc in Environmental Design and Engineering curriculum at The Bartlett, UCL.

The future: towards new policy

Dr Mumovic, project coordinator, is producing a positioning paper (see below) based on the discussions and presentations around this symposium, which will be submitted to government policy makers through the symposium's guest speakers and project participants Lord Teveson (House of Lords) and Ted King (DCLG, now retired but still active in research and policy circles).

There will be continuing knowledge exchange activities through IBPSA-England, CIBSE School Design Group and CIBSE Natural Ventilation Group and CBES at UCL as part of the Sustainable Cities Grand Challenge (see page 36).

Project resources
www.lowcarbonbuildingsdirectory.org

There more than 25 presentations on the Low Carbon Buildings Directory from the symposium, and several more have also been added from related UrbanBuzz and UCL events. The resource will be kept up to date by UCL

Since 2008, more than 800 viewers have downloaded this material, and many professional users have provided valuable reviews, feedback and suggestions to improve the quality of the content and the functionality of the site

The project's positioning paper will be available in late summer 2009 via:
www.ibpsa-england.org
www.cibse-sdg.org

UCL
Symposium promotion to a wide UCL community, and advice on speakers and presentation material

Expert committee
Malcolm Cook, De Montfort University

Ian Ward, University of Sheffield

Mike Davies, UCL

CIBSE School Design Group
Symposium promotion to members, and advice on speakers and presentation material

International Building Performance Simulation Association (IBPSA-England)
Symposium promotion to members, and advice on speakers and presentation material

Symposium and project management
Dr Dejan Mumovic, UCL, with the support of UCL students and doctoral students, organised the symposium activities including establishing links with IBPSA and CIBSE

CIBSE Natural Ventilation Group
Symposium promotion to members, and advice on speakers and presentation material

Low Carbon Buildings Directory
www.lowcarbonbuildingsdirectory.org
Presentations were filmed and turned into multimedia webcasts, and made available as a free online resource

The 165-strong audience

Policy recommendation: material and conclusions from the symposium are being submitted to policy makers through guest speakers and via a position paper, to be published during 2009

Symposium speakers included:

Bill Bordass, the Usable Buildings Trust

Hywel Davies, Technical Director, CIBSE

Ian Ward, University of Sheffield, Immediate Past Chairman of IBPSA England

Professor Robert Lowe, UCL

Matthew Kitson, Director of Sustainability, Hilson Moran

Dr Jake Hacker, Director of Research, ARUP

Professor Steve Sharples, University of Sheffield

Professor Mike Davies, UCL

Professor Kevin Lomas, De Montfort University

Dr David Etheridge, University of Nottingham

John Palmer, Director of Research, Faber Maunsell

Roderic Bunn, BSRIA and Usable Buildings Trust

'We could easily save 20 per cent of the energy use in buildings now by doing relatively straightforward things. Behaviour is a huge issue. One of the things we've learned is that if you don't communicate in the right way, people feel demotivated and not encouraged'
Hywel Davies, CIBSE

Enabled Self Procurement Simulation
(ESP-SIM): a UK model for
communities as decision makers

Lead organisation
UEL

Project coordinators
Michael Kohn, Slider Studio
Joanne Harrison, UEL

Project start and end dates
July 2007 to October 2008

Total UrbanBuzz funding
£255,881

Total CIK
£130,554

Contact details
michael@sliderstudio.co.uk
J.E.Harrison@uel.ac.uk

● Planning/regeneration
● Governance
● Society
● Design/housing

The context: a new housing delivery model

This project is rooted in the need for new, community-relevant housing delivery. Such a concept must, by necessity, offer a robust delivery framework supported by freely accessible tools and processes that enable stakeholders and communities to engage, test and develop ideas.

Most housing developments in the UK are run on a speculative model, taking risks on what the market will pay for, on the granting of planning permission, and on construction-related risk. Speculative housing is subject to fragility in the housing market, as the effects of the credit crunch have revealed. Such a model is not, arguably, a sound way to build sustainable communities and it is currently difficult to see how UK national housing targets can be delivered by the private sector alone. It has also been noted that much of the housing delivered by this sector is of poor design quality (CABE 2004, 2005).

Enabled Self Procurement (ESP) sits between speculative and self-build housing models. ESP is not self-build as we currently recognise it in the UK, nor is it volume house building. It is an imagined hybrid solution that combines the best of both worlds. Such a system would include degrees of design and construction choice for the individual, with some of the mass efficiencies delivered by coordinated volume house building. The larger benefit lies in the social sustainability of constructing a place or new neighbourhood, using a process managed by those who actually want to live there, rather than one driven by market assumptions and commercial speculation.

Essentially, ESP means bringing together an 'enabling' developer, a set of community-wide design codes and a series of customisable 'pattern books' for individual home designs. Future community members select a plot and a home design, and negotiate fees according to the 'enabled' development model. This approach helps to embed sustainability into community design, by giving its future residents much greater input into design, build and planning options.

Key project objectives

The ESP-SIM team is focused on the bold and intelligent adoption of existing planning policy, focusing attention on existing but little-used planning policies, Local Development Orders (LDOs), as a delivery route for ESP, embedding new potential into planning tools. It aims to explore ESP as an approach to community-scale development, involving:

01 the creation of a viable and appropriate virtual world scenario in which development could take place;

02 the application of development and planning rules to each plot;

03 the population of the model with appropriate housing design models, customisable by users according to plot planning permissions;

04 designing and producing downloadable software (YouCanPlan) so that users can select and customise their chosen design;

05 creating a sophisticated tool for simulating design and environmental options along with predictions of energy use and fuel bills;

06 creating a mass collaboration tool capable of enabling online community consultation; and

07 defining the planning policy frameworks within which ESP could operate, including new uses for existing planning policy. ❯

Community building
The ESP-SIM project set out to define a viable model of Enabled Self Procurement for the UK, and to create a virtual world for testing and progressing the concepts

Enabled Self Procurement Simulation
(ESP-SIM): a UK model for
communities as decision makers

YouCanPlan menu functions include:

Design mode

Community view

Rotate view

Simulate designs

View proposals

Show plot
information

External view

Internal view

Show layers

Show
navigation

Show lighting

Community
statistics

Time remaining

Zoom

The project response

Developed by Slider Studio with support from UEL's computing school, bespoke multi-user online software called 'YouCanPlan' simulates the consumer experience of entering an enabled self-procurement project. This software offers future residents a choice of plots within a community, and a range of pre-approved house design choices that are customisable within set parameters.

In exploring Enabled Self-Procured housing, any sustainable development must render a certain social mix, a range of house sizes and include a proportion of affordable houses (or plots). This can be achieved through applying design codes at the level of a plot or group of plots. The design code parameters are embedded in the software.

It is hoped that a convincing illustration will ultimately lead to the delivery of a live ESP housing development using the YouCanPlan software as a supporting tool.

A case study has been completed, in collaboration with housing pathfinder Bridging Newcastle Gateshead, exploring the financial viability of such an approach, and early results suggest that an ESP approach can increase the residual value of land being brought forward for housing, thus making ESP a financially attractive procurement option for local authorities.

The team is currently developing a new version of YouCanPlan for online community consultation around another housing-led regeneration project in Lozells, Birmingham. Working in collaboration with Axis Design Architects for Birmingham City Council and Urban Living, a housing market renewal pathfinder, the new platform has been configured to allow direct uploads from designers, moderated by the Lozells project manager. A new feature supports resident surveys, enabling residents to feed back comments to project officers online. The Lozells project software will be launched during 2009, and will be publicly accessible online: www.vision-lozells.org.

YouCanPlan is, in effect, a mass customisation design tool for house designs, based on offering sustainable pattern book designs, as well as a mass collaboration design tool for establishing urban design parameters, based on embedded design codes for each plot. YouCanPlan ultimately operates as both as design visualisation and project management software for the support of ESP.

Project impact

Pattern books could offer an adaptable and flexible solution to the development of large-scale sustainable housing, offering a higher level of consumer choice than is currently available via UK housing delivery models. 'A combination of pattern book designs and urban design codes can meet all the placemaking requirements outlined in the national Building for Life initiative,' says project coordinator Michael Kohn. The crucial role of the 'enabling developer' is to determine the overall cost of development, and break down these costs into smaller pieces which can be shared by individual developers. Costs will be site- and context-specific.

YouCanPlan software enables widespread community and stakeholder engagement. Design teams and local authorities can test out urban design code and pattern book options. Potential house owners can test design and living options, make decisions about the types of housing they wish to live in, and communicate their views to the local authority and the enabling developer.

ESP enables individuals to have a direct say in the design and delivery of their own home and the surrounding community. The team believes that this innovative form of procurement can help improve design quality, increase delivery speeds and help build sustainable communities. However, the real test will be its implementation on a real development project.

The project team believes that planning should be about place-shaping, and that the planning system should create a framework for investment, not dictate it. Making enabled self- ❯

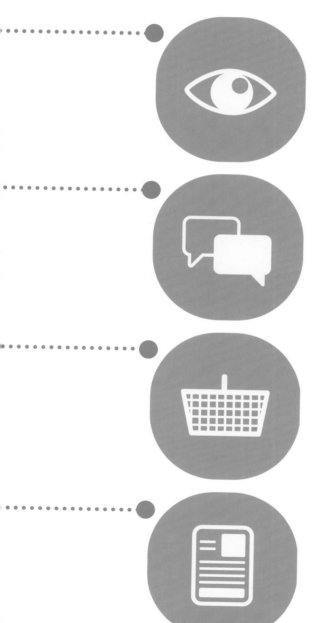

Look

YouCanPlan offers users tools for looking around the virtual environment in real-time and from any angle. Aerial view mode allows evaluation of the urban design; 'walk around' mode affords a view of the community at street level. This mode allows exploration inside individual homes. A simulation feature visualises different permissible design outcomes within the design code

Chat

YouCanPlan integrates online instant messaging so all project stakeholders can chat with one another as the design evolves. Group chat can be set up to host focus group discussions and workshops. Hosted online, 24/7 communication is managed as a 'single conversation' focusing on the design, with the software used supported in live workshops or remotely from home

Shop

YouCanPlan allows individuals to assemble their pattern book design on a plot, selecting parts from the pattern book shop. Prospective residents can select and test design options and assemble components on a specific plot before exploring inside. Each pattern book design allows for different layouts, elevations or environmental features; each choice brings with it cost implications

Manage

This feature records the different designs tested for a plot and allows users to publish preferred designs so that the whole community can see individual design choices. A simple calculator feature adds up the different component costs and 'eco points' of each design so users can determine (site and context-specific) cost and environmental impacts

Enabled Self Procurement Simulation
(ESP-SIM): a UK model for
communities as decision makers

Industry team
Advisors on process,
development models, use of
LDOs and development
economics

Alastair Donald
Audacity
HTA Planning
Mae LLP
Three Dragons

Urban design team
Work on design codes
and community-scale
planning policy

Slider Studio
Mae LLP
UEL AVA

**Winning pattern book
designers**

Clive Gray
David Kohn Architects
Edward Cullinan Architects
Hassan Ali
Howling Monkeys
Featherstone Associates
Geraghty Taylor Architects
Monique Suksmaningsih
Citylab
Jemma Horwood and
Tom Smith

Project management
Slider Studio
UEL Simlab

Overall project
management

'This approach to housing
delivery begins with the
establishment of credible pattern
books. It progresses by bringing
a Government agency or
landowner into the equation, and
by ringfencing land on which the
project can take shape'
David Birkbeck, Director,
Design for Homes

Architectural competition
An open, online competition
for pattern book housing
designs. Ten winning designs
were selected to populate
the virtual world

RIBA competitions office
Meganexus
Mae
Slider Studio

Software design and build

Development of the
YouCanPlan software and
the online virtual world.
Slider Studio
UEL SCoT

Development of project
websites
Slider Studio
Smartlab

The simulation platform: YouCanPlan

A virtual world simulation of a potential community.
Users can download free YouCanPlan software, select
and modify a pattern book house and progress
through the development cycle: www.youcanplan.co.uk

procured housing a possibility through Local Development Orders (LDOs) is one way in which a different form of investment could be encouraged – that driven by ordinary people who want to live in houses designed for their needs. The YouCanPlan software simulation is an exemplar for planning authorities of the possibilities for testing design codes and pattern books, so offering the development certainty required to publish LDOs for additional sites.

Knowledge exchange

ESP requires collaboration between all parties in regeneration, public and private sectors and the individual self-procurer. The project has brought together a range of industry experts to look again at the potential of existing planning policy, and has opened dialogue with two public sector housing pathfinder programmes.

To demonstrate how pattern books can be combined with urban design codes, the ESP-SIM project team ran an open competition to find a range of pattern book designs that could be built into the online simulation. This attracted 38 entries, with 750 online voters each voting for five schemes. Ten designs were selected and built into the simulation. Many competition entrants became members of the UrbanBuzz virtual community.

Dissemination and outreach activities have attracted significant public interest, with team members actively reaching out to members of the public who are interested in design, but who are not built environment professionals. The project has fed into the Office of Fair Trading (OFT)'s *Homebuilding in the UK*: a market study (September 2008) consultation recommending that the government should enable small builders

and self-builders to deliver a larger proportion of UK homes, and that local authorities work with 'enabling developers' to split up land into smaller development plots.

The project has created a tool that could deliver all the objectives spelled out in the 2007 Green Paper for housing development, and which could open up development to a wider range of individual developers – to the point where ESP could become possible on a widespread basis. Interest in finding creative uses for existing planning policies such as LDOs has been stimulated by the project team, and further research is encouraged.

An illustrated report explaining the ESP process and the potential of ESP for further development is to be published in May 2009, and widely circulated to local authority housing and regeneration managers. Copies will be available from the project website: www.esp-sim.org.

Education and training

The YouCanPlan software featured at CABE's Futurescape exhibition in October, exploring digital tools for design education. Project coordinator Michael Kohn has also delivered lectures on ESP, offering material for alternative urban design to UEL, Birmingham, Oxford Brookes and Anglia Ruskin Universities. Calls for further lectures continue as interest in alternative procurement concepts increases.

The future: embedding community choice

Using the enabling developer model, housing plots would have pre-approved planning permission based on the types of pattern books associated with them. Depending on the project parameters, developments could allow for vastly differing types of housing, or the design code could be constrained to allow only similar designs. As the ESP simulation evolves, a wider range of

design components could be offered for each home, with additional environmental specifications. The team is working with architects to increase choice in the design and environmental options available.

ESP development requires a high level of collaboration between house builder, architect and end user to get the job done – a factor that could be of increasing importance as the move to integrated management schemes becomes more widespread.

With traditional models, new communities can take up to 20 years from outline planning permission to first phase completion. Schemes need to be 'future-proofed' against a rapidly changing policy agenda, and ESP is well placed to adapt quickly to change – the YouCanPlan software can calculate and re-calculate the costs associated with each plot, each design and each service provided.

ESP could also work as a percentage of larger development, with a small percentage of homes offered through ESP, encouraging community cohesion and seeding social sustainability – a key aim of the Homes and Communities (HCA) delivery agenda, which pioneered similar interventions in its design code-supported millennium developments. As a development model, ESP can help the public sector to deliver design quality, social inclusion and higher land receipts, especially in times of economic downturn.

The business case barrier is cultural change, and professional capacity within the public sector to manage such innovation. Yet as the credit crunch continues to disrupt traditional development plans, agencies and interest groups across the UK are now frequently heard discussing the need for new and innovative development models – including ESP and ESP-SIM. A bold and well-resourced public sector body such as the HCA is well-placed to take such ideas forward.

Project resources
www.esp-sim.org
www.youcanplan.co.uk
www.vision-lozells.org

'The idea is that the architectural designs relate to the plot at point of sale. Using the enabling developer model, the plots would have pre-approved planning permission based on the types of pattern books associated with them'
Project coordinator, Michael Kohn

FEfUR: Fresh Eyes for Urban Regeneration

Lead organisation
British Urban Regeneration Association (BURA)

Project coordinator
Dr Gareth Potts

Project start and end dates
August 2007 to September 2008

Total UrbanBuzz funding
£33,000

Total CIK
£11,905

Contact details
garethpotts68@aol.com

- Environment
- Society
- Governance
- Policy
- Planning/regeneration
- Design/housing

Fresh perspectives on regeneration

A group of urbanist and non-urbanist academics and practitioners from a wide range of disciplines is bringing fresh eyes to bear on the regeneration process

The context: familiar challenges, new ideas

Urban regeneration is big business in the UK. The Government devotes £4 billion annually to new schemes, but we don't always get it right. The Fresh Eyes project explored the potential of a new, inclusive approach to the regeneration process. Urban regeneration is increasingly interdisciplinary in both academia and practice, but many disciplines such as environmental economics, systems thinking and philosophy have yet to be invited to the table. What insights might theorists from these areas add to perspectives from disciplines such as geography and design – those from which 'urbanists' traditionally come?

Key project objectives

The project sought to explore the possibility of bringing new insight to the regeneration process from academics and practitioners working in areas outside of those traditionally involved in regeneration. Through exploration of an emerging urban regeneration challenge (Deptford in Lewisham, south London), the idea was to go beyond the views of the 'usual suspects' such as architects, geographers and urban designers. The project aimed to:

01 bring together representatives from the fields of cultural studies, philosophy, micro-economics, systems thinking, futures/scenarios work, environmental and community psychology, anthropology and political science to assess a development site, its restraints and its potential, supported by local community groups;

02 bring together an 'urbanist' group that included planners, economic geographers, architects, urban designers, urban sociologists, property developers, estates managers, civil engineers and transport experts, to explore the same site;

03 to overcome mental and practical barriers to collaborative working;

04 to define a framework in which future initiatives of this kind can take place;

05 to define a process by which insights arising from such initiatives can inform the planning process.

The key challenge was to develop new perspectives on building and maintaining sustainable communities. Specifically, the project sought to enthuse academics and the local community, and to demonstrate that innovative new approaches to regeneration can be interesting, enjoyable and productive.

The project response

A regeneration site in Deptford, Lewisham, was selected as a case study for the project. It featured industrial units and a substantial breakers' yard, as well as being near to a large social housing estate and high-end riverside apartment blocks. The Creekside Community Forum and Pepys Estate Community Forum, both local community groups, were approached and their interest and engagement assured.

Academics from more than 20 disciplines took part in the initiative, along with public and private sector practitioners (RPS Group, Atkins, Groundwork and legal firm Bircham, Dyson, Bell). A local history of Deptford and Lewisham was created to provide the participants with background knowledge. ›

The first Fresh Eyes event was held in September 2007, and chaired by John Worthington from international design consultancy DEGW (also a visiting professor at Sheffield University and board member of London Thames Gateway Development Corporation).

The event included a guided tour of the area led by a member of the Creekside Community Forum. This was followed by group working to summarise what each participant would propose in terms of research and/or action, and presentations from the working groups on their findings. The event concluded with group discussion and recommendations, leading to an evaluation of the event.

Post-event, each academic produced a discipline-specific report on the issues raised, and outlined their suggestions for possible research questions or courses of practical action. Each academic also nominated a key book on their discipline as recommended reading for the other participants.

A 'User Panel' was established in the summer of 2008 to discuss the first event and the wider process. Five key stakeholder groups were identified as those most likely to be interested in using the outputs from the Fresh Eyes event: community 'activists', developers, educators, local authority regenerators, and planning/regeneration consultancies.

Representatives from each of the five key stakeholder groups were invited to attend a meeting of the User Panel. Discussion focused in particular upon the different stages at which the perspectives generated at Fresh Eyes events might be used. This discussion fed into the design of a final prototype toolkit.

A second Fresh Eyes event was held in September 2008, with 40 people attending including academics, community group members, developers, local authority workers and representatives from private sector organisations. Also in attendance was a local councillor (also a Deputy Mayor), a member of the local safer neighbourhoods team and the neighbourhood warden.

The structure of the day followed that of the first event – but began with contextual background from a local developer and the local councillor. Following feedback, and including comments and appraisal from the User Panel and attendees, the prototype 'Fresh Eyes Toolkit' for implementation on each development site was refined and created.

The toolkit draws out relevant questions, the stages at which they can be asked, identifies specific 'Fresh Eyes' elements and explains how context may alter the questions asked. The toolkit relates Fresh Eyes insights to each stage of the

Creekside Forum Community Group Workshop participants

Local resident and tour guide Noel Rooney

Development Trusts Association (DTA) Jess Steele Creating historical information

British Urban Regeneration Association (BURA) Dr Gareth Potts Project coordinator, event convener and background research; production of Fresh Eyes toolkit

Local businesswoman and tour guide Rebecca Molina, Raw Nerve Design

Pepys Estate Forum Community Group Workshop participants

regeneration process (strategic planning, masterplanning, detailed development decisions, community consultation and post-development evaluation), and highlights which new perspectives are likely to improve regeneration processes.

Project impact

The Fresh Eyes project demonstrated that experts from a wide range of disciplines can usefully be brought together with a view to broadening the traditional regeneration framework, so informing the wider planning process. The feedback from both events pointed to a willingness amongst the vast majority of participants to repeat the exercise, and to consider taking the process forward through one or more

avenues: research, education, events and engagement with local communities. In this way, the project has created a network of interested individuals who are open to working with colleagues from non-traditional built environment disciplines, but who previously lacked the framework to do so. Importantly, the project created space for interaction and reflection regarding regeneration practice.

The prototype 'Fresh Eyes Toolkit' outlines a framework for assessing locations and developments elsewhere and offers, in effect, a checklist against which local plans or developments can be designed and/or analysed. It enables insights and new thinking to be evaluated in the context of defined regeneration

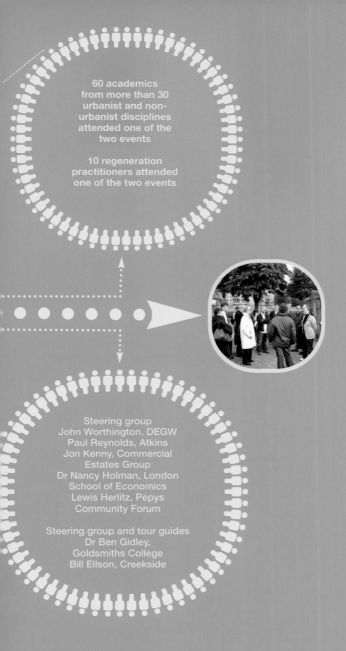

60 academics from more than 30 urbanist and non-urbanist disciplines attended one of the two events

10 regeneration practitioners attended one of the two events

Steering group
John Worthington, DEGW
Paul Reynolds, Atkins
Jon Kenny, Commercial
Estates Group
Dr Nancy Holman, London
School of Economics
Lewis Herlitz, Pepys
Community Forum

Steering group and tour guides
Dr Ben Gidley,
Goldsmiths College
Bill Ellson, Creekside

The project has highlighted barriers that need to be challenged, for example, the cultural and linguistic barriers between many deprived communities, academics and professionals. The language may be mutually unintelligible, and confidence on all sides may be low

establish processes, working within wide partnership for putting such insights into practice in an active regeneration project.'

Knowledge exchange

The project has demonstrated that many perceived and practical barriers to knowledge exchange can be overcome, and has provided a route-map for real-world progress. The barriers to multidisciplinary working on this scale have been shown to be partly mental and partly structural – there were previously no specific schemes that encourage such an approach. They are also partly institutional in that traditional faculty boundaries tend to limit interdisciplinary working, as academic pressure directs academics to excel in a specific discipline rather than experimenting with novel approaches.

Frequently, the lack of a brokerage mechanism to bring academics together has lessened the likelihood of such experiments. The project has also highlighted barriers that need to be challenged, for example, the cultural and linguistic barriers between many deprived communities, academics and professionals. The language may be mutually unintelligible, and confidence on all sides may be low – there is frequently uncertainty about moving forward and embarking upon a dialogue. The toolkit outlines processes for managing these issues.

Education and training

The project is an important step in the establishment of regeneration courses that are even more interdisciplinary in nature than occurs at present. There is certainly interest in the concept. The project coordinator has been contacted by the regeneration course directors at London Metropolitan University and the London School of Economics (both of whom participated in the first Fresh Eyes event) with a view to involving student groups in the Fresh Eyes process.

The future: implementing Fresh Eyes?

The next step is to explore issues raised by the Fresh Eyes process, taking each new theme as the focus for an event. Local residents would be consulted for their views on an issue (using outreach techniques) and academics and practitioners would discuss these findings – thinking particularly about what could and could not be changed in the case study area.

The tool can be used by individual universities to promote interdisciplinarity and community engagement. It can also be used by communities and practitioners working on specific sites to engage with academia and to generate new ideas.

variables such as scale, use, population, community interest and management models.

The toolkit incorporates lessons learned about how the Fresh Eyes process could usefully be put into practice in future. Although the events proved popular, there was an acute awareness from both the project coordinator and participants of the need for a defining structure in which the site exploration and the discussion process can take place. A lack of structure and focus for the debate, and a lack of specific questions posed in advance, resulted in few actionable conclusions being reached on this occasion.

In defining a viable framework for events of this type, the team established that several elements must be in place: a committed and informed Chair who understands both the academic and practitioner

worlds; enthusiastic and informed tour guides; and an effective manager able to handle project management and to make sure that events proceed smoothly.

The discussion and feedback gave rise to 'a mix of thoughts, ideas, stimulating points, description and critical appraisal', says project coordinator Dr Gareth Potts. 'Several participants said that they'd benefited from "looking at my discipline from the outside",' he adds. Others stressed that they'd been made more aware of the intricacy of the regeneration challenge, especially the 'sheer complexity of the planning process'. But to move from being 'novel and interesting' to being really useful, says Potts, the 'Fresh Eyes approach needs to continue to

Project resources
www.urbanbuzz.org (select projects)

GBE: Gender and the Built Environment

Lead organisation
Women's Design Service

Project coordinators
Wendy Davis and Barbra Wallace

Project start and end dates
May 2007 to December 2008

Total UrbanBuzz funding
£127,420

Total CIK
£9,000

Contact details
bwallace@wds.org.uk

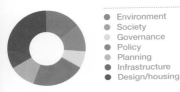

- Environment
- Society
- Governance
- Policy
- Planning
- Infrastructure
- Design/housing

The context: inclusive design

In a planning policy arena peppered with 'community empowerment' and 'inclusive design' soundbites, it is difficult to make a case that gender issues deserve particular attention. Surely women are part of the community, and their needs covered by community-wide inclusive design plans?

'Not necessarily,' says Wendy Davis, GBE project coordinator and director of the Women's Design Service (WDS). 'Treating the sexes "equally" simply doesn't work.'

Project Advisory Group member Professor Clara Greed concurs: 'The project raises the importance of all the so-called "little" things that limit women's experience of cities, not least lack of public toilets and inappropriate transport routes that do not reflect women's "different" journeys to work, home, school and shops.'

The Gender Equality Duty (GED), a legal obligation which came into force in April 2007, requires public bodies and their contractors to actively promote gender equality. However, there are no guidelines on how this relates to built environment issues as there are, for example, in the case of disability.

In the course of its training agenda, the WDS, says Davis, regularly encountered 'ignorance' amongst practitioners of the role gender should play in the design and management of the built environment.

Academics do have some awareness of the issues, stresses Davis, but policymakers seem to ignore the body of evidence recommending that gender issues be addressed in planning. 'We found that even those institutions that have commissioned research are often unaware of, or fail to implement, relevant recommendations.'

Key project objectives

Realising that awareness of existing gender research and its recommendations was very low, the project's aim was to create a comprehensive database of gender resources. 'We wanted to address everyday issues,' says Clare Melhuish, project researcher. 'Why are there never any queues outside men's toilets? Why are women six times less likely to go out alone after dark? Why are 90 per cent of people employed in UK construction-related professions male?' The project aimed to:

01   collate and reference existing research and initiatives relating to gender and the built environment;

02   widely disseminate awareness of the issues and the new resource to built environment professionals through online communications and a launch event/exhibition; and

03   hold training and workshops to raise awareness of gender issues and the implementation of the Gender Equality Duty. ❯

Sex and the city
Gendersite, a comprehensive online resource for gender and built environment information, will help the planning and development community to create inclusive environments that meet the needs of all

CREATE ● ● ● ● ● ● ● ● ● ● ● ●

The project response

The result, Gendersite, is a free online resource for anyone seeking information about gender issues in the built environment. The database lists and references 1,600 books, bibliographies, broadcasts, case studies, conference papers, journals and reports relating to gender and built environment issues. More than 2,600 people had visited Gendersite by November 2008. Gendersite was actively promoted to built environment professionals and policymakers via an email marketing campaign. A launch event and exhibition featuring guest speakers was held, supported by a series of seminars, training sessions and presentations, to raise awareness of both the underlying issues and the new resource. Gendersite will be maintained by WDS.

Project impact

The Gendersite resource will help professionals and communities to focus on gender issues within development policy. It raises awareness of the substantial body of work that is already in the public domain. David Morris, Senior Policy Advisor to the Mayor of London, attended the Gendersite launch event. 'What we build around us will reflect our diversity,' he said, adding that he regularly meets, in policy circles, 'rooms full of non-disabled blokes who don't experience barriers. What we need,' he stated, 'is more people who experience the barriers to get into designing the change.'

Crime-friendly environments such as poorly overlooked alleys, badly-lit public spaces and dead ends impact on us all, but many women have a gender-specific response to safety that is psychologically and socially rooted in the fear of sexual assault. This is why, says Davis, many women object to siting lapdancing and sex clubs within community areas.

The team are sure that debate, and the fact that relevant background information is now easily accessible to all, will help gender-aware campaigns to succeed. Many professionals working in the gender and built environment field agree. 'It is still a man's world when it comes to rebuilding Britain's towns, but if designers and decision makers consult the Gendersite resource, perhaps we will start to see a difference,' says Dr Gemma Burgess, University of Cambridge Centre for Housing Research.

Knowledge exchange

Gender awareness training sessions and seminars were delivered in fora from Urban Design Week, a Public Realm Information Network (PRIAN) seminar, Design Education for

Women's Design Service (WDS)
Wendy Davis
Project management, design of website structure with Fat Beehive

Barbra Wallace
Project management

Hannah Carty
Website design and marketing support

Project Advisory Group (PAG)
Professor Clara Greed, University of the West of England (UWE)
Professor Dory Reeves, University of Auckland
Dr Jos Boys, University of Brighton
Professor Kerry Hamilton, UEL
Virginia Newman, RIBA
Primali Dishna Paranagamage

Fat beehive
Design and construction of the Gendersite resource

Queen Mary University London (QMUL)
Professor Alison Blunt
Supervision of the research stage

Dr Clare Melhuish
Project researcher and editor

'We wanted to address everyday issues. Why are there are never any queues outside men's toilets? Why are women six times less likely to go out alone after dark? Why are 90 per cent of people employed in construction-related professions in the UK male?'
Clare Melhuish, Gendersite researcher

'Gendersite provides an enduring legacy to raise the recognition of gender-aware policy and design resources for the built environment'
Professor Clara Greed

●●●●●●● ➤ PROMOTE

WAND
Creation of the Gendersite awareness campaign, and promotion of the Gendersite resource and events via a customised email database of relevant contacts

Launch event
With speaker Ruth Reed, former RIBA President: 'I greatly applaud the work of Gendersite in promoting the information required for briefing. These are issues that need raising, we all design on the basis of our own experience'

Launch event and exhibition audience
A diverse audience of practitioners, policymakers, academics and the public attended the Gendersite launch event and exhibition

Project supporters
David Morris, Senior Policy Advisor to the Mayor of London

Professor Alison Ahearn, Imperial College London

Professor Despina Stratigakos, Faculty of Architecture at Buffalo, State University of New York

Professor Annmarie Adams, School of Architecture, McGill University, Montreal

Terry Marsh, Director of WISE

Hilary Burrage and Kate Beeching, British Urban Regeneration Association (BURA)

'We all face barriers. We need more people who experience them to get into designing the change. We don't talk enough about our space – there is no democracy in architecture. When people get together and start exploring how they feel about space, change happens'
David Morris, Senior Policy Advisor to the Mayor of London

Seminars and training
Six training sessions and seminars were delivered, disseminating the project's outputs to 170 participants

Sustainability (DEEDS) and the UrbanBuzz showcase, ensuring effective dissemination of the project's message and outputs. Dissemination feedback was monitored and received a positive rating from session participants. Improvements to the website are planned in response to feedback, and the team hopes, through continued fundraising, to continue to add new resources as they are published

Entry and exit surveys aimed at Gendersite visitors were set up using free Web 2.0 service SurveyMonkey.com to establish whether there has been any change in people's knowledge and awareness of the issues around gender and the built environment since the launch of Gendersite. The results suggest that it may be helping to inform users about gender and built environment issues: in the post-launch survey, 59.4 per cent of respondents thought that women experienced the built environment differently from men, compared to 42.2 per cent for a pre-launch survey.

Education and training
Gendersite has been promoted as an informal learning resource at WDS' EHRC-funded 'Promoting Good Relations' project meetings. It will be promoted through all WDS training programmes. Gendersite will also be promoted within WDS's London Council funded project, Women's Design Groups, which aims to set up women's design groups in 12 Greater London boroughs throughout the next three years.

The future: raising awareness
'The legacy of the Gendersite project will be raising awareness of gender-aware policy and the provision of design resources for the built environment,' says Professor Clara Greed, Gendersite participant and Project Advisory Group member. Gendersite has a key role to play in reinforcing and informing GED policy implementation and regulation. For example, it could be a key resource for those advising large public-funded built environment projects such as the development and construction of the 2012 Olympic & Paralympics site.

Through existing initiatives and contacts, there is opportunity for WDS to work with public bodies, such as the Greater London Authority, to inform the effectiveness of Gender Equality Duty requirements within the built environment field. The British Urban Regeneration Association (BURA) has contacted WDS regarding collaboration on the development of BURA's programme on equality and diversity awareness.

Project resources
www.gendersite.org
www.wds.org.uk/www/projects_gendersite.htm
(including video of the launch event)

i-VALUL: The Intangible Value of Layout

Lead organisation
Space Syntax Ltd

Project coordinator
Alain Chiaradia and Christian Schwander

Project start and end dates
September 2007 to December 2008

Total UrbanBuzz funding
£382,803

Total CIK
£840,991

Contact details
a.chiaradia@spacesyntax.com
c.schwander@spacesyntax.com

- Environment
- Society
- Governance
- Policy
- Planning/regeneration
- Infrastructure
- Design/housing

The intangible value of urban layout
The evidence-based i-VALUL urban layout evaluation project brings layout factors into the heart of design, planning and economic appraisals

The context: layout and movement

The impact of street widths, building heights or construction materials on the built environment is directly measurable. The impact of urban layout and its effects on social, cultural and economic aspects of community is much less tangible, and difficult to visualise and measure during the planning and design process.

Research findings from University College London (UCL) have enabled practitioners to understand the ways in which urban layout can shape basic human interaction. 'Space plays a key role in determining patterns of movement in cities, and the everyday activity of people in places is influenced by the way the layout makes it easier, or more difficult, for them to move around,' says Tim Stonor of lead project organisation Space Syntax Ltd. 'These interactions are both social and economic.'

In terms of movement, measures of spatial accessibility are key, he adds. The more accessible a place is, the more movement it experiences. Movement leads to sustainable land use, and so spatial layout is intimately linked to the viability of retail and commercial activity.

However, many new developments in the greater south-east are failing to implement high quality urban layout. The i-VALUL team wished to change this by developing an evidence-based urban layout evaluation programme able to overcome the barriers that prevent layout factors from being considered in economic appraisals.

Key project objectives

The project team, understanding that patterns of space, land use, activity and development are closely related, wished to develop a contextual approach to quantifying and measuring the relational properties of urban layout. Technology and tools exist to analyse spatial layout and forecast movement patterns, but only a handful of local authorities and Regional Development Agencies make use of these methods during the planning process.

The i-VALUL project aimed to develop a user-friendly layout evaluation toolkit, focused on the needs of potential users rather than led by academic researchers, that would lead to an increase in the levels of spatial analysis being undertaken in our towns and cities. It aimed to:

01 use existing knowledge of spatial modelling to create a unified spatial accessibility map of the greater south-east region. This map forms the basis for a layout evaluation tool capable of 'quantifying' urban layouts;

02 integrate and cross-reference valuations from existing economic, social, security and environmental studies of layout, and incorporate this data into the layout evaluation tool. Values of accessibility patterns, land use distribution, safety and environment (traffic, noise and pollution) would be correlated with spatial layout evaluation data;

03 create a training programme to transfer the integrated knowledge stemming from use of the layout evaluation tool to the public, private and voluntary sectors;

04 train representatives of these three sectors to undertake the valuation and evaluation of urban layout;

05 undertake live integration projects to transfer the practice of using layout valuation targeting the three sectors at different scales, and to evaluate the success of the project knowledge transfer;

06 disseminate outcomes and support project legacy; and

07 integrate the evaluation of urban layout into general practice, with the ultimate aim of informing the development decision-making process. >

'The creation of the i-VALUL layout value map is the project's main contribution to enabling spatial analysis. Local stakeholders are much more willing to believe in the case studies when they see the tools applied in their own areas. They can relate the analysis to their own shops, streets and space, and see the evaluation in action'
Christian Schwander, project coordinator

The project response

Planners, transport engineers and urban designers are involved in the specification of urban layout. This project has developed tools and processes that enable these professionals to determine how layout impacts directly on the ways in which places are used, and their value. The project team identified, and overcame, three main barriers to the use of layout evaluation tools.

The layout value map: Urban and city centres function in relation to a large surrounding context. This means that the cost of mapping a large enough area on which to base a layout analysis is often outside the budget for single development stakeholders. The project responded by creating a 'base' model, in the form of the greater south-east layout value map, that would substantially reduce entry costs.

Configurational spatial data that describes the relationship of an area with its wider context is necessary in a layout value map, and the map developed by i-VALUL covers one of the largest city-regions in Europe with a population of 21 million; it takes in an area of 40,000 km² and consists of 2.4 million street segments.

Awareness and training: The second barrier was the need to develop an accessible training programme. There is a lack of knowledge amongst community stakeholders, including local authority planning officers, elected planning committees, private sector developers and professional architects and surveyors, of the nature and potential of the latest tools and techniques for bringing intangible factors into the planning and design process. There is awareness that intangibles need to be managed, but little knowledge of how to progress. The project team organised training sessions for a wide range of project participants, providing computers pre-loaded with the necessary software tools to get around the reluctance of local authorities to install the necessary software on their own systems. Space Syntax employees were 'embedded' into local authority teams in order to train new users.

Developing the tools: The third barrier was the lack of a set of generic, benchmarked layout valuation tools that can be updated with local data as it becomes available. Baseline data necessary to assess the wider context of each development site, for example, data on land use, development density and building condition, is rarely readily available. Other data on crime, or socio-economic and demographic factors, is often aggregated to the point at which it loses meaning. There is a need to make such data accessible in a user-friendly and meaningful way to decision-makers.

The project team developed a layout value tool that calculates these indicators on the basis of simple Ordnance Survey maps. A set of Geographic Information System (GIS)-based computer tools has been programmed to calculate the indicators using available spatial and statistical datasets (Ordnance Survey, Office of National Statistics). The tools can quantify and monetise the socio-economic benefits of urban layout, and can be updated to take in more detailed local data in specific areas.

Project impact

The i-VALUL project has delivered new knowledge, techniques and services for planners, designers and community members by exploiting existing, multi-disciplinary experience.

'The i-VALUL layout value map of the greater south-east enables the systematic analysis of link and space in relation to their wider spatial context, as promoted by the Department for Transport's *Manual for Streets*,' says project coordinator Alain Chiaradia. 'The map can be used for layout valuation, either to assess the value of urban layout in existing places, or to test the impact of new development onto the surrounding area. The map provides a large base model around specific sites, and will be licensed to the project partners,' says Chiaradia.

The pilot analyses using the new tools revealed that town centre vitality is a key concern for local authorities. The tools can help stakeholders to track the relationship between spend and wealth in town centres, and to demonstrate how certain aspects of town centre accessibility, such as the ease with which they can support movement to them, and movement through them, is very tangibly part of how their economies work.

To date, i-VALUL integration projects have been carried out in several areas: Hampshire County Council, and the London boroughs of Croydon, Tower Hamlets and Islington, in the latter case working with the Better Archway Forum. The core project team has supported the transfer of knowledge to pilot project participants, with the layout value map and evaluation tools being tested on live projects. This process is being monitored by an expert review panel.

Academic and professional support enables the pilot partners to produce best practice planning and implementation documents for their areas. The London boroughs of Tower Hamlets and Croydon are using the layout valuation methodology in the evidence base for their Core Strategies, with a particular focus on town centres and their wider residential context.

The Core Strategy is the key document in the Local Development Framework (LDF) which sets out the long-term spatial vision and strategy for the borough, and the strategic policies and proposals to deliver that vision for the next 20 years. As these planning documents are binding for future developments, they determine the quality of urban layout.

In a similar way, i-VALUL has produced publication material for a community workshop with the Better Archway Forum that describes the spatial characteristics of the area, and suggests options for improvement.

Knowledge exchange

Space Syntax is continuing to train project partners from the public and voluntary sectors in layout evaluation techniques by supporting live integration projects on different scales, ranging from the neighbourhood to the regional level.

The project has taken existing academic knowledge and practitioner tools, and formed partnerships in order to establish the best ways of ›

The project team created the greater south-east layout value map, which comprises every street segment of the city-region, and calculates its accessibility according to different radii. The map will be available, under licence, to the public and private sectors, thus allowing layout valuation to be undertaken at all scales and by all interested parties

i-VALUL brought more than 20 partners together through a series of workshops. The partners identified themes where the impact of urban layout has been demonstrated, and where tangible spatial design, social and economic indicators for the performance of the layout can be found. Five Knowledge Integration Themes (KITs) were defined, each with a set of specific analytical tools:

The creation of the layout value map, using both existing space syntax tools and those developed by the project team, provides a basis on which to apply layout evaluation tools across south-east England. Before, each local authority would have had to invest resource in creating a layout value map of its region

The outcomes of i-VALUL enable economic appraisal of the positive or adverse impact of urban layout design. This can be done at the early stage of the design process to assess the feasibility, viability and predictability of a specific project

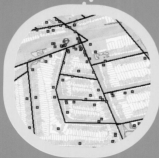

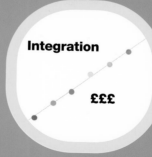

The value of property security
Based on the analysis of burglary patterns over five years in a London borough, Professor Bill Hillier and Oezlem Shabaz, both from UCL, identified four major layout factors that contribute to safer places. One of these factors reducing burglary risk is the existence of a residential culture, which can be measured by the number of dwellings per street 'segment'

The value of personal security
Existing research suggests that three spatial factors reduce the risk of street robbery; one of them being the relationship between sufficient movement rates resulting from an integrated spatial layout and residential culture measured by dwellings per street 'segment'

The value of urban centres
The recently published study *Paved with Gold* (CABE/Buchanan 2007) that showed the impact of street design on the economies of 10 London high streets was complemented by a strategic layout component. It shows that successful urban centres have particular spatial features, for example significantly smaller urban blocks and higher accessibility streets, that distinguish them from their context. Importantly, this study enables us to distinguish spatial effects and compositional effects

The value of residential property
Analysis carried out by UCL and Savills Research on more than 100,000 dwellings in a London borough showed that the distribution of residential property values, measured by council tax band data, follows a clear spatial pattern. A concentration of higher value properties is found at globally integrated places, whereas locally integrated places tend to have lower property values but higher densities. Savills Research showed that tax band trends are in line with property sales

The value of public realm design
Based on the recently completed public realm improvements in the Walworth Road, Southwark, a before and after assessment of the detailed public realm has been carried out comparing the results of the Pedestrian Environment Review System (PERS2) with analysis of the area's spatial layout. The case study also suggests a way to capture the health impact of pedestrian-friendly streets

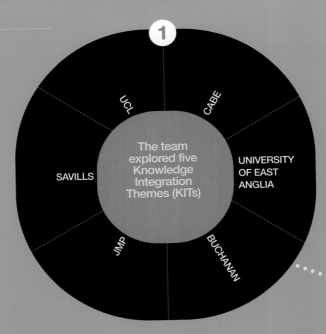

1

The team explored five Knowledge Integration Themes (KITs)

UCL
CABE
UNIVERSITY OF EAST ANGLIA
BUCHANAN
JMP
SAVILLS

'i-VALUL has developed an evidence-based urban layout evaluation programme able to overcome the barriers that prevent layout factors from being considered in spatial planning economic appraisals'
Alain Chiaradia, project coordinator

'i-VALUL findings suggest that place geometry does correlate with house values: higher value, single residential properties have greater accessibility to the large scale system, but less local accessibility; and have more passing larger scale movement passing the door, but less local movement'
Yolanda Barnes, Savills, project partner

Space Syntax Limited

Live integration project partners

Hampshire County Council
London Borough of Croydon
London Borough of Tower Hamlets
Better Archway Forum
London 21
Renaisi
UrbanBuzz secondments

Training and knowledge exchange

Space Syntax has developed a wide range of knowledge transfer services for the public, private and voluntary sectors. These support the in-house appraisal of urban layout and development management, and help to embed layout value in spatial design and planning practice from policy to delivery processes. The following formats have been tested during the i-VALUL project:

Training workshop 'Layout design for everybody' for local community groups

Training courses for local authority officers from planning or transport backgrounds (onsite and offsite)

Trainee scheme for local authority officers at Space Syntax Limited

Secondments of experienced Space Syntax consultants to local planning authorities

Licensing of the software package UrbanValue

Training and knowledge exchange partners

Hampshire County Council
London Borough of Croydon
London Borough of Tower Hamlets
Better Archway Forum
London 21
Renaisi
Student internships

3

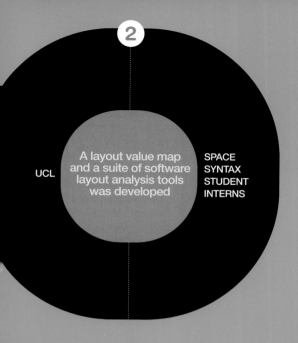

② UCL — A layout value map and a suite of software layout analysis tools was developed — SPACE SYNTAX STUDENT INTERNS

'Cities and towns are large collections of buildings held together by a network of space – the street network. The network has an architecture, a geometry and a topology manifest as a pattern of connections. Our interest lies in analysing this network. By doing so, we can design urban forms with the best chance for economic and social success'
Professor Bill Hillier of UCL, founder of the UCL spin-out company Space Syntax Ltd

Dissemination and peer review

Communities & Local Government
South East England Development Agency
East of England Development Agency
Greater London Authority
Hampshire County Council
London Borough of Croydon
London Borough of Tower Hamlets
Sustainable London 2012
The Housing Association
Department of Health
London 21
EDAW
Skanska
University of East Anglia
Cardiff University
UCL
Highways Agency
Housing Corporation

④

further developing the tools for use in the public sector. Input from local authorities and community groups as to typical workflows, access to data and access to software determined what form the tools should take. In turn, the finding that town centre viability is a major concern for local authorities is being fed back to academics and professionals for further analysis.

The project findings support the case for improving street layout design, and provide evidence of the likely economic returns to be gained from investing in high-quality residential and town centre street layouts. The new tools that i-VALUL has created will help to identify public sector development priorities, offering private sector investors a greater level of confidence and a more secure framework in which to invest.

Education and training

There is an ongoing relationship between academics at UCL and the UCL spin-out company Space Syntax Ltd. Information about the tools, processes and data needed by local authorities will inform future UCL research. Training courses based on use of the layout value map and tools have been developed for three different user groups – layout for everybody, layout for transport planners and layout for local authority planners.

The future: work in the field

The layout valuation tools are already being used in practice out in the field, with feedback informing further development. The layout value map and tools will be taken forward by Space Syntax Ltd as a licensed service.

One current application focuses on town centre accessibility in Hampshire, where the project partners are measuring which elements of their urban layout work well, and are making sure that these properties are captured in future designs.

In Archway, the team is working on a community-led project with a number of partners, exploring issues of accessibility, transport and housing, and is already producing findings that are challenging the preconceptions of private sector developers. The i-VALUL tools are also being applied to the development of town centre spatial strategies in two London boroughs; helping to create a key part of the evidence base for emerging Core Strategies.

Project resources
www.spacesyntax.com/en/valuing-urban-layout.aspx

Lead organisation
London Borough of Camden

Project coordinator
Chit Chong

Project start and end dates
May 2007 to December 2008

Total UrbanBuzz funding
£133,106.25

Total CIK
£362,730.00

Contact details
chit.chong@camden.gov.uk

- Environment
- Society
- Policy
- Planning/regeneration
- Design/housing

The context: energy-efficient period homes

The urgency of climate change has brought to the fore challenges of energy use and adaptation in housing. Huge investment will be required if we are to reduce CO_2 emissions from the housing sector. There is an urgent need to add to the evidence base that will inform housing and environmental policy. Robust monitoring and feedback will play a key role in developing this evidence.

Accurate information relating to performance, costs, usability, economic viability, process, supply chains and conservation issues needs to flow between all parties concerned with reducing carbon emissions from homes. New thinking is required. The knowledge exchange, discussion and actions arising from this project will help to inform a new approach to both housing and climate change policy.

Key project objectives

The project aimed to improve and monitor the energy performance of a Victorian house in Camden, north London. The house has been renovated and fitted with energy-efficiency measures that were projected to reduce its carbon emissions by 80 per cent. Since December 2008, the house has been occupied by tenants and its performance is being monitored under normal living conditions.

The energy-performance data from the house, along with information on how occupants are using it, will add to an emerging evidence base for design and construction professionals, policy makers, energy experts, academics, heritage bodies and sustainability campaigners. Millions of homes across the UK will need remedial energy-efficiency work in the next decade. The project aims to:

01 ensure that opportunities for energy reduction are being maximised;

02 collate, analyse and disseminate the costs and relative values associated with the performance of each of the energy-reduction technologies, along with knowledge gained during the construction, renovation and installation processes;

03 enable heritage professionals to review the project in order to assess the potential impact of energy-reduction measures on heritage and conservation policy.

The project response

The house was renovated and fitted with energy reduction measures in May 2008, and has since achieved an estimated 80 per cent reduction in carbon emissions and a Standard Assessment Procedure (SAP) equivalent to the Code for Sustainable Homes Code Level 4 rating. Project partner Kingspan undertook a predicted energy assessment of the property in April 2008. The house achieved an energy efficiency rating of B (90) and environmental impact rating of B (90). Testing between June and October enabled the team to establish a baseline for the house's energy performance, pre-occupation. Comparison data from similar properties in the area was also compiled for reference. Monitoring equipment was installed in the house during renovation, and performance tests are being carried out on a regular basis.

Project impact

The house was open to the public every Sunday between the end of July and October 2008 with more than 1,800 people visiting – a number far exceeding project expectations. The house also won 'Low-energy upgraded social housing project of the year' at *Inside Housing*'s Sustainable Housing Awards.

The results of blower door tests, carried out in October, showed that the refurbishment had transformed the once leaky Victorian house into an airtight property. The house achieved an air permeability of 6 $m^3/hr/m^2$ of façade, a value that is better than that of many newly-built UK homes. The results of the co-heating test were also very promising, with a heat loss of 280W/k, below the target 300W/k. During the summer of 2008, monitoring of the house showed that it performed ❯

Low Energy Victorian House
Academics and building professionals are learning from an energy-efficient Victorian house in Camden, London, one of only three period homes in the UK to have its energy performance robustly monitored

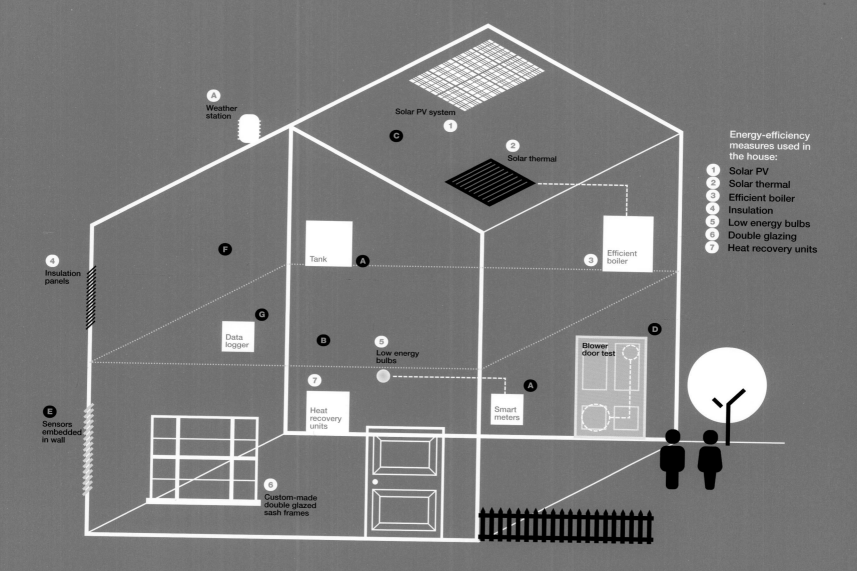

Energy-efficiency measures used in the house:

1. Solar PV
2. Solar thermal
3. Efficient boiler
4. Insulation
5. Low energy bulbs
6. Double glazing
7. Heat recovery units

Weather station ⒶⒶ

Solar PV system ①

Solar thermal ②

Ⓒ

Ⓕ

Tank Ⓐ

Insulation panels ④

Efficient boiler ③

Ⓓ

Data logger Ⓖ

Low energy bulbs ⑤

Ⓑ

Blower door test

Sensors embedded in wall Ⓔ

Heat recovery units ⑦

Smart meters Ⓐ

Custom-made double glazed sash frames ⑥

Key monitoring processes are being carried out:

Ⓐ Gas and electricity
EDF, the utility company, will install intelligent meters in the house. These will give a detailed readout of how much electricity and gas the house is using

Ⓑ Heating
Heat meters have been installed on the central heating system to measure the energy used to heat the house. The temperature in the main rooms will also be measured and compared with the external weather, as measured by a weather station

Ⓒ Renewable energy
This is produced by the photovoltaic system for electricity generation. The solar thermal system produces hot water. Both systems will be monitored

Ⓓ Airtightness
Before the house was occupied by tenants, a blower door test assessed the house for airtightness, identifying leakage sites where cold air comes into the building. Infrared camera and smoke sticks also identified leakage sites

Ⓔ Humidity and air quality
Relative humidity sensors have been installed behind the insulation to test for condensation forming on the colder surface of the external wall. As the airtightness of the house is increased, lack of adequate ventilation could lead to indoor air quality problems

Ⓕ Coheating
Testing for building fabric heat loss. This measured the fabric heat loss of the building. Electric heated fan heaters heated the house to a constant temperature for a week. By measuring the internal temperature and the external temperature, the actual heat loss co-efficient of the house was calculated

Ⓖ Remote data collection
The monitoring system has been designed to be as unobtrusive as possible, with data collected and downloaded automatically by computer and modem

London Borough of Camden, housing department
Assessing the house for livability and potential to adapt the successful interventions across Camden housing stock

London Borough of Camden
Project management, overseeing construction

'Camden's Low Energy Victorian house is a pioneering project. Sustainability is a top priority for the council, and we are committed to creating more sustainable homes throughout the borough'
Cllr Chris Naylor, executive member for Homes and Housing Strategy, Camden Council

London Borough of Camden, conservation department
Report on heritage value of the house's features and liaison with heritage consultants and English Heritage

Planning

Construct

Oxley Conservation
Initial heritage assessment for the house

English Heritage
Co-funder of the house's heritage assessment

University College London
Advisors on energy efficiency, ventilation, construction methods; devising and conducting training sessions; modelling and simulation

'Millions of UK homes will need remedial energy efficiency work in the next decade. We need to know that we can repeat with confidence what we've done here for other homes '
Dr Ian Ridley, manager of the monitoring process

'We need to understand how the energy efficiency of these buildings can be improved, whilst retaining as much of their heritage value as possible'
Chit Chong, London Borough of Camden, and project coordinator

The results of blower door tests, carried out in October 2008, showed that the refurbishment had transformed the once leaky Victorian house into an airtight property. The house achieved an air permeability of 6 m3/hr/m2 of façade, a value that is better than that of many newly built UK homes

Landers and Associates
Surveyors for the construction work

Energy Centre for Sustainable Communities
Advisors on energy efficiency

ParityProjects
Advisors on the assessment of building function and opportunities for energy and water consumption

Kingspan
Manufacturer, supplier and installer of insulation panels; energy use assessment

Lengard
Contractor for the construction phase and installer of insulation and solar thermal systems

University College London
Design, installation and management of monitoring equipment, interpretation and dissemination of monitoring data

The 1,800 visitors to the house
Learning from the project; considering applications at home

Monitor and inform

Sustainable Energy Academy
Organising open days and public awareness via the Old Home, SuperHome programme

Friends of the Earth Camden & Green Homes Concierge
Organising and managing public access to the house

Local authorities across UK
Learning from the project; considering future applications

The replacement windows are double-glazed and highly efficient, but retain the look and feel of the original sash frames

Local resident and conservationist Mr Rowley is pleased that the house 'can become a viable home for future generations'

better in terms of summertime overheating than comparable 'superinsulated' dwellings.

The project has also focused attention on the energy performance of heritage properties. A stated goal for the Low Energy Victorian House project team, according to project partner Oxley Conservation, was to look at ways of refurbishing our traditional building stock to low-energy use whilst preserving the nation's heritage in a considered way. 'As the project developed', its final report reads, 'the agenda for the refurbishment became driven by energy conservation ... the individual heritage value of the building, and what we can learn from it, has been lost for future generations.'

Project coordinator Chit Chong takes a different view. 'Unfortunately,' he says, 'Oxley Conservation had decided that, in their view, the house should be refurbished to prioritise heritage, which would result in a 30 to 40 per cent saving in energy.' This was clearly not compatible with the council's aims. 'The house protects the heritage values of today, as it shows that it is possible to refurbish these houses to low-energy standards,' says Chong. 'More importantly, it is likely to protect the heritage values of tomorrow. We should see the house, and others like it, as embodying Victorian heritage, rather than as unwanted monuments from a profligate age that could turn energy-inefficient Victorian suburbs into future areas of urban blight. It is time to evolve today's intellectual foundations of heritage so that they can be the intellectual foundations of tomorrow.'

Knowledge exchange

Over the past few months the house has attracted a great deal of interest, with tours being organised by the Sustainable Energy Academy as part of its Old Home SuperHome initiative. This promotes exemplar energy-efficient existing homes across the country with the aim of inspiring homeowners to transform their own houses.

During construction, the team held regular 'toolbox talks' and hands-on training sessions with UCL academics, the construction team and the insulation specialists, exchanging views and expertise. Many of these were recorded for possible future uses in developing and delivering training. Through the channels open to project partners, construction and training policy informs parties along the supply chain, from initial guidance to product specification and construction.

The lessons learnt from this project are feeding into English Heritage's 'Hearth and Home' research programme. English Heritage will explore ways of measuring energy use in 20 inhabited Victorian houses. When a robust method has been developed, it will be used to monitor the buildings,

Costs and estimated carbon savings		
Method	Cost	Tonnes CO$_2$ saved
Solar PV	£25,000	1.4
Solar thermal	£8,000	0.5
Double glazing	£24,000	1.3
Roof insulation	£6,600	3.4
Wall insulation	£11,000	3.3
Leakage reduction	£2,666	1.0

first without adaptations and then to test the effects of different adaptations (such as roof insulation).

The construction and installation process highlighted some interesting challenges: how to install insulation effectively, how to hang fixtures and fittings, such as sinks and toilets, on insulated walls, and how to mitigate the impact of an extra 100mm of internal insulation in tight spaces, such as narrow hallways.

Education and training

The project will give rise to a computer simulation model and substantial amount of data on the process and subsequent performance of the house. This is to be written up into reports and papers as the data is collected. Material will feed into UCL courses: MSc Environmental Design and Engineering, and MSc Sustainable Heritage.

The future: informing policy

Information about the performance of a refurbished house, the cost of the refurbishment process and the problems involved in carrying out refurbishment will all feed into the national policy development for improving the energy performance of existing building stock. These issues are at the top of the UK policy agenda as the target for reducing UK carbon emissions approaches.

Project resources
www.levh.org.uk
Features information, images, monitoring results and videos of the project's progress

The Sustainable Energy Academy's (SEA) Old Home SuperHome is an ongoing programme to transform the energy efficiency of existing housing stock in the UK. Visit www.sustainable-energyacademy.org.uk/

For information on related UCL MSc programmes, visit: www.bartlett.ucl.ac.uk/web/ben/ede/ and www.ucl.ac.uk/sustainableheritage/msc.htm

'We remain committed to the target of reducing emissions by 60 per cent by 2025. We will be focusing our public resources into a large scale rollout of retrofitting homes with energy efficiency measures, saving carbon and also helping people with energy bills. The Low Energy Victorian House project is a very interesting example of what can be done with some of the most difficult properties'
Sir Simon Milton,
Deputy Mayor of London

LOWCARB4REAL

Lead organisations
UCL, Leeds Metropolitan University (LMU)

Project coordinators
Bob Lowe (UCL), Malcolm Bell (LMU)

Project start and end dates
January 2008 to December 2008

Total UrbanBuzz funding
£120,699.72

Total CIK
£192,635.50

Contact details
robert.lowe@ucl.ac.uk, m.bell@leedsmet.ac.uk

- ● Environment
- ● Society
- ● Governance
- ● Policy
- ● Design/housing

The context: the knowledge gap

There is growing evidence, from both academic research and initial monitoring and certification of housing energy performance (the introduction of Energy Performance Certificates in 2008) of a 'performance gap' between design and delivery of new-build homes. This gap has strategic implications for the Government's 2016 zero carbon target for new housing.

The challenges and barriers to be overcome in the move to delivering energy efficient homes are considerable. Culturally, the UK has no tradition of energy performance measurement, or of design and production processes that follow sound manufacturing principles, in which measured performance is fed back to create system improvements. This issue was identified in the Egan report, *Rethinking Construction*, almost 10 years ago.

Lack of data on performance is coupled with, and reinforces, low levels of knowledge and understanding throughout the design and construction chain in regard to the principles of effective thermal envelope and systems design, with the result that these key principles are neither well-understood nor prioritised within design or construction processes.

Key project objectives

The project, coordinated by Professor Robert Lowe of University College London and Professor Malcolm Bell of Leeds Metropolitan University, draws on a pioneering, six-year Participatory Action Research study of more than 700 new build homes at Stamford Brook, near Altrincham, undertaken by Leeds Metropolitan University. The project team includes the Good Homes Alliance, whose members have been pioneering the construction of energy efficient homes around the country, and Dr Lai Fong Chiu of Leeds University, an expert in participatory action research.

The Stamford Brook study established the existence of a significant gap between predicted and actual energy demand in new low energy housing. Using a participatory knowledge exchange approach, the project team has worked with design and construction professionals, developers and policymakers to reflect on evidence from Stamford Brook, and to develop a new model for knowledge transfer that can address gaps in technical knowledge and understanding within the industry, aiming to:

01 develop a knowledge exchange programme for low carbon (energy efficient) new housing, based on action research principles and using learning captured from an existing seven-year field trial of current design and build principles;

02 to assess, in a comprehensive way, the issues involved in improving the carbon performance of mainstream house building;

03 to generate new learning related to airtightness, envelope integrity and systems performance at all levels, including building physics, dwelling design, site management, workforce training and procurement systems;

04 to refine, contextualise and embed this new learning within national house building workflows; and

05 to act as a model for industry-based research and knowledge exchange designed to make zero carbon housing a reality. ❯

Working together to build low carbon homes
Academics, design and construction professionals and developers are working together to overcome the energy 'performance gap' created by imperfect housing design, construction and production processes

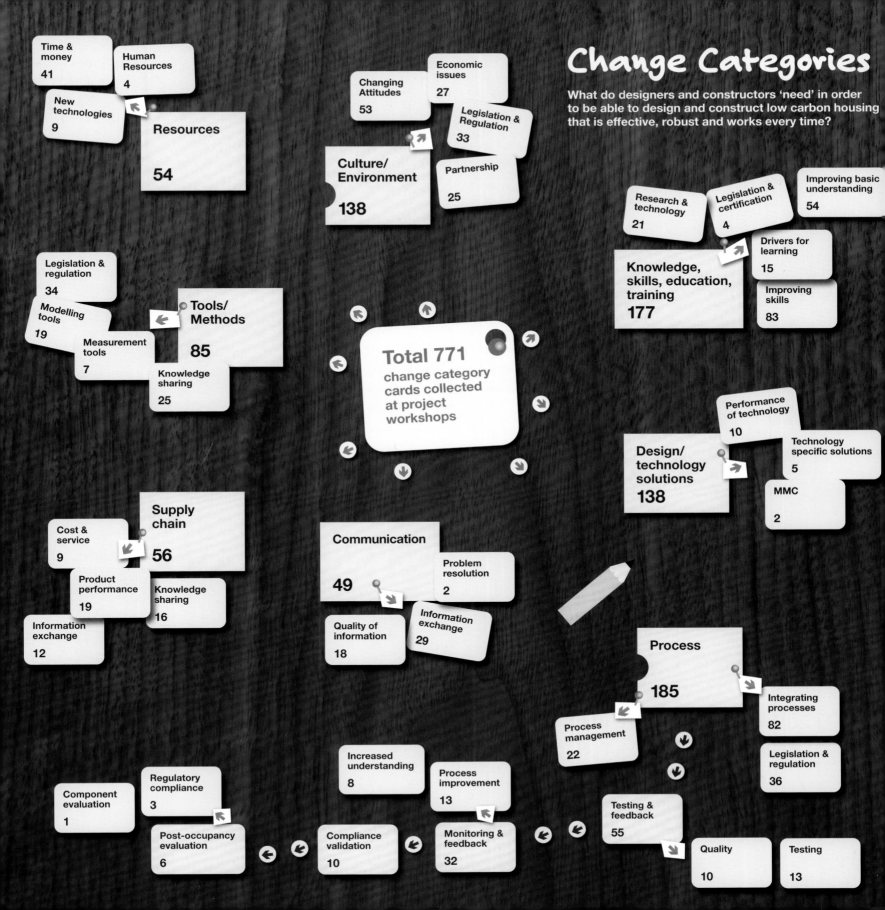

Change Categories

What do designers and constructors 'need' in order to be able to design and construct low carbon housing that is effective, robust and works every time?

Total 771 change category cards collected at project workshops

Resources — 54
- Time & money — 41
- Human Resources — 4
- New technologies — 9

Culture/Environment — 138
- Changing Attitudes — 53
- Economic issues — 27
- Legislation & Regulation — 33
- Partnership — 25

Knowledge, skills, education, training — 177
- Research & technology — 21
- Legislation & certification — 4
- Improving basic understanding — 54
- Drivers for learning — 15
- Improving skills — 83

Tools/Methods — 85
- Legislation & regulation — 34
- Modelling tools — 19
- Measurement tools — 7
- Knowledge sharing — 25

Design/technology solutions — 138
- Performance of technology — 10
- Technology specific solutions — 5
- MMC — 2

Supply chain — 56
- Cost & service — 9
- Product performance — 19
- Knowledge sharing — 16
- Information exchange — 12

Communication — 49
- Problem resolution — 2
- Quality of information — 18
- Information exchange — 29

Process — 185
- Integrating processes — 82
- Process management — 22
- Legislation & regulation — 36
- Component evaluation — 1
- Regulatory compliance — 3
- Post-occupancy evaluation — 6
- Increased understanding — 8
- Process improvement — 13
- Compliance validation — 10
- Monitoring & feedback — 32
- Testing & feedback — 55
- Quality — 10
- Testing — 13

Stamford Brook developers

Leeds Metropolitan University
David Johnston
Link to Construction Knowledge Exchange and Low Carbon Learning Zone

SD Foundation
Jon Bootland
Supervision of materials from the Good Homes Alliance

Communities and Local Government
Ted King and Paul Decort

Simon Corbey, Good Homes Alliance (GHA)
Researcher for exploratory workshop and delivery of case study material at workshops

Bob Lowe
University College London

Malcolm Bell
Leeds Metropolitan University

Project coordination, leading workshops

Jez Wingfield, Leeds Metropolitan University
Lead researcher on Stamford Brook

Dominic Miles-Shenton, Leeds Metropolitan University Research assistance, Stamford Brook

Lai Fong Chiu, University of Leeds
Advisor on participative action research and action learning

Home Builders Federation
Dave Mitchell
Industry representative body: members account for around 80 per cent of new homes in England and Wales

Workshop participants
Drawn from large developers and GHA membership

National Trust
Catherine Prasad and Rob Jarman
Stamford Brook landowners and prime mover (funder) in the development of the sustainability standard for the development

Good Homes Alliance (GHA)
Access to GHA members and experience

'We focused on the gap that exists between what we think buildings should do when we did the calculations and the models, and what buildings actually do when you measure them'
Professor Bob Lowe, UCL

The project response

Evidence from Stamford Brook shows that the performance gap is more than a narrowly technical issue; the project was therefore built around a series of five workshops that aimed to support mutual learning on three levels – technical knowledge, on-site management, and system transformation.

These enabled participants to place the technical information provided in a practical perspective, and to tease out technical, process and contextual factors that were responsible for both successes and failures. This deepened the learning of all participants, including the LOWCARB4REAL team. Views from the workshops were then fed back to senior industry executives and policymakers at a Strategic Forum.

Feedback showed that a combination of clear, visual presentation of research evidence on performance; opportunities to work through and discuss the issues in a workshop format; and examples of good practice (provided by members of the Good Homes Alliance) produced significant improvements in self-reported knowledge and understanding amongst workshop participants.

Recorded responses also suggested improvements in awareness of problems and their solutions and, perhaps more importantly, of personal commitment to improve practice. The major project lesson is that the key to low carbon housing is not just the facilitation of learning, but enabling industry to retain and apply it.

Project impact

During the course of the project, the team realised the value of participatory learning workshops, especially in a complex sector like construction. 'There is a category of insights that we only get from learning by doing,' says Lowe. 'Taking part in this process convinced me that engaging in this kind of process is an essential tool for any academic working in this area.'

Valuable though the lessons and insights from Stamford Brook and the GHA experience are, their absorption, adoption and impacts are primarily determined by the culture and structure of the house-building industry.

To maximise the value of research and experience in the development of low carbon housing, it is important that all sections of the house-building industry are able to share their knowledge of the industry and of the issues and barriers that arise.

Such knowledge-sharing is key when seeking the sort of fundamental change that is needed to achieve the demanding targets for low carbon housing set by the government. Given that the LOWCARB4REAL project began with the Stamford Brook study, there are several key lessons to be taken from that project:

01 technical change and improved performance are possible. Dwellings at Stamford Brook had roughly half the air leakage of typical dwellings of the time, and around half the heat loss. This conclusion was particularly important in the light of the view, widespread in the early years of this decade, that site-built load-bearing masonry construction represented a technological dead end;

02 unless performance is measured, it is hard to make and sustain change. This was most clearly visible in respect of air leakage, which demonstrated a robust tendency to drift upwards between campaigns of pressurisation testing;

03 change does not stick unless cultural and structural issues are dealt with. This lesson was fully corroborated by GHA contributions to the LOWCARB4REAL workshops, and was not disputed by any participants;

04 the construction industry is complicated, and academic support for change works best in a participatory framework. The best illustration of this is that the technique used at Stamford Brook to make walls airtight was proposed and demonstrated not by an academic, but by the developer partners in the project.

LOWCARB4REAL built on these lessons in a number of ways, but the real contribution of both projects has been to reveal the technical, social, cultural and structural complexity of the housebuilding industry, and to demonstrate models of participatory, industry-based research and knowledge exchange needed to make very low carbon housing a reality.

Lessons from LOWCARB4REAL are being taken forward in a number of ways. UCL is currently working with Barratt Homes on an investigation of the performance of the Barratt Greenhome, one of the UK's first Code for Sustainable Homes (CSH) level 6 (zero carbon) homes at the BRE Innovation Park, and Leeds Metropolitan University is working with the Joseph Rowntree housing trust on a CSH level 4 housing scheme incorporating heat pump technology. The intention is to use participatory techniques developed from LOWCARB4REAL to engage with the design and construction teams, and to work through issues that emerge from monitoring.

The workshops and Strategic Forum identified regulation as a key area for improvement, with deficiencies in the system of regulatory advice and the disjunction between Building Regulations and the Code for Sustainable Housing currently causing problems for housebuilders. Lessons from LOWCARB4REAL have been fed into the ongoing review of Part L of the Building Regulations, via a working group dealing with compliance and feedback.

Knowledge exchange

The project has clearly demonstrated the need for, and a potential model to deliver, knowledge exchange in a complex industry. Technical knowledge 'shifts' as a result of attending the workshops were monitored by questionnaire during the project, and proved statistically significant in several categories. For further information, see the project report, available from www.urbanbuzz.org (select projects).

Education and training

The LOWCARB4REAL advisory group included ConstructionSkills, and it is expected that experience from the project will feed into developments in training through this route. LOWCARB4REAL has demonstrated successful knowledge transfer in three key areas – thermal bridging, airtightness and thermal bypassing – and it is likely that the approach developed by the project will be widely used in training and education in these areas.

Output from the project has already fed into the development of a Low Carbon Housing Learning Zone, part of Leeds Metropolitan University's participation in the Construction Knowledge Exchange, in conjunction with AECB (The Association for Environment Conscious Building). UCL Energy Institute and Loughborough University have recently won £5.8 million to establish a Doctoral Training Centre in Energy Demand Reduction in Buildings. Project outputs will feed into the development of an MRes course which will provide the taught element of doctoral training at this centre.

The future: informing the agenda

The most important developments for the UK construction industry are around proposals for dealing with existing housing stock. The experiences gained from LOWCARB4REAL have enabled members of the project team to inform the agendas of a number of organisations (English Heritage, the Homes and Communities Agency, Communities and Local Government, the Zero Carbon Hub, Arup) on how major refurbishment programmes should be constructed and supported, particularly with respect to engagement between industry and academia.

Project resources
http://www.lmu.ac.uk/as/cebe/projects/lowcarb4real/index.htm
http://www.cke.org.uk/

Workshop materials and a series of project posters are available online
A more detailed version of this article is available from: www.urbanbuzz.org (select projects)

LSTS: London Students Towards Sustainability

Lead organisation
London Sustainability Exchange (LSx)

Project coordinators
Kirsty Balmer and Shalini Jayasinghe

Project start and end dates
May 2007 to November 2008

Total UrbanBuzz funding
£66,000

Total CIK
£50,590

Contact details
K.Balmer@lsx.org.uk

- Society
- Governance
- Infrastructure

The context: addressing sustainability

In the move towards creating sustainable communities, all organisations – and not only those involved in creating green products or technologies – need to address sustainability issues. These issues may relate to efficiency in the supply chain, communications, behavioural change, corporate social responsibility initiatives, internal management or environmental policies.

The student population of London is a huge resource of skilled, knowledgeable individuals with time, energy and access to resources. The 2004 Egan Review *Skills for Sustainable Communities* called for efforts to encourage entrants into the 'core occupations' of sustainable communities.

The report suggested that, to new graduates, the lure of financial reward from competing sectors threatens to undermine the work of educational institutions that are increasingly addressing the issue of sustainable development through degree courses. The challenge is to maintain, encourage and mobilise student enthusiasm for sustainability.

Key project objectives

The project aimed to help students to feed knowledge of sustainability initiatives gained from the university environment, for example the use of footprinting sheets to assess ecological footprints, to real-world companies through internships.

This would enable London students to support the development of sustainable communities through their studies and future careers by providing motivation, knowledge and connections. It would also enable students to gain valuable experience of sustainability in practice. The project aimed to:

01 create a student/employer network for students, with input from students;

02 develop an internship scheme, with targets for numbers of placements during 2007 and 2008;

03 facilitate knowledge exchange between students and practitioners on sustainable communities; and

04 build a legacy of activity with the impetus to continue and develop once UrbanBuzz funding came to an end.

The project response

LSTS has developed a supportive network of just under 800 members: 730 students and 60 employers. Although a key aim was to connect students with potential employers, LSTS has become more than a brokerage service. The network promotes knowledge exchange on key sustainability factors between students, employers and potential employees across the south-east. Strong links have been created with like-minded organisations: Sponge, the network for young professionals in the construction sector; University of East London Employability Services; Imperial College's Department of Environmental Technology; and Thames Water, as well as a range of public, private and third sector organisations.

'We've been successful at "matchmaking" students with employers, but our feedback tells us that both parties are getting considerable added value,' says project coordinator Kirsty Balmer. At the end of December 2008, LSTS was receiving more requests from employers than it could handle. Its success was due to the care taken when connecting students and employers. ❯

Students networking for sustainability

A network and managed internship scheme gave London students the motivation, knowledge and connections to support the development of sustainable communities through their studies and future careers

The network was built up through a series of networking events, stalls at Fresher's Fairs, e-bulletins, student-led and employer-led seminars and workshops, and a social networking group, all bringing network participants together for discussion and debate. The project team worked with existing support organisations such as university volunteering services and UEL's Projects and Placements Coordinator.

A detailed internship criteria and 'matchmaking' methodology was developed, and placements advertised widely through university channels. Between July and October 2007, 14 placements went ahead, with 20 more taking place during 2008. A key element of the internship criteria was reflective evaluation of sustainable development issues and the intern process by both interns and employers. To this end, the LSTS team developed reporting systems to capture aspects of sustainability in practice in businesses and colleges across London and the south-east.

Project impact

The LSTS activities raised the exposure of students in London universities to a wide range of sustainability issues, and to how sustainability works in practice: more than 500 network members (46 organisations linked to 11 universities and more than 400 students) exchanged information on sustainability issues at a series of project-supported events and activities.

Increased sustainability literacy was evidenced by the use of footprinting sheets (questionnaires to help assess ecological footprints): 150 of these were completed by attendees at one LSTS event and followed up by discussions on sustainability amongst the network.

Both interns and employers were encouraged, once the internship was complete, to reflect on ways in which the two-way exchange of experience between them has supported sustainability initiatives. 'Once interns were placed, the detailed reporting structure devised by the project team (based on the sustainability initiatives outlined by the UrbanBuzz external evaluator, see page 26) generated a wealth of information on sustainability issues and processes through reflective practice and feedback,' says Balmer.

'There is significant value added by the matchmaking offered by the LSTS programme' Graham Mallett, Thames Water

The steering group

Strategic oversight for the project, expertise and advice, supporting the development of the project and its key objectives, for example promoting the project through members, existing networks and contacts

Darryl Newport, UEL

Antony Day, London South Bank University

Yvonne Rydin, UCL

Martin Fry, City University

Shaun McCarthy, Action Sustainability

Paul Edwards, Hammerson

Euston Ling, Hyder Consulting

Chit Chong, London Borough of Camden

Graham Mallett, Thames Water

Tom Randall, Sponge

London Sustainability Exchange (LSx) Project management, engaging the steering group, organising events, developing a network of students and employers, overseeing internships and evaluation

Kirsty Balmer, project coordinator (replaced Shalini Jayasinghe)

Samantha Heath
Gayle Burgess

Sourcing project interns
LSx
Action Sustainability
Thames Water
London Borough of Camden
UCL
UEL

'Once interns are placed, the reporting structure that we've devised generates a wealth of information on sustainability issues and processes through reflective practice and feedback' Kirsty Balmer, London Sustainability Exchange

Project lead organisation LSx endeavours to utilise and build on this knowledge and momentum, and is progressing relationships with partners, for example European student network StudentForce. It will use this knowledge to continue to engage networks of students and employers, and to promote sustainability through LSx initiatives.

Several employers indicated that they benefited from the sustainability expertise of interns, and have incorporated elements of sustainability practice into their work processes as a result.

In turn, students have benefited from seeing the sustainability implications of existing employer practices, and several network members and former LSTS interns are now pursuing careers within the sustainability field. Eleven of the 14 first year interns now have permanent jobs within the sustainability sector. Many of them state that their placement helped them secure a successful position, with one being offered a permanent position by their LSTS employer.

Establishing relationships and offering value (for example practical skills and support in CV writing and networking) has encouraged past interns to continue to support the network and to participate in an ongoing programme of events.

Students have both enhanced their employment prospects and have been made aware of the wider implications of sustainability. LSTS intern Alex Michelsen, for example, worked with ISEAL (an umbrella body that represents the organisations behind social and environmental standards such as Fairtrade and Organic) for 12 weeks in 2007, and found the experience particularly useful. 'The internship was a chance to "test the water" for a career path. My thesis looked at sustainability in retail supply chains. Throughout my degree I had been interested in the role of communications in promoting sustainability.'

The network has helped students to bridge the gap between academic knowledge and practical skills to support sustainability. For example, the LSTS network participated in a workshop with professionals reviewing Sustainability Appraisal Tools. The event offered opportunities for students to think about the principles of sustainable development and how they are – and should be – applied, and about how the London Sustainable Development Commission's framework can be integrated into policy frameworks.

Knowledge exchange

Placement completion reports (self-evaluation in discussion with employer) indicated that satisfaction was high and that considerable knowledge transfer took place between intern and employer. LSx invited students from all programmes to join LSTS and aimed (through events and bulletins) to improve sustainability literacy in students from courses outside of 'environment-related' degrees. The network aimed to encourage universities to institute at least one sustainability-related lecture or elective in every programme. The team encouraged fellows on the project Steering Group to champion this across their universities.

The future: sustainable careers services

LSx will continue to develop the network jointly with Sponge, the network for young professionals in the construction sector, and aims to establish further partnerships in a number of different areas, for example with StudentForce – LSx has negotiated a Memorandum of Understanding with StudentForce for Sustainability. This partnership aims to continue to support students and employers through signposting, events and network collaboration. Plans include offering membership to LSx's network of professionals to graduating students who are now working in the sustainability field. LSx is putting together a brief to send to careers services with the aim of highlighting opportunities in the growing sustainability sector, and to encourage careers services to cater for this niche.

The network

In November 2008, a network of nearly 800 members was recorded; 730 students and 60 employers. The chief contributor to the growth of the network is word of mouth between students

'Exposure to the reality of working within an organisation made me more aware of the constraints of working on sustainability projects' LSTS student, reflecting on budgets and funding

Project resources
http://www.lsx.org.uk/whatwedo/LSTS_page3067.aspx
http://www.studentforce.org.uk/

MCSC: Mapping Change for
Sustainable Communities

Lead organisation
UCL

Project coordinator
Dr Muki Haklay

Project start and end dates
May 2007 to December 2008

Total UrbanBuzz funding
£175,683

Total CIK
£63,480

Contact details
m.haklay@ucl.ac.uk

- ● Environment
- ● Society
- ● Governance
- ● Planning/regeneration
- ● Infrastructure
- ● Design/housing

The context: mapping for change

East London and the Thames Gateway are facing major and accelerating changes. If local people are to engage effectively with the processes of development, they need to understand how proposed changes may affect them, and feel confident about playing a positive role in those changes.

Currently, communities have limited access to decision-making processes and key data sources, for example information about planned new developments in their area. Many people feel excluded and alienated from the changes that are happening around them, and report that typical consultation exercises are frequently over-technical and time-consuming.

Ensuring that local communities can influence change is a major challenge, as is the management, assessment and interpretation of the masses of demographic, cultural, socio-economic and planning data that will be generated as the Thames Gateway grows.

GIS-based mapping systems have been shown to be logical ways of managing such data, and making it available to communities and stakeholders.

Key project objectives

This project planned to deliver a set of GIS-based maps of the region that could be used by communities and stakeholders. Four online maps would be created by, and for, four east London communities. The project team wished to:

01 improve access to community information through mapping. Although information is available in the public domain, knowing where to find it and, more importantly, how to interpret it, is key. Maps can help to collate and visualise such information;

02 develop new ways of handling data via maps and displaying it online;

03 engage east London communities in the mapping process, and demonstrate how to use the mapped information to plan action;

04 help to build community communication channels via mapping;

05 provide communities with a means to express their views;

06 address the inequalities of access to information and work towards bridging the digital divide; and

07 build links between academia, communities and a range of organisations working across east London. ❯

Community mapping for change
From noise annoyance to local trouble spots, communities across London are using community mapping projects to focus on making connections, common interests and planning for change

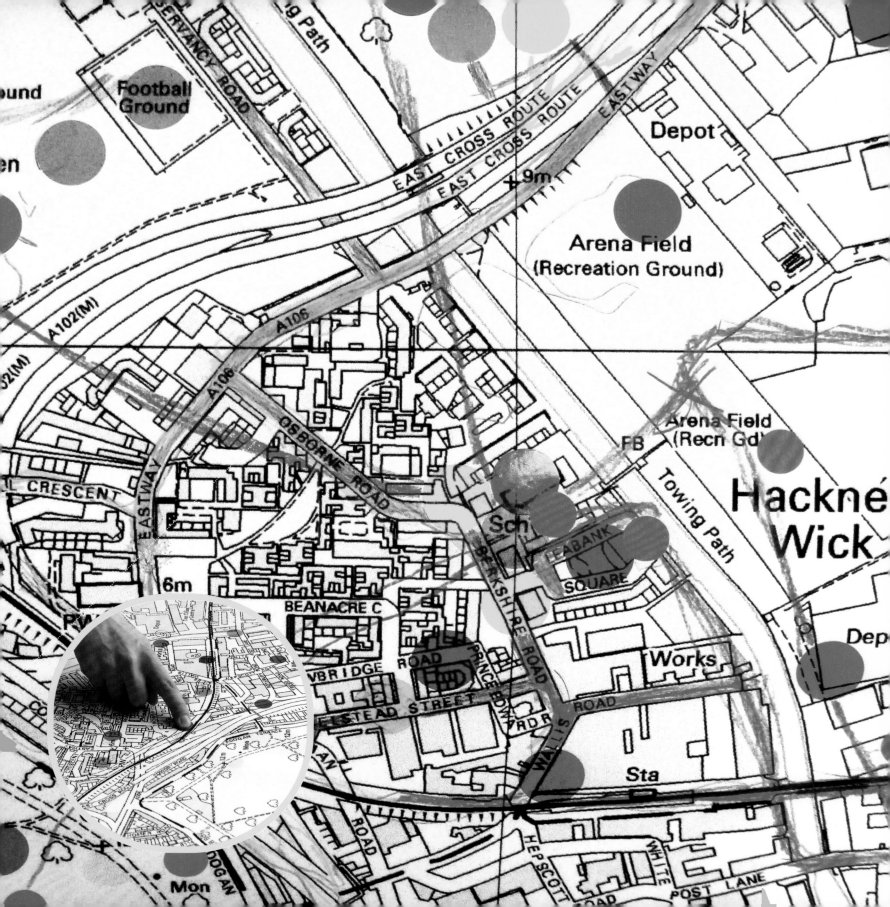

The project response

The project team, working through project partners, made links with four local community groups in Royal Docks, Hackney Wick, Marks Gate and Archway. A series of workshops was held with each group to discuss which issues were important to each community, and to explore these issues through mapping. The team built on a London Green Map that had been created a few years ago by project partner London 21, with technical help from UCL, that enabled communities to 'post' details of green initiatives onto an online map.

When it became clear, through workshops, that each of the project's four community groups had very different concerns, the team created a unique map with each community. In the Royal Docks, a key issue was noise. In Archway, it was traffic; at Marks Gate, it was local behaviour. The major concern for the Hackney Wick group was the massive changes brought about by the Olympics development.

The workshops included sessions on the planning process, familiarity with map data, exploration of historical maps, participatory mapping exercises, bio-mapping (a bio-mapping report from artist Christian Nold is available online, see project resources), walking tours and noise monitoring. Although the final maps are technologically complex, technology took a back seat in the planning sessions; discussion, stories and ideas came first. 'Throw away the computer and involve people with paper mapping,' says London 21's Louise Francis, project partner. 'Set up projects with paper and pens, then go on to digitise the material.'

Maps were produced for the four community groups, and made available online. Community members can update their maps, which are hosted by London 21. To help locals keep in touch, and up-to-date with events, UCL PhD student Hanif Rahemtulla developed ECOTEXT, an SMS service that sends text messages about events and meetings to registered users of the maps.

An 'action pack' has been produced by the project team, aimed at communities, published by London 21. This outlines the processes involved in setting up community mapping projects, along with advice on participatory mapping initiatives. It is available via the project website (see project resources). >

'We offer technical help and guidance, but locals have led on developing their maps'
project coordinator
Dr Muki Haklay

HACKNEY WICK
COMMUNITY

'Mapping raises awareness. It gives the community an impetus, and a reason to go to the council and say right, we've got something to show you'
The team from London 21, Colleen (left) and Louise

3rd Sound Reading (dBA
76·6

Constant
Repetitive
Abrupt
Random

ROYAL DOCKS COMMUNITY

Planning Aid for London
Michael Parkes
Held workshops assisting local communities to read plans, understand the planning system, and identify planning issues in their local environments, signposting key development proposals of interest to local communities

Community Environment Associates

Chris Church
Coordinating and leading on community engagement activity, developing engagement with London Thames Gateway Forum and Planning Aid for London

UCL

Dr Muki Haklay, Department of Geomatic Engineering
Project coordinator, development of online maps, supervising MSc students

Mr Hanif Rahemtulla, PhD student, Department of Geography
Developed the localised SMS used to encourage participation in local events

Claire Ellul, Department of Geomatic Engineering
Development of the website and relevant software

THAMES WARD COMMUNITY

London 21

Colleen Whittaker
Engaging local communities in mapping activity

Louise Francis
Project manager, working with local communities on mapping activities

Christian Nold, artist
Working with communities to bio-map the 'feelings' of a given space, using GPS, 'lie detector' technology and Google Earth

ARCHWAY COMMUNITY

ble
ng
rtable
able
ng
sting

Aircraft engines - descending and also taking off. Makes standing outside unpleasurable - at 1½ min intervals.

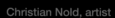

'The project has led to a new social enterprise, Mapping For Change (MfC), that promotes innovation in participatory mapping, and provides services to public, private, voluntary and community sectors with the aim of supporting sustainable communities' project partner Chris Church, London 21

Project impact

Using a shared web-mapping resource has promoted the exchange of information within communities and local authorities. The mapping process has also benefited community cohesion. The Rev Gualter De Mello, Community of Reconciliation And Fellowship, took part in the Hackney Wick mapping project. 'Making the map enabled us to see some focal points where the community needed support,' he says. 'The population of Hackney Wick has changed greatly over the past few years. Mapping our community has been a very positive exercise, helping us to find and access new groups in the area. Many people around here use the online map, and ask me all about it.'

Some project partners, Rev De Mello included, are hoping to begin new mapping initiatives. The project has demonstrated that mapping can be used to create an 'evidence base' to support community activism. Locals living in one of London's noisiest areas, the Royal Docks, Newham, used their maps to record and map noise levels from nearby London City Airport (LCA). They found a clear correlation between unacceptable levels of noise and LCA operational hours. The project team captured the noise levels using noise meters, as well as noting down residents' perceptions associated with the noise.

'Many readings exceeded levels deemed to cause serious annoyance under the World Health Organisation community noise guidelines,' said Colleen Whittaker, London 21. The results also showed that residents' perceptions of noise, pre-mapping, had been surprisingly accurate. They findings were shown to the planning officer involved with LCA's planning application, who responded by progressing further monitoring. 'We're raising awareness,' says Whittaker. 'The

mapping is giving the community an impetus, and a reason to go to the council and say right, we've got something to show you.'

A social enterprise, Mapping for Change (MfC), has been launched to continue this type of project across London. The aim is to provide ongoing GIS services to the four communities and others, helping them to understand and use spatial data to further community development. In addition, MfC will provide services that enable communities to collate and present data in order to support proactive action around specific development and environmental issues.

Knowledge exchange

An initial aim of the project was to help locals to engage with planning and development issues across the Thames Gateway. But despite the input of Planning Aid for London, an organisation offering planning advice to communities and a project partner, accessing up-to-date information on live projects proved to be far from easy. From the point of view of communities, it's very difficult to get information on major projects from developers or from borough councils. 'Even for our project partner Planning Aid for London, this was a substantial, time-consuming challenge. This is an area that needs more attention,' says project coordinator Dr Muki Haklay.

The project also revealed issues with community access to data and services. Whilst much of the information available to community organisations can be easily mapped using paper maps, or freely available Google maps, more complex analysis requires access to Ordnance Survey or local authority data, and to GIS software. It is difficult for most members of the public to access such resources.

This issue highlighted the key role of 'experts' and professionals in supporting community engagement, as well as the range of skillsets involved. Expert input and facilitation is required, which places the style and performance of the facilitator in focus.

The experience gained from workshops also yielded useful information, for example the fact that shorter and more focused workshops produce better results, when dealing with engaging communities, than single day-long sessions. The need to manage expectations effectively was also highlighted. Given the complexity of the 'back end' systems for online mapping, the community needs to know what's possible at each stage.

The type of mapping task was also found to impact upon how much support communities need. It proved easier to engage people, and to keep them engaged, when specific issues such as noise pollution were being mapped.

A one-day community mapping event and project exhibition was held at UCL in June 2008. More than 100 individuals from non-profit, local authority, government agencies, academic institutes and community organisations attended in order to share information on participatory mapping practices and initiatives. Project participants from the four communities gave short presentations on their mapping experiences.

The action pack provides information on creating community maps, drawing on lessons learned and demonstrating outputs from the project. A further publication, addressing community engagement and working with a mix of online and offline information sources in the process of community mapping, will be available in summer 2009: details on the project website.

Education and training

Experience taken from this project will be taken forward into the teaching materials of Dr Haklay. Collaborating with the Development Planning Unit (DPU), UCL, the team will provide 40 MSc students with a better understanding of urban sustainability and equality in practice at local level, and expose them to participatory mapping, among other techniques, with a focus on Hackney Wick and the Olympic Site. Two MSc students (funded by bursaries) worked on this project as part of their studies, and acted as knowledge transfer ambassadors to their peers.

The future: community mapping in practice

The Mapping for Change (MfC) social enterprise is beginning work on several new community mapping projects. A forthcoming publication will be available to the public, private and voluntary sectors to draw attention to the viability and utility of participatory mapping, and to outline how the MfC initiative can work with communities.

@

Project resources
Online maps: www.communitymaps.london21.org
Action pack and further information on Mapping for Change: www.mappingforchange.org.uk

Online video
Royal Docks noise mapping project: iTunesU
http://www.youtube.com/user/uclurbanbuzz

Presentations, papers and biomapping
http://www.slideshare.net/mukih/tags/ppgis
(slides from the workshop)
http://www.softhook.com/green.htm (Christian Nold's biomapping experiences)

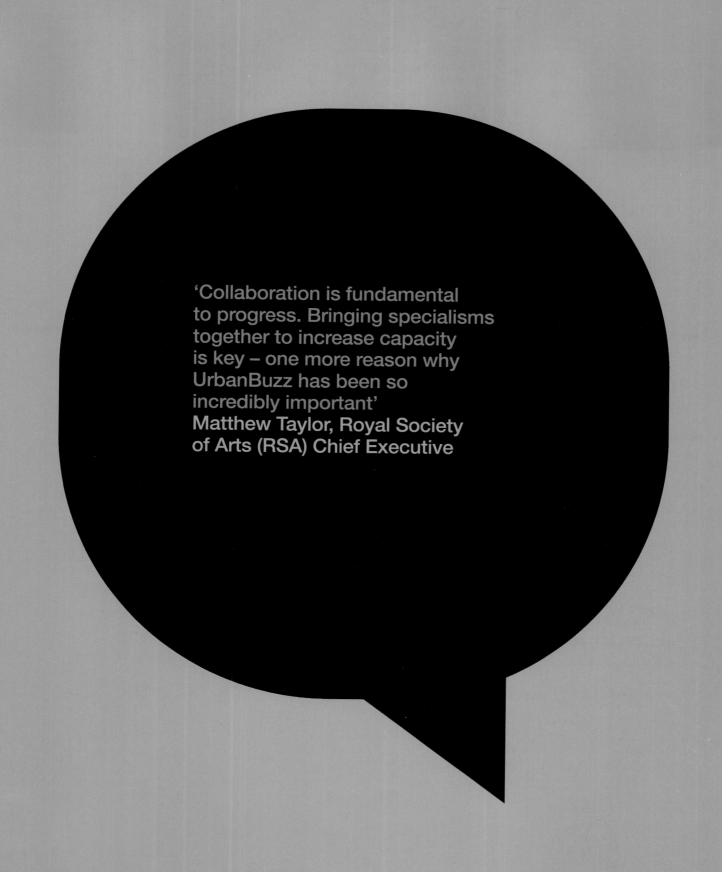

'Collaboration is fundamental to progress. Bringing specialisms together to increase capacity is key – one more reason why UrbanBuzz has been so incredibly important'
Matthew Taylor, Royal Society of Arts (RSA) Chief Executive

Lead organisation
Helen Hamlyn Centre, Royal College of Art

Project coordinator
Paul Clarke

Project start and end dates
December 2007 to October 2008

Total UrbanBuzz funding
£9,951

Total CIK
£38,311

Contact details
paul-david.clarke@rca.ac.uk

- Environment
- Society
- Governance
- Policy
- Planning/regeneration
- Infrastructure
- Design/housing

Exploring new measures of urban density
The METRICITY project is exploring ways in which contemporary patterns of work, leisure and travel affect the way new urban developments are designed and occupied

The context: today's live/work patterns

The density metrics currently favoured by planners – such as the number of dwellings per hectare, or people per hectare – are static and do not reflect the immense upheaval of social and demographic change evident in dynamic cities such as London. Yet these current metrics, based on numerical measures of density, are widely used to inform policy and planning. It has frequently been suggested that these standards should be modified to take into account more complex interrelationships – accessibility, occupancy levels, car use, parking, open space and distribution of facilities, for example.

Density measures apply to both regional and local development plans as a means to achieve a greater balance within key areas of housing, economic development and transport planning. Direct application of density metrics – through Planning Policy Statement 3 (PPS3) housing density guidelines, for example – could create a link between housing numbers and more qualitative and socio-economic factors such as work patterns.

Key project objectives

The METRICITY team recognised a need to explore alternative measures of urban density that go beyond a conventional and prescriptive numerical approach, and instead reflect more animated and realistic descriptions of emerging patterns of living and working. The project focuses on how urban density is measured, and on how such measures affect the way urban developments are designed and occupied. High-density often means high-risk to a developer, and as a result the opportunity to develop a site to its full potential can be missed. A key project aim has been to create and evaluate new urban density metric principles, and to consider their application and potential benefit in an urban planning framework.

The team wished to explore the urban design implications of social and demographic change in order to make cities more liveable, inclusive and sustainable, especially when development is placed within the context of successful community engagement and support for new development. Specifically, the project aimed to:

01 initiate cross-disciplinary discussion between planners, policymakers, architects, developers and relevant government departments/agencies on policy measures in relation to density;

02 explore the possibilities of new density metrics supporting the development of dense, animated environments;

03 stimulate debate about the planning process, and possibly improve it for all those involved. More relevant measures of urban density could afford communities a stronger voice in the planning process and support community-based decisions;

04 begin to develop a design framework that will allow design and planning professionals to be more creative, and to make use of qualitative data in order to make the development process more responsive to both market and social needs;

05 explore the impact on urban density measures of socio-economic, social demographic, political and technological drivers of change;

06 investigate the creation of a sustainable new settlement, not solely reliant on transport connections to provide much needed employment options and services to this new community; and

07 investigate the potential impact that density and the related critical mass of a development has in the creation of a 'destination' rather than an unsustainable 'dormitory' settlement.

The project response

To evaluate new measures of urban density, the METRICITY team has created a series of theoretical design scenarios applied to an actual development site within the UK: Ebbsfleet in the Thames Gateway. Importantly, this site has been described by developer Land Securities as 'large enough in scale to define its own way of life'. Smaller-scale settlements are unlikely to deliver the sort of coherent development planning and associated benefits of scale that would attract the employment opportunities, amenities and services able to make the difference between 'destination' and 'dormitory' settlements.

The project has focused on the role of the workplace in influencing urban form and, in particular, considered the drivers of change that affect economic sustainability and influence city development.

In conducting the initial research, it was necessary to 'unpack' the complex issues around density, land use, transport policy and ways of working. The study homed in on the ways in which planners address high-density urban environments around transport nodes. An evidence base of trends and data was compiled from policy papers, newspapers and reports relevant to strategic urban planning.

The new density measures put forward by the project team are organised around design scenarios rooted in socio-economic, social demographic, political and technological drivers of change. Four such design scenarios for 2018 were created, each representing a new way of exploring urban density (see below).

Project impact

The project has collated an evidence base of information relating to changing social trends and demographics. This has been related to potential strategic policy approaches for the designated test site.

Within the context of work and changing live/work and travel patterns, a framework within which to evaluate the design scenarios was created, informed by users' experiences and narratives regarding their work and lifestyles. The research investigated these issues, 'testing' the framework and assessing the 'trade-offs' between the density metrics across the four design scenarios, while simultaneously considering the qualitative effects on users and their relationship to density, transport and land use.

The innovative multi-disciplinary debate pioneered by the project has suggested that the creation of community-led Local Development Frameworks could combine both user aspirations and market realities in a sustainable manner. To take this further, the urban density principles considered by the project signal the need for new processes that support qualitative dialogue and can demonstrate the effectiveness of community consultation. ❯

CONTROLLED POLICY OF
HIGH-DENSITY AT
TRANSPORT NODES

GREATER
CENTRALISED
EMPLOYMENT
AND
SERVICES

GREATER
DE-CENTRALISED
EMPLOYMENT
AND
SERVICES

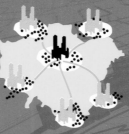

Scenario B
Timeshare towers

Scenario D
Open source city

Scenario A
Disconnected suburb

Scenario C
Incorporated cluster

NO ENFORCED POLICY
OF DENSITY AT
TRANSPORT NODES

Knowledge exchange

This project has underlined the necessity for robustly-managed knowledge transfer at the level of policy and decision-making. It has also raised other issues: the need for more evidence-based design and constraint-based modelling, clarity in relation to data analysis and data quality, and the development of ways in which to use qualitative data as part of a strategic analysis.

Knowledge exchange has underpinned the project's progress, through interviews, workshops, seminars, design workshops, presentations and a series of expert forums. During these forums, metric principles were tested against the views of local authority planners, architects and other experts, using scenario-based design, to explore the drivers and possible implications for planning policy. The scenarios were presented to, and developed by, the project team after a series of Expert Forums.

With a knowledge exchange project of this type, in itself a model for future urban development scenario-planning initiatives, robust means of capturing communication streams and evaluation methods need to be in place. These should be developed around qualitative criteria; particularly those relating to sustainability. Whereas hard data, such as that from fiscal analysis, is usually dealt with efficiently, less tangible metrics can remain unchecked or simply considered as an afterthought.

There is a need for more integrated people management with relation to qualitative data capture when working on large and complex projects. 'Mobilising the correct project team, and organising data exchange and the most appropriate means of knowledge transfer, is key to developing the right solutions,' says project coordinator Paul Clarke.

The project's final report (available online; see resources at the end of this article) is being circulated widely among planning and design professionals to spark continued debate.

Child Graddon Lewis
Provided a lead role on the project steering committee and enabled in-depth insight into current practice, including work with high-density projects related to Transport for London development areas; hosted an Expert Forum to develop core issues around the design scenarios

Arup
Provided a lead role in the steering committee and links to expert disciplines, including the Sustainable Solutions Team, Transport and Infrastructure Planning, and the Integrated Urbanism Team. Enabled links to possible future cross-council partnership and explored development with third parties

British Council For Offices (BCO) and the Urban Affairs Committee
Explored the role and impact of offices as a catalyst in urban regeneration, and best practice and new thinking in urban regeneration and renewal. Committed to follow a broader remit within this field so that concepts of urban and master planning, mixed use development, and social engagement, may be fully explored

3D Reid
Provided a lead role in the steering committee, as well as supervision and guidance, including the final METRICITY event; hosting an Expert Forum and developing core issues around the design scenarios

Fletcher Priest
Provided a lead role in the steering committee

Education and training

The project findings are feeding directly into the Royal College of Art's Department of Architecture MA course. Links have also been made with UCL (MSc Environmental Design and Engineering and the MA Urban Design programmes), and with other training providers such as the Royal Institute of British Architects (RIBA) and the Commission for Architecture and the Built Environment (CABE).

The future: applying the metric

The project team has pioneered new approaches to codifying qualitative data derived from project-based discussion: these could prove useful in a future seeking to involve more diverse communities in design and development. Building on an established working relationship with the Planning for Housing Team at the Department of Communities and Local Government (DCLG), project coordinator Paul Clarke plans to organise a further series of workshops to provide a 'test laboratory' for refining the metric and processes of defining and measuring density. The aim is to assess the impact of such measures on the way urban developments are designed and occupied, with a view to making cities more inclusive.

The project team has investigated the potential of further research development with the support of Arup. This could take the form of a combined analysis and data collection tool that could be aligned with the interests of Arup's Sustainable Solutions Team.

As the knowledge economy and leisure industries mature, the city of the future continually transforms to attract people and jobs. Emerging pervasive internet-based services, citywide telecommunications, and Geographic Information Systems (GIS), all harnessed by online social networks, will have enormous potential to change the way we perceive and administer the planning of cities. The planning process, by its democratic nature, should rely on evidence-based practice and cross-disciplinary involvement. Enabled by emerging online technologies, communities will be able to gather the necessary critical mass around frameworks for planned development.

This enables a community to view, in advance, the trade-offs that higher densities can provide: more housing, sustainable amenities, transport connections and job opportunities. In the light of current consistent opposition to large-scale developments, community-led planning could ensure that development will reflect the needs of end-users and organically adapt with the use of land and building management.
See Debating density, page 60.

Project resources
The METRICITY publication outlines the toolkit for assessing density and illustrates four scenarios that show potential applications. The report is available from the project website

www.metricity.net will continue to act as a hub for the development and dissemination of findings from the METRICITY project

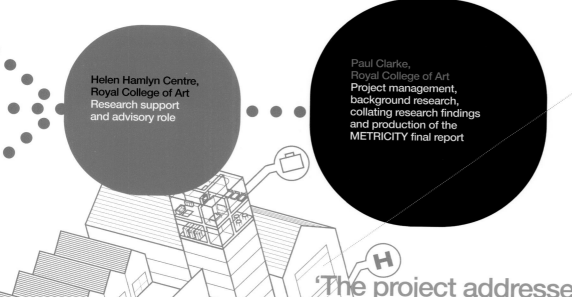

Helen Hamlyn Centre,
Royal College of Art
Research support
and advisory role

Paul Clarke,
Royal College of Art
Project management,
background research,
collating research findings
and production of the
METRICITY final report

'The project addresses the urban design implications of social and demographic change. Its aim has been to stimulate debate, engage the key players and ask how exploration of alternative principles can offer a framework for change. We badly need new development to be planned in a more animated and holistic way'
Professor Jeremy Myerson, Director, RCA Helen Hamlyn Centre

MOBILISING KNOWLEDGE: Solving the interaction gap between older people, planners, experts and general citizens within the Thames Gateway

Lead organisation
Goldsmiths College

Project coordinators
Dr Alison Rooke and Dr Gesche Wuerfel

Project start and end dates
May 2007 to December 2008

Total UrbanBuzz funding
£34,678

Total CIK
£13,956

Contact details
a.rooke@gold.ac.uk

- ● Environment
- ● Society
- ● Governance
- ● Planning/regeneration
- ● Infrastructure
- ● Design/housing

The context: community empowerment

The 2008 Planning Bill seeks to re-activate local democracy and local decision-making, and so community engagement is high on the agenda. The *Communities in control: real people, real power* White Paper, July 2008, states that a key government aim is to 'pass power into the hands of local communities ... But while people do want to have a greater say, they also want to know that their voices will be heard. This is what empowerment is all about – passing more and more political power to more and more people through every practical means'. Local authorities and planners need to be ready.

Alongside planning reform, the UK must manage an ageing population. Office of National Statistics (ONS) figures predict that over 65-year-olds will constitute more than 24 per cent of the UK population by 2036. Older people have a wealth of experience, and the MOBILISING KNOWLEDGE project set out to create channels for capturing this experience and feeding it into the planning system.

Key project objectives

Communities can claim to be 'sustainable' if they meet the needs of all members, including older people. This project aimed to mobilise 22 Lewisham residents, aged above 60 years, to share their experience and knowledge with technical experts and professional decision-makers. According to Lewisham Primary Care Trust, almost 11 per cent of the population is aged 65 or over, and the borough needs to find strategies that will integrate this key group and promote social cohesion. The project aimed to:

01 engage a range of older Lewisham residents from different class and ethnic backgrounds in dialogue about planning;

02 increase older people's involvement in planning decisions;

03 increase the awareness that urban planners and others have of the needs and wishes of the elderly;

04 empower a section of the population that is often excluded from official decision-making processes;

05 include older residents in planning processes, to create communities that are more sustainable in the long-term; and

06 overcome communication barriers through knowledge exchange between older people, planners and academia.

Closing the generation gap
The MOBILISING KNOWLEDGE project explored older people's experience of the city and created ways of incorporating their views into the planning and design process

The project response

The 22 local residents, once engaged, took part in a series of six interactive sessions together with local stakeholders (planners, local councillors and community workers) during a three-week summer school. The participants explored a range of themes, including transport, schools, hospitals and GP access, through workshops, walking tours, photography exercises, discussion groups and a participatory street workshop.

The summer school explored older people's experience of their borough, drawing out ways in which today's decision-makers and developers can understand how past and present developments are experienced by older residents – and how they would like to live in the future.

Several planners and designers from the London Borough of Lewisham joined the local participants for planning workshops, outlining the developments that would be happening in Lewisham over the next five years, and discussing planning, travel and masterplanning options.

Local resident participants documented aspects of their borough with digital cameras, and drew mental maps of neighbourhood experiences. Professor Julianne Hanson from University College London shared her research on inclusive design, and demonstrated how, by incorporating simple design features, planners can vastly improve older people's experience of the city.

Project impact

The summer school addressed the disconnection of older residents from their borough's complex new regeneration framework. It critically explored future developments from the perspectives of local older people by teaching, and applying, communication skills. The experience has begun a dialogue between older people and policy and planning professionals in order to explore older people's experience of the city.

The participants made many interesting observations that 'really got us thinking', said planning policy officer Lovelace Poku, a summer school expert participant. For some, mobility is an important issue, as is the need for more public toilets, and for benches in hilly areas. Others reflected on their younger years and the changes they'd seen in the community; many felt that community life has suffered, and that housing policy should accommodate a social mix of all age groups. Poku also agreed that the project had encouraged him to think 'outside of the box' when it came to communication and engagement techniques – experience that planners could really benefit from as new local empowerment legislation is put into practice.

The findings from these sessions have been published in a comprehensive 'toolkit' and short video on DVD, each linking theory and practice. As well as outlining the case for involving older people in planning, the toolkit offers good practice guidelines for organising workshops and information-gathering events, including sample budgets and logistics. Copies have been sent to local authorities and to professionals seeking to work with older people.

Beneficial relationships have been developed with Lewisham Regeneration Department, and members of the team have been invited to participate in future borough-level participative planning events, and are featured on Lewisham's intranet database as contactable experts in the field of participative planning.

A key project goal was to find ways of incorporating inclusive views into the planning and development process. Local authorities are frequently slow to incorporate new ideas, but there are signs that the project experience is moving towards practice recommended by the project team – at a recent consultation event in Catford, planning officers rented a shop so as to interact with local passers-by, and gave them cards on which to make suggestions. >

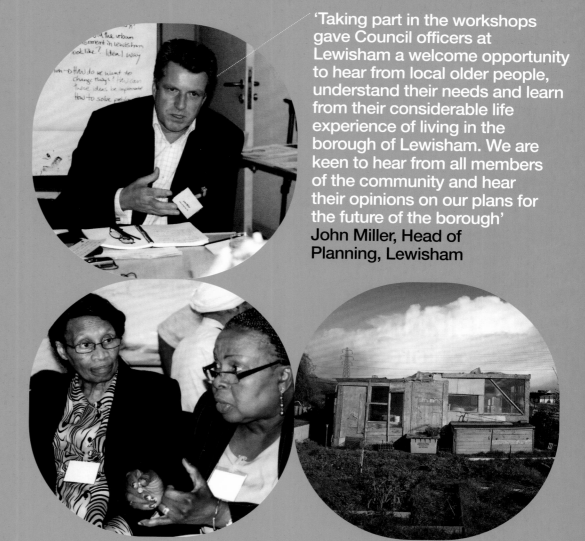

'Taking part in the workshops gave Council officers at Lewisham a welcome opportunity to hear from local older people, understand their needs and learn from their considerable life experience of living in the borough of Lewisham. We are keen to hear from all members of the community and hear their opinions on our plans for the future of the borough'
John Miller, Head of Planning, Lewisham

Knowledge exchange

Several summer school events, including a 'Lewisham Futures' workshop, were attended by planning officers, councillors, the borough Mayor and senior policymakers, both locally and nationally.

The resultant dialogue has allowed the participants to reflect on each other's needs and priorities, and to propose concrete solutions for ways in which developments can be more inclusive. Importantly, the practical means by which the dialogue was facilitated have also been captured and documented in the toolkit. The project team also noted that the project focused on one borough with complex and contradicting planning and regeneration processes underway. While officers were willing to take part in the project itself, and are convinced that the consultation approach needs to be more inclusive, the extent to which these 'good intentions' have been converted into action by local authority teams remains to be seen.

Developers were also invited to participate in the project events, but were unable to attend. They are important players in regeneration, but proved difficult to engage in this inclusive design process. Their lack of interest in the project may reflect their different priorities.

summer sch

City mine(d)
Led by Jim Segers, the group organised a participatory event in Deptford market with project participants and the public

London Older People Strategy Group
Professor Singh, project advisor

Michael Keith
Presentations at the summer school

Rebecca Maguire
Organising dissemination events, and connecting partners via the Building Conversations initiative

Goldsmiths
**Gesche Wuerfel, Alison Rooke
Project coordination and management**

**22 local residents
took part in summer school events over a three-week period, along with planners, academics, government officials, local authority workers**

Simon Rowe
Workshop on digital photography for summer school participants

Ben Gidley
Lecture at the summer school, organising a participant walk through Deptford

summer school

Education and training

Learning from the project will be fed into course material at Goldsmiths across a range of programmes: MA Culture, Globalisation and the city; MA Photography and Urban Culture; and BA Sociology: Visualising the Social World.

There are also plans to work with the London Borough of Lewisham on creating training programmes for employees in the education, leisure and planning departments. The team delivered two days of teacher training with Deptford Green School as part of London Borough of Lewisham's Links Regeneration Project.

The future: embedding best practice

The toolkit has been disseminated across local councils. The next step, which is ongoing, is to embed the process into the planning workflow process. Several of the officers working within Lewisham council are exploring ways in which this can be done.

A final project event helped to raise awareness of the toolkit and DVD, and to consolidate the connections that could be made between experts and potential partner organisations such as Knowledge East. The project has been incorporated into the 'Building Conversations' initiative, organised by the Business Development Office (BDO), and links with the London Assembly and Women's Design Service are being actively taken forward.

Project resources
www.goldsmiths.ac.uk/cucr/pdf/mobilizing-knowledge.pdf

The 'Building Conversations' educational pack combines the Mobilising Knowledge toolkit with a participative planning project for younger people. Contact the project coordinators for details

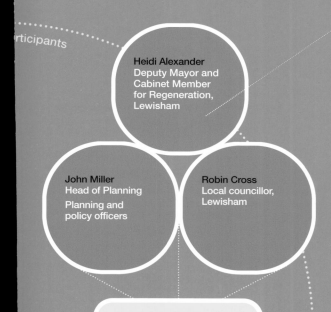

Participants

Heidi Alexander
Deputy Mayor and Cabinet Member for Regeneration, Lewisham

John Miller
Head of Planning
Planning and policy officers

Robin Cross
Local councillor, Lewisham

Lewisham Council

Chris Brodie, Louise Holland, Nigel Adams, Lesley Lee
Advisors and summer school participants

Barbara Gray
Area Initiatives Officer, Lewisham
Initial engagement of participants and advisor on embedding best practice into council workflows

Outcomes

'Working with local residents is at the heart of what policy makers should do. These summer school events have inspired us with new ways of connecting with our communities'
Heidi Alexander, Deputy Mayor and Cabinet Member for Regeneration, Lewisham

'It was a challenge to reach people, and in the end we worked with individuals who were already active in the community. We thought of the summer school as a testing process. Now we have a process in place, we can bring in other groups'
Barbara Gray, Area Initiatives Officer, Lewisham

DVD: short project film
Screened for participants, at local workshops with project stakeholders, and available from Goldsmiths

The toolkit
Widely disseminated to members of Lewisham Council, the Thames Gateway Forum and Women's Design Service via a round table discussion event and at workshops

Embedding inclusive practice
Event/workshop bringing together all participants and stakeholders to focus on embedding good practice into council workflows

REBOPSE: Reducing Barriers to Opportunities
for People Socially Excluded

Lead organisation
Meganexus

Project coordinator
Dr Dan Brown

Project start and end dates
June 2007 to December 2008

Total UrbanBuzz funding
£174,354

Total CIK
£294,617

Contact details
dan@meganexus.com

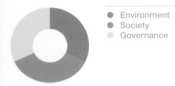

- Environment
- Society
- Governance

The context: enhancing social capital

Sustainable communities are built on trust, equal opportunity and social inclusion. The jobless often have limited opportunities for interaction beyond their local area and social group. This project aimed to identify a community of jobless people and introduce them to opportunities for social interaction via both online social networking and offline volunteering opportunities, with the aim of helping them to find work. By interlinking a green business network and local job seeker networks, the REBOPSE scheme aimed to provide job seekers with new experiences and knowledge.

Key project objectives

The project aimed to widen access to employment opportunities and support the skills and enterprise agenda of the emerging green economy. The project team planned to provide volunteers for green events and raise awareness of the social issues related to joblessness. The project aimed to strengthen network members' choice: 'groups that are too much alike find it harder to keep learning, because each member is bringing less and less new information' (Surowiecki; *The Wisdom of Crowds*). The project aimed to address sustainability through:

01 widening access to employment opportunities (particularly for the disadvantaged);

02 improving the matching of skills and enterprise needed for the emerging green economy;

03 extending the area of search open to job seekers through the use of interlinked web-based and offline social networks;

04 setting appropriate institutional rules (registration and membership procedures), common to web-based social networks in order to reinforce trust, confidence and social inclusion;

05 interlinking job seekers, employer and green networks with the aim of increasing the employment search space and diversity of choice available for members;

06 undertaking analysis and benchmarking of social networks to provide a baseline from which to monitor and evaluate the effectiveness of the project; and

07 developing agent-based models to simulate the take-up of jobs in the network, and reviewing the importance of increasing connectivity between individuals.

The project team aimed to create a densely-populated, independent network ranging across social and economic divides, based around an online hub where job seekers, employers and potential volunteers could interlink. Creating links between this network, and job seekers and employers' networks, was a key element of the project.

The intention was not merely to increase the number of jobs and job seekers available, but also to increase members' social diversity (and thus improve job chances based on the idea of the strength of 'weak ties' in social networks). These ideas are well-known, widely accepted and grounded in the theoretical framework of social network theory (Granovetter). The project also aimed to take advantage of demand for 'green' skills (retrofitting solar panels, energy conservation advice, insulation fitting and recycling).

It was intended that the network would lead to real job creation, rather than job listing, through associated networks. These social and economic clusters would, it was hoped, continue to enhance the growth of new markets, products and services in the 'green economy' in future.

Connections that may change your life

REBOPSE is addressing sustainability by widening access to employment opportunities for the socially excluded and disadvantaged, using a social networking model

The project response

The project created the GreenManiac offline and online network. On joining the network, 148 small and medium enterprises (SMEs) were given an environmental 'health check', so helping to improve knowledge, skills and the working environment for the local community. These businesses have been supported economically and environmentally: the team has provided them with potential business opportunities, advisors and mentoring, as well advice on environmental management and sustainability.

Through the site, and via offline communications such as calls and texts to those registered on the network, members were offered volunteering and, potentially, employment opportunities. 'People who have been without jobs for a long time might be richly connected to other people,' says project partner Sue Batty from UCL, 'but usually the people they're connected with are exactly the same as them. We were aiming to get jobless people to connect with people who *do* have jobs and opportunities.'

With Camden selected as the base location for the project, many of the job seekers were invited to join as members of the Camden Working recruitment website; a traditional 'job advice and job matching' site aimed at local disadvantaged job seekers. Others joined through GreenManiac stalls at local events; or were invited by members wishing to expand their networks. To date, members have been actively engaged in voluntary activities such as street cleaning, graffiti removal and helping out at green events.

To evaluate project impact, social networking benchmarks were generated using data gathered by the project team. This involved identifying the networking patterns and geographic concentrations that are characteristic of groups of jobless people in the study area.

Project partner Volterra designed agent-based models (ABM) to simulate the take-up of jobs in the GreenManiac community, and to analyse the strength of the network.

The team also surveyed 200 workless individuals: 100 were registered on the GreenManiac site and supported by offers of volunteering experience and job alerts, while a control group of 100, registered with the Camden Working job recruitment site, received no additional support.

Project impact

These two groups were surveyed at the end of the project, with impressive results. Of the 100 people that had been supported through GreenManiac, 15 people had gained employment since registering on the network. Out of the 100 that received no assistance, only four people had found employment during the life of the project.

The agent-based models have also delivered interesting results, using the project data to predict the degree of linkage needed in the population to ›

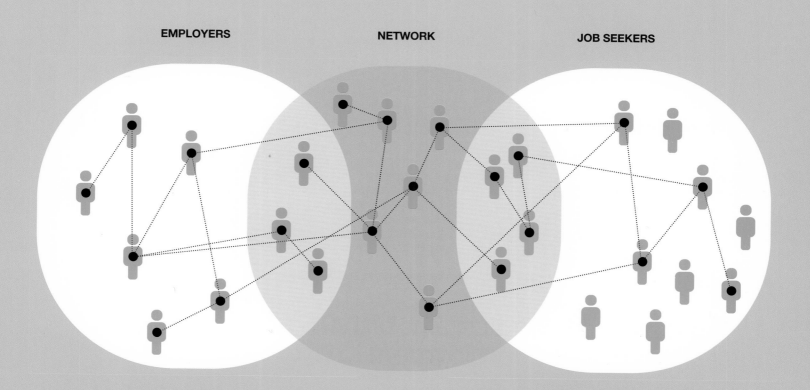

EMPLOYERS   **NETWORK**   **JOB SEEKERS**

Prospects for job seekers becoming active members of green networks are raised significantly as network connectivity increases

REBOPSE: Reducing Barriers to Opportunities for People Socially Excluded

Key findings:

22%
increased the links they had with businesses and job seekers

16%
were helped towards job opportunities

47%
will continue to use the GreenManiac website

53%
got a job or job offer in the period they were involved in the project

Goldsmiths College
Providing contacts and advice on green networks

UCL
Providing contacts and advice on green networks

Meganexus
Development of social networking website

Engaging people and businesses in online and offline networks

Organising volunteering opportunities for jobless network members

Volterra
Development agent-based models (ABM) to analyse the strength of the network, simulate the take-up of jobs in the job seeker community, and demonstrate the importance of increasing the connectivity between individuals

Centre for Advanced Spatial Analysis (CASA)
Social networking analysis and benchmarking the usage and impact of the network

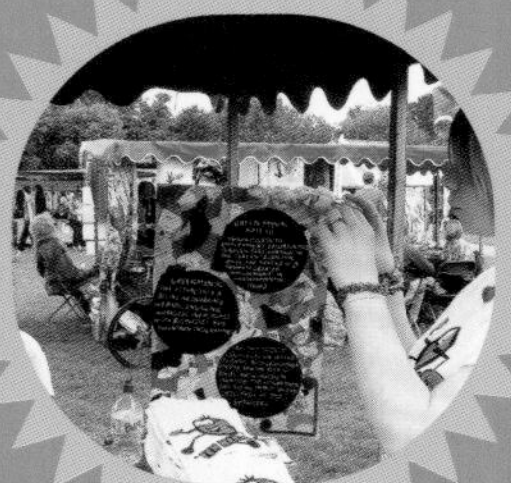

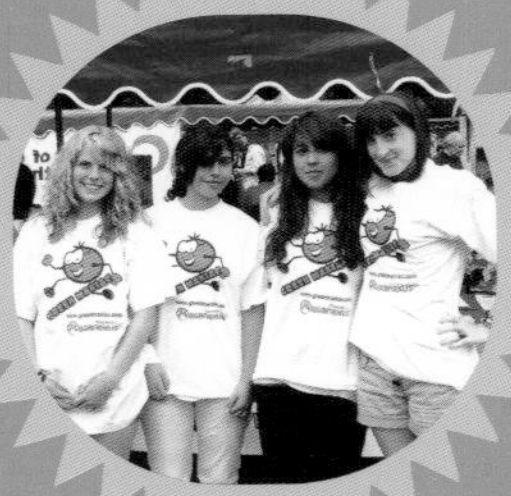

Camden Green Fair and other events
Providing training and voluntary experience for jobless individuals

The British Library
Future development of the network

Sutton Council
Urban Futures
Action Acton
Populating the network, online and offline, with data and jobless people

'We couldn't have run the event without the volunteers, their input was terrific. They were really reliable and made the day run really smoothly'
Cathy Maund, Camden Green Fair Coordinator

increase employment levels. The model simulates the take-up of jobs in the job seeker community, demonstrates the importance of increasing connectivity between individuals, and explores the role of information spread in a community. Broadly speaking, if every job seeker passes on information about a job to just one other, take-up improves by almost 50 per cent.

The model was benchmarked on local socially-excluded job seekers from the borough of Camden at the beginning of the project, and calibrated using GreenManiac survey data. The key dynamic of the model is the passage of information through a group. Knowledge about a job is first given to one job seeker who may get the job but, if not, can pass the information on to their contacts.

Further versions of the model indicate that for low numbers of connections – the starting point for the analysis – only one job seeker finds out about a job and, if they don't take it up, then knowledge of the job is missed by others. As the number of connections increases, job seekers are able to pass on information to other members of the network. By the time the network becomes very highly connected, almost all jobs are taken up by someone in the network.

Offline, businesses registered on the GreenManiac site have access to a pool of experience in the form of more than 800 other London businesses and mentors registered on a linked site run by project lead organisation Meganexus. 'As people join the network, we have linked them with people who have a common interest,' says Batty.

In terms of volunteering, the project's most successful event so far has been the Camden Green Fair. 'We provided hundreds of volunteers, and made a huge impact, both on the event and on our network members,' says project coordinator Dr Dan Brown. 'In terms of sustainability,' he adds, 'it also seems possible that event support has the potential to become a commercial service in future. We've demonstrated that we can bring large numbers of volunteers to events, and that they do a great job.'

The volunteering sessions brought the jobless into contact with people who have opportunities. 'We've already seen cases where trust builds through voluntary work – employers tell us that they are more confident about offering somebody a job after seeing them working in a voluntary situation,' says Batty.

As part of the project evaluation, feedback has been collected on how REBOPSE has benefited members. Overall, positive feedback was received, with many network members stating that they would like to be more involved with green volunteering, and others wanting the project to continue across other regions in England.

The GreenManiac network has:

01 signed up 148 businesses that were provided with information regarding the environment and how to develop an eco-friendly business;

02 undertaken an environmental 'healthcheck' with the 148 businesses; 35 have now developed an environmental policy;

03 registered 149 individuals on the network;

04 established 2,796 connections throughout the network, including direct and indirect links;

05 generated 35 new jobs, according to evidence from questionnaires and telephone surveys

Knowledge exchange

One of the lessons of the project is the critical importance of timely information and the need to ensure that all individuals have equality of access to information. A second lesson is the importance of combining offline and online social networking. Members value personal invitations to events and activities that improve their confidence and skills and introduces them to others, along with website reminders and announcements that help them to network effectively.

London Sustainability Exchange (LSTS project, see page 150) has included a link to GreenManiac on its regular email bulletin for sustainable businesses: LSTS provides internships, temporary and voluntary placements for students from a wide range of backgrounds that have a common interest in sustainability.

Education and training

The GreenManiac network is helping to educate job seekers and businesses about sustainability issues. Academic working papers and articles on the power of networks will be published in professional journals during 2009.

The future: growing the network

As the GreenManiac network matures and builds links with other networks, the team expects to receive more offers of mentoring and job experience, and to support the growth of advice and green awareness services for SMEs.

Project resources
www.greenmaniac.com
www.urbanbuzz.org (select projects)

A range of reports and papers is being produced by the project team: contact dan@meganexus.com for more information. Details are listed on page 48

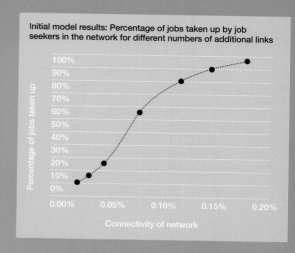

Initial model results: Percentage of jobs taken up by job seekers in the network for different numbers of additional links

Project partner Volterra's models simulate the take-up of jobs in the GreenManiac job seeker community. Initially, Volterra was provided with a sample of 7,841 'nodes' and the links between them. The vast majority of the 'nodes' were individual job seekers living in the London Borough of Camden, and just 68 had multiple roles – for example job broker, employer and advisor. Almost all of the links go between job seekers and the 68 nodes with multiple roles. This indicates that connections between the workless individuals were very sparse, and there is little opportunity for information about job opportunities to spread across the network.

This network data was used as the basis for the initial agent-based model. It simulated how increasing job take-up could be generated by increased connectivity in the social network. As more links between job seekers were created, more job seekers found employment. The benefits rose quickly after the number of links passed an initial threshold.

A further model was developed which distinguished between the 22 per cent of job seekers that increased their links during the period in which they were involved with GreenManiac, and the 78 per cent that did not. The model reveals a potentially dramatic difference between the two groups in terms of potential employment – those who'd increased their links increased them even further.

The model can benchmark the potential impact on employment of increasing the number of connections within the social network of the workless. This is based on a range of assumptions about the propensity to pass job information on to others in the network, and the rate at which employment offers are made to people in the network.

RETILE COMBEEP: Real-Time Learning for Community-Based Environmental Projects

Lead organisation
UCL

Project coordinator
Gemma Moore

Project start and end dates
July 2007 to December 2008

Total UrbanBuzz funding
£125,233

Total CIK
£21,573

Contact details
gemma.moore@ucl.ac.uk

- Environment
- Society
- Governance
- Planning/regeneration
- Design/housing

Capturing evidence for place-changing impacts
The RETILE project has focused on developing effective self-evaluation and project management techniques for environmental regeneration charity Groundwork

The context: changing places changes lives...

For many charities, there are gaps in relation to the evaluation of project process and outcomes. Environmental regeneration projects require complex partnerships between a range of stakeholders, and managing such interaction effectively can be problematic. In terms of project outcomes, many community-based organisations struggle with time and resource for defining and implementing effective project management mechanisms, and with processes to evaluate and review their ways of working. Current systems of measurement/monitoring revolve around 'quantitative' measurements such as NPMs: national performance measures.

'Many evaluation tools aren't really useful for capturing key aspects of our work,' says Anna Walnycki from environmental charity Groundwork North London, a key RETILE project participant. 'We may have changed someone's life or made someone happier, and we know, anecdotally, that we're building up partnerships and bringing people together. But this hasn't been captured or shared amongst staff.'

Capturing and sharing knowledge is also a key challenge across the third sector. Success is frequently linked to individual skills and approaches and, as many third sector organisations have high a staff turnover, it's important that neither information nor community links are lost when members of staff move on.

Key project objectives

This project is about self-evaluation and learning from intangible impacts. The project team worked with national environmental regeneration charity Groundwork, which has undertaken thousands of practical projects in its field, project managing the reworking of local spaces such as playgrounds and community gardens as catalysts for broader community regeneration. There is evidence that well-designed and well-managed public space plays a key role in the creation of sustainable communities. Recent UK policy (ODPM 2002) has stressed that 'public spaces play a critical role in creating pride in places where we live which, in turn, is essential to building community cohesion and successful communities'.

However, the process of capturing, evaluating and reflecting on the added value that quality public spaces deliver is challenging – especially for the tightly-resourced third sector. The key aim was to strengthen evaluation and knowledge capture processes for Groundwork North London through real-time learning. Collaboration between academics and practitioners connected the 'know how' to the 'how to' for community-based environmental regeneration projects. The project aimed to:

01 undertake a participatory review of existing/recently-completed projects, including process mechanisms;

02 develop an active review methodology;

03 test the methodology using diaries, visual ethnography, interviews and focus groups;

04 collate and apply learning from the review to ongoing projects;

05 produce an evaluation guide;

06 develop a participatory training package for internal Groundwork staff;

07 disseminate training and evaluation experience to other Groundwork trusts; and

08 feed back (via guidance and training) to practitioners and the local community to improve practice for future projects.

The project response

The project team was conscious from the outset that various approaches to evaluation have been tried in Groundwork over the years – for example in response to national approaches (Prove It). Furthermore, it was assumed that, prior to the recent merger of Groundwork trusts across London into Groundwork London, each trust had used its own approaches to project evaluation and internal learning. ❯

'WE KNOW THAT WE MAY HAVE CHANGED SOMEONE'S LIFE OR MADE SOMEONE HAPPIER. WE'RE BUILDING PARTNERSHIPS AND BRINGING PEOPLE TOGETHER BUT, UNTIL NOW, THIS INFORMATION HASN'T BEEN CAPTURED'

ANNA WALNYCKI, GROUNDWORK NORTH LONDON

RETILE COMBEEP: Real-Time Learning for Community-Based Environmental Projects

The review of a variety of evaluation methodologies using existing Groundwork North London projects was undertaken collaboratively by UCL and Groundwork, concentrating on three completed projects and one live project.

The project team developed methodologies, including a 'walk & talk' process, to evaluate qualitative experience. This approach, along with interviews, surveys and visual audits, was used to undertake the project reviews. The project team noted which techniques proved effective with particular stakeholders (residents, funders, Groundwork staff), and/or at particular stages of the project, and which proved useful for capturing particular project processes, outputs and impacts.

During the development of the evaluation framework, senior management at Groundwork were involved in trialling the developing evaluation tools for speed and cost, thus reducing the risk of the RETILE team creating an overly complicated and expensive framework. As a result of management feedback, a two-tiered framework was developed (GPE and GPE+): a standard evaluation, and an enhanced evaluation methodology for longer term or more complex projects. It is hoped that the framework will remain flexible enough to be incorporated into all projects.

The two-tiered project framework incorporates tried and tested evaluation methodologies and involves a range of project stakeholders. It is designed to:

01 provide a structure for project-focused self-evaluation;
02 build evaluation into projects from the start;
03 ensure that project management systems are robust, with clear aims and objectives;
04 give guidance about the kinds of evidence needed to assess projects: have specific aims or quality features been met?;
05 provide a standard, comparable but adaptable framework that can be applied to a range of projects;
06 encourage learning and reflection through methods and information being collected throughout the life of the project; and
07 provide evidence of what works well/not so well to ultimately improve practice and performance.

Project impact

Through undertaking reviews of completed projects it was possible to understand the social contribution of Groundwork's activities. 'We realised through this exercise that Groundwork had been very project-delivery focused,' says Walnycki. 'We moved from one project to the next very quickly, and didn't have much opportunity to stay in touch with project stakeholders. But the evaluation framework we have developed ensures that we follow up on our work. This is really helping us to be aware of the "hidden" added value that we can bring to projects in terms of creating lasting links in the community.'

Previously, Groundwork had struggled to understand the impacts of its projects, post-completion, because of the rush to move onto new projects. To this end, the review of a project on Brecknock Road, Islington, driven by the local tenants and residents association, revealed that the community had benefited from improved self-confidence as well as developing new skills in planning, dealing with contractors and project budgets, gaining consensus amongst themselves, organising events and gardening.

'Measuring the success of these projects can be fraught with difficulties, but we've come up with a framework outlining what can be done at certain stages of a project, what questions should be asked, and who should be involved in the process'
Gemma Moore, project coordinator

University College London

Gemma Moore
Project coordinator
Providing academic resource and establishing networks

Ben Croxford
Project management and support

Groundwork North London

Urvisha Mistry, Anna Walnycki, Karen Partridge
Advisors on project activities and charity networks

Sandra Hoisz
Strategic direction and uptake

Ben Coles
Roll-out and legacy of the evaluation framework across Groundwork trusts

London 21
Chris Church
Contribution to the development of a project evaluation framework and strategy

AOC
Daisy Froud
Advisor on stakeholder engagement and consultation

Saima Iqbal
Advisor to the project, reviewing evaluation strategies

Local communities
Communities across north London worked with the project team on project reviews

Reviewing the completed projects has also meant that links have been re-established with a number of communities and stakeholders. As a result, some follow-on work is to be undertaken by Groundwork's 'Green Team' at the Regent's Park Estate: an initiative that aims to give people experience in the horticulture sector. Reviews have also demonstrated the extent to which many projects created spin-offs that stimulated other youth work and regeneration in the area.

The team has noted the importance of effective communication and reporting, both during and after projects. Stakeholders and the public are more likely to be involved in projects if they believe that the information they deliver will be valuable.

The GPE and GPE+ frameworks have been adopted by the Groundwork North London trust. Following the recent merger of local trusts into Groundwork London, the new processes have been adopted as a common approach. A Groundwork London project team is taking the framework forward. Groundwork London and Groundwork UK are potentially committing £20,000 to support the practical implementation of the framework.

For Groundwork London, the use of a consistent approach to project evaluation and internal learning will have positive strategic benefits. It will help to influence and shape policies and learning, and to demonstrate positive impact. Operationally, it will help Groundwork London to improve its project delivery. Groundwork UK will monitor the progress of the implementation within London and, if it proves successful, will adopt the GPE and GPE+ evaluation frameworks in all Groundwork Trusts across the UK.

Knowledge exchange

The project team developed an implementation training workshop for the evaluation methodologies, with the aim of stimulating discussion. An open exercise was undertaken to share experience of what works well, and what does not, within projects. These will continue to be held for Groundwork London staff.

During the development of the framework, it emerged that little was known of other Groundwork trusts' monitoring and evaluation procedures. The project team decided to engage other trusts by undertaking a 'baseline' survey, conducted during November to December 2007. This was considered a key step in the engagement of other trusts.

The 'walk & talk' methodology is rooted in knowledge-sharing. It involves an individual, possibly a resident or a local community group member, giving a guided tour of the project site to other stakeholders, followed by questions. This method was found to be valuable, eliciting much richer information than that volunteered in a typical Q+A session, although it was recognised that walk & talk sessions might need to be supported by a detailed briefing note, sent out to stakeholders before the event.

Reflecting upon the walk & talk methodology, the facilitators agreed that the method may also prove useful for staff training.

Education and training

A key member of the project team, Dr Ben Croxford, is course director for the MSc Environmental Design and Engineering course at the Bartlett School of Graduate Studies, UCL. A new module, Social Dimensions in Sustainability, was introduced in the academic year 2008-09, drawing upon the work of the RETILE project.

An MSc course run at the UCL's Development Planning Unit (DPU) approached Groundwork North London for several case studies as part of its course on Socially Sensitive Development. Gemma Moore (UCL) and Anna Walnycki (Groundwork) took part in a session with the students, introducing the RETILE project. Contact will be maintained with the course convener to enable results from student projects to be fed to the RETILE partners, and vice-versa.

The future: wider applications

Further funding is being sought to enable the continued involvement of UCL, and the wider application of the framework within other UK regeneration organisations, for example local authorities' regeneration teams, and New Deal for Communities.

Additional work has been undertaken by Groundwork in developing an evaluation plan for Well London at Noel Park, a three-year project addressing access to parks, encouraging positive uses in the form of physical exercise classes, a healthy eating café and arts-based activities. Well London is managed by an alliance of partners that has already commented on the quality and structure of the evaluation that Groundwork is now using. Groundwork hopes to trial and disseminate its new processes and methodologies by working with partners.

Environmental regeneration charity Groundwork has undertaken thousands of practical projects, such as the regeneration of playgrounds and community gardens, as catalysts for broader community regeneration. Participatory reviews of existing and recently completed projects Groundwork enabled the RETILE project team to develop new and effective active evaluation methodologies

Project resources
http://www.bartlett.ucl.ac.uk/web/ben/ede/Intro.htm

The evaluation toolkit

Groundwork Project Evaluation (GPE)

The standard approach to evaluation maps onto existing project management systems, therefore incurring minimal time and resource investment. It involves incorporating tried and tested evaluation methodologies into key partner meetings involving a range of stakeholders, for example inception meetings and end of project reviews.

Groundwork Project Evaluation Plus (GPE +)

This approach involves the standard evaluation (GPE), but also provides project officers with a methodology to undertake tailored evaluation in the case of larger, longer term projects with more complex aims. This framework can be used from the beginning of a project to:

01 capture the outcomes as well as the outputs;
02 self-evaluate;
03 encourage learning and reflection and think about methods and information being collected throughout the life of the project;
04 remain aware of what project aims are and how to achieve them
05 act as an alternative to outcome tools such as Prove It.

SCREAM: Urban Screens as a Medium
for Communication

Lead organisation
UCL

Project coordinator
Ava Fatah gen. Schieck

Project start and end dates
April 2008 to December 2008

Total UrbanBuzz funding
£9,272

Total CIK
£23,400

Contact details
ava.fatah@ucl.ac.uk

- Environment
- Governance
- Policy
- Planning/regeneration
- Design/housing

The context: digital media cityscapes

In the last decade, cityscapes have been undergoing major transformations. LCD screens and LED billboards are appearing as part of the city architecture, flashing dynamic moving images and messages with the potential to affect our perception and understanding of the space around us. Both the screens and the content they display take many forms – movies, news, city information and, of course, commercials.

There is currently a lack of information in the public domain relating to the institutional framework surrounding the set-up of big screens. Who can put up a screen? What policy and regulation governs the content on show? How loud or bright they can be?

Beginning a dialogue, and creating a debate, between the parties concerned was a key driver of the SCREAM project. 'Whilst initially trying to collect information about big screens, says Ava gen. Schieck, UCL, SCREAM project coordinator, 'it was difficult to contact the officers concerned, or to track down the planning applications or consents. We need to understand how urban big screens can be implemented, to establish funding models, and to explore the relationship between the built environment, screen content, and the potential of urban digital media for interaction and engagement.'

Big screens could have a major impact on the public space of many towns and cities in the UK, says the Commission for Architecture and the Built Environment (CABE). Sarah Gaventa, director of CABE Space and a project participant, has commented: 'Having a fun, relaxed time in our streets and squares should come from the character and design of a place, not something that feels like an outdoor Currys.

'This is not urban regeneration. If it is going to work, funding needs to be earmarked for physical improvements to the spaces for which screens are proposed, and for proper curating to ensure the cultural programme is high quality.'

Key project objectives

This project aimed to place big screens in context and to explore the ways in which they affect our experiences of the public spaces they occupy. 'The use of these screens will bring new potential and new challenges for city regulators, artists, architects, urban designers, producers, broadcasters and advertisers,' says Fatah gen. Schieck. 'We are just beginning to understand their potential for public information, art and community engagement. We need to see more negotiation between commercial, public and cultural interests.' The project team aimed to:

01 influence developments related to the sustainable implementation of urban media screens by bringing stakeholders together to debate the issues in a series of workshops; and

02 produce a framework that will influence developments related to the implementation of urban screens. ❯

Connecting the community through media screens
Can the use of outdoor screens be broadened to include art and community engagement? The SCREAM project explores the potential impact of big screens on the urban environment

The project response

The project team identified a range of individuals and organisations playing an active role in the development and implementation of media screens in the UK. These stakeholders came from a range of backgrounds: academic research, art, screen management, screen curation, technology providers, curators, funders and the regulatory sector. A potential agenda for debate was outlined, and participants attended two seminars at which big screen-related issues were raised. Representatives of all the stakeholder groups were invited to attend.

The discussions addressed the ways in which screens could drive urban regeneration if managed effectively, or potentially hinder it by degrading the urban environment. Participants also considered how screens and content providers could potentially engage with audiences through user-generated input, and what might happen if screens fail to show balanced content that reflects the diversity of the urban area. The workshops addressed a range of issues:

01 the motivations for implementation of screens: providing information or entertainment, being an innovative outlet for cultural content and art, or to support regeneration approaches;

02 the identification of stakeholders and their respective interests in the media screen implementation process, and the need to bring them together;

03 the role of commercial screen and content providers;

04 how to understand the long-term impact of screens, and screen content, on urban space and communities. The importance of identifying ways of integrating the screens in the built environment, or as part of the building fabric, was also highlighted;

05 how to reach diverse communities, using various approaches including permanent, temporary and mobile solutions;

06 how screens can play a positive role in engaging the viewer with the urban space by relating screen content to public space activities;

07 technical issues related to the provision of sound and vision in urban space, including the size, shape and resolution of screens, and their energy sources;

08 the context and selection of screen locations;

09 potential funding models; and

10 lessons learned from beyond the UK; in the EU, Australia and South East Asia.

UCL
Ava Fatah gen. Schieck
Project coordinator and workshop organiser

body>data>space
Ghislaine Boddington
Moderation and knowledge transfer in the area of performing arts and the integration of body responsive technologies

Art2Architecture
Peter Fink
Knowledge transfer in the area of application, legislation and evolving technologies related to large-scale LED display screens in an urban context

'The use of these screens will bring new potential and challenges for city regulators, artists, architects, urban designers, producers, broadcasters and advertisers. We are just beginning to understand their potential for public information, art and community engagement. We need to see more negotiation between commercial, public and cultural interests'
Ava Fatah gen. Schieck, project coordinator

Workshop participants
UCL
The Arts Council England
CABE
BBC Liverpool
Tank TV
Addictive TV
body>data>space
Art2Architecture
Live Sites – LOCOG
Foundation for Art and Creative Technology (FACT)
University of Salford
UEL Smartslab
Middlesex ResCe

The framework considered:

Funding models

Content

Technology

The built environment

Community engagement

Communication

media communication experts
architects
body technologists
academics and theorists
software creatives
film video artists
engineers
display technologists
lighting experts
urban planners
interactive digital artists
generative digital artists

the SCREAM project and source new input from the media screen experiences of cities around the world. Fatah gen. Schieck also attended the Media Facade Conference in Berlin to discuss the SCREAM project and engage new participants.

The project's framework document will be disseminated to a wide audience via various newsletters and websites including the Urban Screens Association.

Education and training
To address the potential of media screens raised by the SCREAM project, a module will be developed to be part of the e-ArchiDoct (virtual campus) project; a postgraduate study in architecture offered online using the free e-learning platform Moodle. The e-ArchiDoct is a major EU-Erasmus project that is testing experimental collaboration to offer an online course in architectural research. Fifteen universities across Europe are involved. Each university offers at least one module to create a syllabus rooted in knowledge exchange. The SCREAM project module is 'Media screens: potential, challenges and risks', providing a series of lectures and presentations, aimed a wide audience from the e-ArchiDoct registrants, including graduates and practicing architects.

The future: defining social interaction
Urban screens could transform public space into environments for the creation and exchange of culture. If a positive balance of content, location and type of screen is created to support social interactions, media screens could also promote new types of shared encounters – Fatah gen. Schieck hopes to explore the potential of linking different locations through screens in future. For the present, there are opportunities to build on the work begun by the SCREAM team in building a network of urban screen stakeholders.

The project team is currently in discussions with a number of organisations about participation in further media screens projects. It has been invited to work with Sutton Council and the Sutton Screens project involving the local council, architects and town centre management; on initiatives with professional digital media providers; and on community art and engagement projects across London and the south-east.

Project resources
The project documentation is available online:
www.vr.ucl.ac.uk/projects/scream/
and from body>data>space: www.bodydataspace.net

Project impact
Based on workshop input, the project team produced a framework document, *How to deal with issues related to the implementation of media big screens and how they work in the field*, available from the project website. This document informs a more creative vision for an alternative, socially-oriented approach for the implementation of urban screen in London and the south-east – a critical time as London, and the Live Sites initiative, gears up to deliver big screens for London 2012. CABE is planning to use the framework to inform its work in relation to Live Sites.

Several key stakeholders and policymakers, including Mike Gibbons, Head of Live Sites and UK Coordination for The London Organising Committee of the Olympic and Paralympic Games (LOCOG), and CABE Space director Sarah Gaventa, attended the first SCREAM workshop. The project experience and outputs will be incorporated into forthcoming guidance on Live Sites and the siting of digital TV screens in public spaces, currently being developed by CABE in collaboration with the English Heritage.

Following the workshops, Fatah gen. Schieck was invited by Live Sites and LOCOG to collaborate on running a workshop in Liverpool with potential 2012 screen managers and creative programmers. She has also been invited to present SCREAM's work to a professional development workshop at the National Media Museum, Bradford, in June 2009.

Knowledge exchange
The workshop participants benefited from being able to explore the issues involved with media screens with key stakeholders, many for the first time in an open forum, and gave highly positive feedback. In October 2008, Fatah gen. Schieck was invited to the professional development workshop at the Urban Screens Conference in Melbourne to share findings from

SEDUC: Socio-Environmental Degradation
and Urban Configuration

Lead organisation
UEL

Project coordinator
Professor Allan Brimicombe

Project start and end dates
May 2007 to November 2008

Total UrbanBuzz funding
£192,897.95

Total CIK
£126,907.60

Contact details
a.j.brimicombe@uel.ac.uk

- Environment
- Society
- Policy
- Planning/regeneration
- Design/housing

The context: place and anti-social behaviour

Sustainable communities are perceived to be safe and attractive, with low levels of fear and disorder. Anti-social behaviour (ASB) and environmental disorder such as flytipping, litter and graffiti can be viewed as barometers of sustainability. Areas of high ASB frequently have high levels of deprivation and environmental disorder, attracting crime and fear of crime, promoting insecurity among residents, and eroding community cohesion.

Local authorities record reported ASB and environmental disorder using various methods. Analysis of such data, following innovative GIS-based coding, along with further analysis of the configuration of the built environment (using a method known as space syntax) at identified ASB hotspots, can inform thinking about effective interventions for designers, social infrastructure planners and community safety officers.

The 'space syntax' approach to spatial analysis considers the city as a collection of buildings linked by a network of spaces – the street network. This point of view emphasises the fact that in cities, the structure of the street network determines movement flow, both for pedestrians and traffic. 'We had a clear understanding that spatial layout shapes basic human interactions,' says Tim Stonor of Space Syntax Ltd, a project partner. 'Everyday social and economic activity is influenced by the way layout makes it easier or more difficult to move around.'

Accessibility and movement potential define activity patterns for the street network. These activity patterns are closely linked to patterns of land use, and relate to how busy, active and safe the street is likely to be. The key question is: do specific spatial factors of our urban environments increase the level of ASB occurrence and risk?

Key project objectives

This project aimed to bring together local authority staff, police officers, designers, practitioners, planners and data analysts to discuss the challenges faced by neighbourhoods experiencing ASB, and to understand current design responses. The project team wished to identify and map areas in east London with high levels of ASB. Once located, selected case study areas would undergo spatial analysis to determine which urban layout factors, if any, were impacting on reported incidences of ASB, and to consider appropriate responses relating to urban layout. The project team aimed to:

01	develop automated methods of 'cleaning' and geocoding data from local authority datasets for analysis;
02	use 'cleaned' data to geomap reported cases of ASB in east London boroughs;
03	use space syntax to analyse ASB and environmental disorder against urban layout metrics;
04	design appropriate responses to minimise the potential for recurrences of ASB
05	create a toolkit of good practice resources, including information on data analysis, designing out ASB and design for community cohesion; and
06	widely disseminate good practice resources, thus ensuring the sustainability of knowledge transfer in this area beyond the life of the project. ❯

How place impacts on behaviour
The SEDUC project is geographically locating and mapping antisocial behaviour (ASB) 'hotspots'. An analysis of these, in terms of both urban form and social demographics, will help to inform future planning and policy relating to 'designing out' ASB

'Street-based' layouts
In dense residential
street-based layouts with
many 'active frontages',
or doors and windows
overlooking the street, ASB
incidents (blue dots) tend to
happen on the edges of
street grids, as if being
'pushed out' towards the
main roads, which frequently
coincide with neighbourhood
boundaries

'Estate' layouts
In 'estate' layouts
with tree-like street
organisation, fragmented
street structures and many
free-standing buildings,
such as urban blocks
without significant numbers
of street entrances, ASB
incidents (blue dots) are
often found in the centre
of the neighbourhood

SEDUC: Socio-Environmental Degradation
and Urban Configuration

UEL
Centre for Geo-Information Studies

Professor Allan Brimicombe

**Project coordinator, data mining
and crime analysis**

**Dr Yang Li, programmer/simulation
modeller**

UCL
JDI: Jill Dando Institute
**Dr Shane Johnson, Senior Lecturer JDI, criminology
and forensic psychology**

**Bilkis Begum, Research Fellow JDI, crime and antisocial
behaviour analysis**

CASA: Centre for Advanced Spatial Analysis

**Professor Mike Batty, Director CASA, advisor on
community-based online information systems**

**Dr Andy Smith, Research Fellow CASA, advisor on
community-based online information systems**

CSCS: Centre for Security & Crime Science
Kati Carter, administrative support

Bartlett
**Professor Bill Hillier, Professor of Architecture and Urban
Morphology, advising on space syntax and crime analysis**

**Professor Alan Penn, Professor of Architectural and
Urban Computing, advising on design and management
of safer built environments**

Terra Cognita
**Dr Chao Li, partner, advanced data preparation
and geocoding techniques**

Space Syntax
Alain Chiaradia, Director, advising on spatial analysis
Eva Friedrich, space syntax analysis
Antonin Gosset, space syntax modelling
Fiona Wholey, space syntax modelling
Saussan Khalil, administrative support

Phaeton Consulting
Mark Deane, design against crime

London borough of Tower Hamlets
Participants in the case study
Supplying data; feedback on the analysis

London borough of Newham
Participants in the case study
Supplying data; feedback on the analysis

London borough of Barking & Dagenham
Supplying data

Central St Martins
**Professor Paul Ekblom,
Co-director, Design
Against Crime Research
Centre, advisor on design
against crime**

'These outcomes are the most striking that I've seen
suggesting that traditional street-based patterns are the right
way to organise housing' Professor Bill Hillier, UCL

The project response

The project team has developed consistent
and automated ways of collating and cleaning ASB
data (such as correcting the spelling of street
names), geographically locating (geocoding) and
mapping ASB 'hotspots' and analysing these in
terms of their urban form.

The team collected data from three London
boroughs – Newham, Tower Hamlets and Barking
and Dagenham – on recorded ASB incidents,
noting major variations between the three in the
methods used for recording, storing and analysing
such data. These variations mean that individual
models were created and tuned to each borough.

Traditional methods of mapping 'hotspots'
can be misleading, for two reasons. First,
'counting' incidents implies nothing about risk. On
a busy high street, the actual figures for mugging
might be high although the risk for the individual is
lower than, for example, in a less busy side street.
Second, datasets of reported incidents can be
biased by data collection and reporting styles.

The project aimed to address both these
issues. The team cleaned and geocoded the data,
a process led by project partner Dr Chao Li from
Terra Cognita. This complex process involved
assigning a geographic location to the incident
reports, making sure that the incident site, rather

than the location of the reportee, is recorded.
Accurate geographical locations for each ASB
report were recorded without giving away personal
or postcode data, as required by data protection
legislation. 'For street crime or antisocial behaviour
on the street, the geocoding success rate (for
example how many addresses are matched to
geographical coordinates) can be lower than 50
per cent using standard methods. Our enhanced
geocoding methods have taken us to a 90 per cent
success rate,' says Li.

The complex process, which has been taken
up by the Metropolitan Police for its crime data
geocoding, delivers recorded ASB data relating to

type of incident, date and time, geocoded to a short street segment for accurate mapping.

The geocoding analysis identified several ASB hotspots across the three boroughs. A team from Space Syntax Ltd selected several neighbourhood areas from Tower Hamlets and Newham for further analysis.

This factored in urban layout variables that give a measure of 'integration' for sections of the street network: the movement potential of a street (the likelihood of any section of a street to be used by pedestrians); and the accessibility (closeness) of any section of a street within the local street network.

The analysis detected two key types of layout in each of the case study areas: 'street-based' layouts and 'estate' layouts. For each layout type, generic patterns of ASB were demonstrated, with similar outcomes in both boroughs. The analysis of of ASB incidents was conducted at the neighbourhood level, resulting in incident patterns that are more comparable in terms of reporting issues, and more closely related to movement. Urban residential areas, surrounded by the 'foreground' network of main streets that connect urban centres at all scales, constitute a quieter 'background' network.

'Neighbourhoods can be usefully distinguished as 'street-based' or 'estate' layouts in the way they are internally organised, and in the way they connect to the foreground network,' says Space Syntax's Eva Friedrich.

Project impact

Two aspects of movement and land use that could prevent ASB have been highlighted: the presence of pedestrians on the street, and 'protection' by a large number of residential entrances or 'active frontages' opening onto the street – this configuration is common in London terraced housing ('street-based' layouts). There is less ASB in busy public realms, such as high streets, and more in poorly integrated back and side streets. Notably, the positive aspects of urban layout occur more frequently in street-based layouts.

It had been thought that movement, land use and high and low activity patterns are linked to crime and ASB, according to earlier Space Syntax findings. 'Yet we were taken by surprise by the results of the spatial analysis,' says Professor Bill Hillier, UCL, a founder of Space Syntax Ltd.

'It indicated that there were contrasting patterns of ASB relating to different kinds of layouts; estate layouts and street-based layouts. This was especially unexpected as it applied to areas with different urban characters. These results are the most striking that I've seen suggesting that traditional-street based patterns are the right way to organise housing.'

Integration and area edges

Residential areas are embedded into the more accessible urban 'foreground network', which is why the edges of an area often coincide with the more highly integrated spaces of the street pattern, and why integration values decrease the deeper one penetrates into the area (see graphs below). It is not integration or movement alone that can impact on the level of ASB incidents, but the relation of these to the spatial system of streets, land use and buildings.

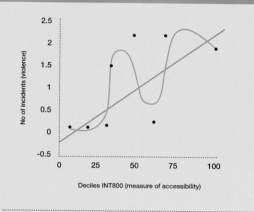

01 Incidents of violence on the edge of the residential area in 'street-based' layouts. Incidents tend to happen on the edges of the area

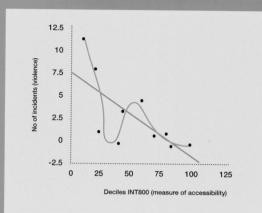

02 Incidents of violence on an 'estate' layout. Incidents are scattered all over the area, and also occur in the centre

The project analysis has generated tools and processes to help practitioners, planners and local authority officers understand the potential impact of urban layout on ASB, and to prepare and use local data to inform further analysis.

Knowledge exchange

Local authorities are already responding to the challenges of ASB, and the project's partnership approach has highlighted the challenges faced by local authorities. Local authority officers have shared their current understanding of how they are dealing with ASB problems, and have been introduced to new thinking and new evidence that could help to make designing out ASB a possibility.

Local authorities have been made aware of the value and utility of the data they hold, and given options for data analysis that can inform design and planning policy. ASB and crime data are sensitive from a confidentiality perspective and there can be a reluctance to distribute such data. The team, however, was able to assure data owners that their data could be safely treated with due data protection consideration.

Academics have been made aware, first hand, of the issues facing local authorities aiming to tackle ASB through design. A good practice resource kit, detailing learning and findings from each stage of the project and a literature review on ASB and community cohesion, is available to local authorities and the police, supported by training and consultancy as required.

The future: developing the analysis

Although the UrbanBuzz funding period ended in November 2008, the project team is continuing to actively disseminate its findings, with a particular focus on local authorities. The team is actively seeking opportunities to develop the analysis. As there is keen interest in the project outcomes, training workshops for professionals and local authority officials are planned for 2009.

Project resources
www.uel.ac.uk/geo-information/SEDUC
A wide range of project documentation is available on the project website

SSSP: Smart Solutions for Spatial Planning

Lead organisation
University of East London

Project coordinator
Paul Coates

Project start and end dates
July 2007 to November 2008

Total UrbanBuzz funding
£82,844

Total CIK
£31,605

Contact details
christian.derix@aedas.com; p.s.coates@uel.ac.uk

- Environment
- Society
- Governance
- Policy
- Planning/regeneration
- Infrastructure
- Design/housing

The context: joined up masterplanning

The masterplanning process is not currently 'joined up', says project coordinator Paul Coates, UEL, with no possibility of integrating planning and design information. There is a 'disconnect' between Geographic Information Systems (GIS) data, social infrastructure data, planning data and site information, resulting in 'jerks and breaks' between various stages of the masterplanning process. Digital links, supporting efficient data exchange, would enable the widespread use of efficient computer-based analysis. Such scenario testing capability could answer complex 'what if' planning questions quickly, allowing the development of well-informed design options.

Key project objectives

The project aimed to create new ways of exchanging knowledge and data between planners, policy makers, urban designers and computational designers. The team plugged in GIS data, social infrastructure planning data (from the 2001 census and Index of Multiple Deprivation, or IMD), urban design best practice and planning policy guidance to create urban development simulations for case study sites in east London. The project set out to outline how such a digital approach can work, using techniques and processes created at Aedas' Computational Design Group and at UEL, for the testing of accessibility, circulation networks, land use distribution, density and massing within a masterplanning context. The project aimed to:

01 create a series of digital tools enabling the integration of GIS and social infrastructure data into the design process, facilitating the focused application of spatial analysis techniques and scenario testing;

02 demonstrate how urban planning can benefit from the use of design systems currently in use in the engineering and architecture sectors;

03 enable feedback between generative and analysis processes, and GIS data, so as to develop sustainable social and environmental infrastructure models;

04 provide a new feedback loop from simulation to urban planning data;

05 seed new thinking regarding design processes. The idea that urban layouts can be generated from mapping data and digital urban codes is unfamiliar to many stakeholders in the design and planning process;

06 enable and support greater participation in urban design and planning via a series of user-friendly tools;

07 involve local authorities, with differing planning policy and data collection and processing policies, in the development and use of a 3D digital design simulation model for assessing spatial planning and speeding up the masterplanning process;

08 develop masterplanning services for the public and private sectors; and prepare teaching material for academic use.

Digital masterplanning
SSSP is exploring ways in which planners, policy makers, urban designers and computational designers can work together to generate and analyse masterplans using digital workflows

The project team has successfully created a set of digital tools that enable the analysis of accessibility, pedestrian mobility, density, urban structure and massing during the masterplanning process. 'We're creating digital processes that can improve the speed and flexibility of masterplanning at the urban block scale,' adds Christian Derix, a key project partner from Aedas' Computational Design Group. The new digital tools were used to explore design issues in relation to a site straddling the border of Newham and Tower Hamlets, a cross-borough site that highlights both masterplanning and data manipulation challenges for any digital workflow.

The SSSP analysis and scenario testing tools can be used to generate initial design scenarios, to assess existing plans, and to ask key 'what if' or 'what else' questions. 'For example, if I need 5,000 houses, all a maximum of three minutes' walk away from the nearest bus stop, I could run a scenario test to see if – and how – this is possible for a specific site,' says Coates. 'SSSP can quickly generate and analyse a range of different potential scenarios, both for "tabula rasa" sites and those within urban contexts.'

A classic example is a developer stating that a particular housing development is no more than 15 minutes' away from open space, and ❯

illustrating this with a circle drawn around an epicentre. 'But that's not the way it works,' says Coates. 'Roads bend and wriggle around, and sometimes there's no access due to a river or a railway line. Our software will tell you exactly how far you can get in 15 minutes, based on actual site conditions.'

The participating boroughs identified a set of performance indicators for the test scenarios, for example 'what if' exercises for specified uses and densities, and improvements in walking times for designated areas. The SSSP outcomes were compared with current TGLP/GLA published plans. The goal of the case study was to show how the SSSP tools could be used to generate spatial planning scenarios that add value for local authority teams exploring sustainable outcomes.

Project partner Jennifer Currier works on Newham's regeneration team. The value of some of the SSSP tools was immediately apparent, she says. For example, one tool can predict and visualise on a map how far people can actually walk in a given time, according to actual conditions. Another can assess site permeability, specifying and visualising specific points on the map where an 'intervention', such as a bridge or a new crossing, needs to be placed. 'In terms of using the tool, the application that we really liked is assessment of real-time walking distances. If every planner could have a desktop tool to analyse this, then that would be really useful,' she added.

Mandar Puranik, project partner and an urban designer from Tower Hamlets, was keen to see how the generative SSSP tools could be aligned with designers' skills and expertise. For the project team, this is not an issue. 'Using SSSP is a technical matter. We are not removing the need for designers' skills or judgement,' says Coates. 'We've simply developed a framework in which they can manipulate variables more effectively. Planners, designers and local residents know things about their environment. What we're doing is finding ways to define and use all available data on the actual dynamics of an urban system, plug these into a model and then let it do its work in finding effective solutions.'

Project impact

The team has overcome many of the technical problems that traditionally have prevented data exchange between planning policy data and the GIS, digital mapping and urban modelling systems used by designers

'We've created digital processes that can improve the speed and flexibility of masterplanning at the urban block scale'
Christian Derix, Aedas

Aedas R&D Computational Design Group

Development of the urban generative models and urban codes; implementation of the model with inputs from GIS; outputs to architectural design generative models; design and implementation of simulation systems and generative models of urban form and structure

Advisor and liaison with local authority partners

4M Architects and Urban Planners
Masterplanning advice and subsequent design development in collaboration with Aedas

Urban Initiatives
Liaison with partners and local authorities, review of data requests, input of sustainability criteria from national and good practice guidance

Commission for Architecture and the Built Environment (CABE)
Advisor on the interpretation of project outputs

'Our take on sustainability is it has to be somehow measurable. If it isn't measurable, then we are not moving towards evidence-based design. If you can't measure something, you don't know whether you've achieved it or not'
Paul Coates, project coordinator

University of
East London
(UEL)

School of Architecture
and the Visual Arts (AVA), UEL
Paul Coates,
project coordinator

Centre for Geo-Information
Studies, UEL
GIS data analysis and data
cleaning

Centre for Evolutionary
Computing in
Architecture (CECA), UEL
Computational design
consultants, detailed
design services

Alternative Urbanisms
MA team, UEL
Design consultancy: urban form,
architecture and technology in relation
to social life and environmental
sustainability, links between
computational work at CECA, Aedas
and UEL, development of urban codes
and other design criteria

London Borough
of Newham
regeneration team
Design and development,
input into case study

London Borough of
Tower Hamlets
regeneration team
Design and development,
input into case study

'The application that we really liked is
assessment of real-time walking distances.
If every planner could have a desktop tool to
analyse this, then that would be really useful'
Jennifer Currier, London Borough of Newham

and developers. The development of the new tools could help to overcome barriers between planners, developers, architects and urban designers by creating a series of digital workflows that span the design and evaluation process, developing new digital tools to perform key tasks such as scenario testing and accessibility analysis. 'The key thing that we learned is that people don't want to be given a design solution to a complex problem. They want to explore the parameters of the problem to see what different sorts of solutions might be more or less appropriate. This is what SSSP can offer,' says Coates.

The creation of such a digital chain has enabled, for the first time, the impact of urban spatial design on social and environmental sustainability to be analysed. The use of traditional, non-digital methods precluded such analysis as there is no easy way to interrogate non-digital models. Planners tend to rely on generally accepted best-practice guidance and standards that are not well-defined, the use of which rules out monitoring and evaluation.

'With our tools,' says Coates, 'input data has to be rigorously examined. Our take on sustainability is it has to be somehow measurable. If it isn't measurable, then we are not moving towards evidence-based design. If you can't measure something, you don't know whether you've achieved it or not. So we're saying it's got to be measurable, it's got to be explicit, it's got to be open for discussion and transparent. If what comes out at the end of the generative process doesn't appear to be working, then maybe we haven't used the right data, or haven't made the right judgments.'

The computer models developed by the project team could be developed into useful training tools to aid the demonstration of new possibilities in terms of urban analysis. The project documentation is moving towards a software specification for creating models of this nature. In effect, SSSP has created a new workflow and data exchange that can speed up the design cycle, as well as providing an audit trail for the impact of different variables on the design process.

Knowledge exchange

During the development of the tools, significant knowledge exchange took place between planners, policymakers, urban designers and computational designers. Initially, the project team reported unexpected problems with data access and map data due to a lack of understanding of GIS data and formats. Project partner Dr Yang Li, UEL, worked closely with the local authorities to overcome this problem, and invested much more time than originally planned in cleaning and preparing data. Finally, Dr Yang, Coates and the Aedas programming team ❯

collectively developed methods of exporting and reformatting data from GIS to CAD.

The team realised that, given the power and effectiveness of the computer in evaluating large amounts of data, it is best deployed in the widest possible context. With this in mind, the team extended the study to allow better use of contextual information.

When drawing upon planners' implicit design knowledge to encode the SSSP tools, the project team found it interesting to see how local authorities worked with design principles, suggesting that the latter found it difficult to design numerically (to quantify and calculate a design rather than see it graphically). Drawing up a performance specification for the case study was therefore an interesting challenge to their way of working.

Education and training

UEL's Master of Alternative Urbansims lecturers will be integrating the SSSP digital masterplanning applications into student workshops, enabling students to understand the assumptions behind masterplanning decision-making processes that are not explicitly qualifiable.

Further teaching and dissemination is taking place through the Aedas Computational Design and Research group, which has been demonstrating the SSSP workflow at various academic and professional conferences. Further workshops at a range of universities are planned.

The future: towards new policy

While each aspect of the SSSP process provoked much discussion, the local authority representatives were confident that, provided the SSSP tools could accept a wider range of inputs and planning policy criteria in future, they could form the basis for useful enhancements to the tools currently available. This would include:

01 a more intelligent accessibility planning tool for Area Action Plans and other policy and planning tasks;

02 the ability to test developers' assumptions in pre-planning application meetings with developers;

03 the ability to test ways in which a development sits in its context;

04 the possibility of conducting in-house studies to explore site-loading possibilities in redevelopment areas.

As the usability of SSSP is teased out, it is clear that it could have a variety of applications, particularly in the private sector – it was also noted that development pressures derive from private partners rather than public partners such as local authorities. 'SSSP could be useful for designers and developers seeking investors to get a scheme up and running. It can estimate how much development can take place on a specific site, what infrastructure would be needed and how much would need to be invested,' says Derix. Aedas has plans to further develop SSSP as a commercial service.

Project resources
http://aedas.com/Europe/RandD/SmartSolutionsforSpatialPlanning/

Overall, the SSSP tools generated useful outcomes and scenarios in three main areas:

Accessibility and connectivity
Fine-tuning access levels, and proposing new connections within the network, worked well and there was a good match between the outcomes from the software and the proposals in the existing plans

Movement framework
The automatic generation of main routes and second order pathways using the software was a good match with the proposals outlined in the plans. The results showed that SSSP would be able to analyse and report on much wider plots than the case study areas

Site density and land use
This component worked as expected, using the supplied performance targets from the planning documents. However, the SSSP tools did not provide for more 'global' outcomes

'We live in a world where if you can't do partnerships, you can't do things properly. UrbanBuzz has been a really interesting addition to the partnership experience. It has extended partnerships from local private companies and the public sector to major research institutions. We've demonstrated that we can combine forces to make things happen that are genuinely of value, both commercially and in the public interest'
John Lock, Development Director, UEL

Lead organisations
UCL and David Adamson, former Director, Estate Management, Cambridge University

Project coordinators
David Adamson and Peter Morris

Project start and end dates
November 2007 to June 2008

Total UrbanBuzz funding
£45,334

Total CIK
£94,646

Contact details
dma23@cam.ac.uk
pwmorris@ucl.ac.uk

- Environment
- Governance
- Policy
- Planning/regeneration
- Design/housing

The context: towards joined-up policy

In November 2005, the Public Sector Construction Clients' Forum (PSCCF) presented a summary of its work relating to sustainable construction. The project team considered that there would be value in reviewing and seeking responses to that work, as well as to other emerging government policies.

The project was timed to investigate how well policy is being implemented around the country, to review how well policy is understood by professionals, and to seek the views and recommendations of senior members of the construction and development industries, policymakers and senior academics on the development and implementation of future policy.

Key project objectives

This project aimed to explore policy implementation in England and Scotland via a series of seminars. The aim was to share knowledge and critique how best, in practice:

01 to debate and facilitate the adoption of recent and emerging government policies relating to sustainability in the built environment sectors;

02 to identify and comment on practical difficulties in implementing government sustainability policies;

03 to help feed emerging government sustainability/construction policies into universities to inform and stimulate their research and teaching; and

04 to input relevant academic thinking into development of government policies in this area.

The project response

Between May and December 2007, one pilot event and seven seminars were held around the regions of England and Scotland. Up to 20 senior representatives from the public and private sectors, from the demand and supply sides of the construction industry and from academia were invited to each seminar.

A total of 129 people attended the seminars. Each seminar lasted for a day, and conclusions and recommendations were collated and reported. The final consultation event was held in January 2008, at which Stephen Timms MP, then Minister for Construction, gave the keynote speech.

Project impact

Recommendations and discussion points from the seminars and the January event were consolidated into a final report, which was launched in April 2008. The report made key recommendations in the areas of higher education, skills, policy implementation, policy standards and technology. This report has been circulated to a wide range of senior construction industry officials, many of whom are now taking the recommendations forward through their own channels and communities of interest. 'The evidence from the seminars, collated in the report, resulted in more than 50 recommendations and many observations for all involved in sustainable construction. Many recommendations have been widely accepted, and at least some implementation has begun,' says project coordinator David Adamson. ❯

Towards sustainable construction
The SUSTAINABLE CONSTRUCTION POLICIES project brought together leading academics, practitioners and policymakers to debate and inform emerging government policy

Knowledge exchange

The report was circulated to government departments, professional institutions and higher/further education institutions, the construction industry's decision-makers and investors, and those who set regional policies and grant planning applications.

Government, professional institutions and campaign groups have informally taken on board much of what the report has to say, but are reluctant to go 'on the record', say the report's authors. They give the distinct impression that there are a number of different agendas being progressed across the policy spectrum.

Following the initial seminars, a series of locally-funded follow-on events have been, or are due to be, held within the regions. Several local knowledge networks combining public and private sectors and academia are now helping to bridge the construction sector knowledge gaps, especially as the project team found that there is less awareness of government policies the further removed organisations are from London.

Many delegates brought together initially by UrbanBuzz, recognising the importance of such contacts, have continued to meet and hold regular 'round tables'. Others are picking up on 'seminar methodology' as an effective method for knowledge exchange, with project coordinator David Adamson being requested to lecture on this approach, most recently at the National University of Estonia. The process suggests that connecting with those who are already involved in consultations in a professional capacity enables them to feed back new knowledge effectively, with the result that the knowledge exchange process develops its own momentum.

The project organisers also noted, during the project cycle, a lack of enthusiasm for electronic communication and a strong preference for face-to-face contact.

Education and training

A graduate programme in sustainable construction at UCL is currently in development, led by project coordinators Peter Morris and David Adamson. Many of the construction policy gaps and weaknesses identified by the project can be addressed via focused educational courses, and the UrbanBuzz work has made a valuable contribution towards the design and construction of this new programme.

'I warmly welcome UrbanBuzz in bringing together partnerships, and commend the team's efforts. I very much welcome different sectors working together and finding solutions'
Stephen Timms MP, former construction minister

The future: informing policy development

The key outcomes from the seminars and the report create an outline for policy development. One recommendation is that Government should provide clarity about targets and requirements, as the property industry will make investments only if there is a level playing field of requirement, or a costed business case. There could also be fiscal incentives such as carbon trading. Another suggestion is that Regional Development Agencies become hubs for the dissemination of sustainability information between different tiers of government and the private sector.

In line with the report's recommendations, The Centre of Expertise for Sustainable Procurement (CESP) is being set up within the Office of Government Commerce (OGC) during 2008/09 and a new post, Chief Sustainability Officer, will take forward a culture of change across all government departments in sustainable operations and procurement. In February 2009, Lord Mandelson, the business secretary, announced a review of the construction and engineering industries.

Several members of Royal Institution of Chartered Surveyors (RICS) reacted favourably to the report, describing it as a useful piece of work that highlights issues that need to be kept on the agenda. In line with the report's recommendations, the RICS Construction Faculty is developing a life-cycle costings analysis that it hopes will replace the differing models and become the industry standard.

Project resources
The project report can be downloaded from www.urbanbuzz.org (select projects)

Bath pilot event

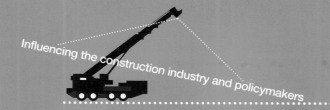

Influencing the construction industry and policymakers

David Adamson
Project management, organising and leading seminars

'The professions, the sector skills councils and academic teaching need to be much better integrated to meet the skills challenge of sustainable construction'

Peter Morris, UCL
Project management

'This project has brought people together in a way that had not happened before. Many delegates have agreed to continue meeting to discuss these issues, indicating that they found this approach valuable'

Project advisors and regional support
Hedley Smyth, UCL;
Andrew Edkins, UCL; Roy Morledge, Nottingham Trent University; Andrew Shaw, DTI; John Ioannou, OGC; Jonathon de Souza, Constructing Excellence; John Betty, BANES; Barry Clark, University of Newcastle

'I found the UrbanBuzz report useful and the meetings informative. The report speaks a lot of common sense and I think that it represents the industries' view well'
Tony Isles, Associate Director, Water and Environment, Atkins, on secondment to Construction Industry Council/BERR

Seminars held:
Bath
London (UCL)
Newcastle
Nottingham
Cambridge
Dundee
Salford

Industry professionals meet to collate workshop findings

Conference with 150 attendees (academic and private) to discuss the report's recommendations. Supported by Stephen Timms MP, at the time Minister for Construction, DBERR

Report produced and disseminated to professionals and policy makers

Lead organisation
Lancefield Consulting

Project coordinator
Julian Hart

Project start and end dates
May 2007 to November 2008

Total UrbanBuzz funding
£170,806

Total CIK
£177,265

Contact details
julian@lancefieldconsulting.com

- Environment
- Society
- Governance
- Policy
- Planning/regeneration
- Infrastructure
- Design/housing

Skills for a new planning framework
Training sessions based on technical review panels could give local authority planners access to the technical skills and expertise they need to address the modern sustainability agenda

The context: the expanding skills agenda
Having spent several years writing sustainability statements to support planning applications, and drafting supplementary planning guidance on sustainable design, project coordinator Julian Hart became increasingly aware of the challenges inherent in securing high standards in sustainable design through the planning process.

'The advent of the sustainable design agenda has seriously added to the technical knowledge that the average development control officer needs to be aware of. Go back 10 years, before the Urban Task Force of 1999, and development control officers mainly handled land use according to the Local Plan,' says Hart. Today, local authority officers are expected to possess considerable expertise in the thermal performance of buildings, energy systems, renewable energy technologies, green materials and water consumption, not to mention understanding space syntax, inclusive design and accessibility criteria.

Hart provides an example. 'I have met development control officers who have spent the last two years negotiating renewable energy provision on major projects. Prior to the UrbanBuzz training, these officers did not realise that there was a difference between thermal and electrical energy. And why should they?'

To support the planning process, design review panels comprising architects and urban designers are being adopted across the country at regional and local levels to advise planning committees. However, it is not clear that these initiatives are widespread enough to make a real impact, whether the panels comprise experts from appropriate disciplines, or if panel members are qualified to advise on sustainability.

Key project objectives
The key project aim was the delivery of focused training, based on live development projects, to a selection of local authority planning teams. The training was developed to help planners to gain awareness of the knowledge and skills necessary to secure better standards in sustainable design, with regard to new planning consents.

The project wished to create, and evaluate the use of, a Sustainable Design Review Panel to assist local planning authorities to address the broad range of issues raised by sustainable design, and the ways in which these factors interact. There is plenty of knowledge 'out there' on what represents higher quality design, and on the key issues of sustainable design. But much of this knowledge has been generated subsequent to the initial training of many planning professionals, whose knowledge base needs updating.

There is also a need for knowledge transfer from the 'real world' of local authority planners to academics, informing the latter how to create education and training that delivers the necessary design expertise to students and professionals undertaking Continuing Professional Development (CPD). The project aimed to:

01 provide a 'stop gap' to help a selection of planning teams improve their skills and understanding of sustainable design;

02 trial and evaluate the use of multi-disciplinary Sustainable Design Review Panels and Technical Panels in a training context; and

03 inform academia of the practical training needs of students and professionals working in sustainable design.

'A key conclusion from the process of running the Sustainable Design Review Panel has been that there is an urgent need to review the built environment design and delivery process'
Julian Hart, project coordinator

Sustainable Design Review Panel

Dr Ben Croxford, UCL
Air quality

Professor Barry Gibbs, Liverpool University
Noise quality

Professor Cedo Maksimovic, Imperial College
Urban water management

Dr John Mardaljevic, De Montfort University
Lighting and microclimate

Professor Mike Davies, UCL
Building design and energy

Dr Rajat Gupta, Oxford Brookes University
Urban carbon emissions

Dr Aylin Orbasli, Oxford Brookes University
Conservation, building re-use

Professor Julienne Hanson, UCL
Inclusive design

Professor Alan Penn, UCL
Space syntax, security

Professor Nick Bailey, University of Westminster
Community consultation

Professor Yvonne Rydin, UCL
Sustainable development/planning

Dr David Shiers, Oxford Brookes University
Green materials

Dr Philip James, University of Salford
Urban ecology

Julian Hart

Lancefield Consulting
Project coordinator
and trainer

Greater London Authority

London Borough of Barnet

Regional and local planning officers
Providing case studies; planning officers participated in training sessions

London Borough of Barking

London Borough of Kingston

London Borough of Islington

'We all work and operate in our own subject areas, so this was a great opportunity to meet across boundaries. The project generated ideas and up-to-date information that I could feed into my teaching. It also confirmed some things that we guessed were happening. There is a narrow definition of sustainability that fails to go beyond green roofs and efficient boilers, or to encompass wider issues and take a holistic view'
Aylin Orbasli, Oxford Brookes University

The project response

The novelty of this particular training project was the approach taken to creating training material and delivering the training. Five planning authorities were engaged in the project from across London – Kingston, Barnet, Islington and Barking and the Greater London Authority (GLA). The planning departments committed to send at least 10 staff each to a series of workshops.

Hart selected a range of panel members,

all academics recognised as technical experts in their disciplines. Whilst panel members were not familiar with the planning application and determination process, they were knowledgeable regarding the application of 'their' technologies in the built environment. Their distance from the planning process ensured that panel members reviewed the submitted planning applications with fresh eyes, looking specifically at how their technical subject area was dealt with by the

applications, with no preconceptions arising from familiarity of how the planning system 'works'.

In preparation for the workshops, the planning authorities provided Hart with details of current or recent planning applications to use as case study material. Hart presented this to the panel. Criticisms and comments from the panel were discussed in subsequent workshops. In total 15 projects were reviewed, three from each partner planning authority.

Project impact

The 18-month project has established that there are gaps in the knowledge base of local authority planners when it comes to technical aspects of sustainable design, and that such lack of expertise could have a negative impact on sustainable design standards. The project team has suggested a methodology for creating practical training sessions in order to fill these gaps. Two documents have been produced in order to help planning officers to secure better standards in sustainable design through the planning system. These are:

01 *A Planner's Guide to Carbon*: This document provides planning policy and development control officers within local authorities with the essential information that they need to know about energy in the built environment. It focuses mainly on residential development, but the general principles apply to all development types.

02 *Rules of Thumb for Sustainable Design*: Workshop material based on this document has been produced in collaboration with Urban Design London, (a department of Design for London, a sub-group of the GLA). The workshop will be hosted by UDL in September 2009.

What became apparent to Hart and the panel is that the planning system has simply not undergone the structural change required to deal with sustainable design. The Code for Sustainable Homes (CSH) 'by no means addresses the fundamental problems' says Hart.

The panel consensus was that members gained little comfort that many technical issues associated with sustainable design are being adequately addressed through the planning process. Many planning applications simply do not spell out what new development projects will actually provide, and lack clarity on specific deliverables. As planning officers made clear during the workshops, the planning process does not have the capacity to penalise poor performance. 'If a developer comes back to us with CSH certificates of level 2, when the planning condition required level 3, then what are we to do?', said one development control officer. 'Tell them to knock the whole building down?' At present the planning system can only punish with a sledgehammer; it needs much more sophisticated tools to incentivise developers to meet sustainable design standards.

In one review session, the panel concluded that a planning application for a 250-unit, high density residential scheme should absolutely not receive permission because of blatant misrepresentation in the energy statement and fundamental flaws in urban design. Unfortunately, by the time the feedback was given to the planning officers, the project had already received consent. The panel felt that several other projects were also 'on the borderline', at a minimum requiring major amendments.

'The evidence shows that poor development is slipping through the net,' says Hart. 'But this is not due to any fault of the planning officers themselves – they are just operating within a system which is not suited to the task.'

The trial of panel-based training has highlighted the fact that reliance on design review panels, even those including 'token' sustainability experts, does not necessarily ensure design quality. In this respect, it is important for local authorities not to assume that the 'all clear' by a design review panel necessarily means that a development is acceptable.

It is important to be clear what skills the panel as a whole encompasses, and to follow up on areas of expertise that may be poorly represented. In the context of increasingly technical urban design, it is vital not to rely on architects, who specialise in buildings, to assess masterplans and public realm design.

The project's potential impact on policy and regulation comes at a local level, via a combination of direct commentary made on the projects submitted to the panel, and in terms of the ability of the planning teams involved to secure better standards on developments in their area in future. In several cases, comments from the panel helped planning teams seek improved standards in relation to specific case studies submitted.

Knowledge exchange

Training workshops have been delivered to five local authorities. Significant knowledge transfer has taken place: academics have been made aware of the practical constraints inherent in the planning framework, and have been informed about the technical sustainable design skills gap, which can now begin to be addressed through education and training at UCL. Says Yvonne Rydin, UCL: 'This was a fascinating experience, bringing together a range of expertise in a way that is rarely attempted. I certainly learned from my panel members.' Via project partners such as the Good Homes Alliance (GHA), the project documentation will be distributed to planning authorities across the country, and the GHA will also advise on future training policy. Local authorities that were not originally project partners have expressed interest in the panel approach to training: content from various workshops has been developed into a full-day workshop, delivered on a commercial basis to the planning team at the London Borough of Newham.

Education and training

Learning from the project is feeding into a new UCL module on social sustainability as part of the MSc Environmental Design and Engineering, with project coordinator Julian hart acting as a guest lecturer.

Ongoing workshops based on material in both the *Planner's Guide to Carbon* and *Rules of Thumb on Sustainable Design* will delivered by Lancefield Consulting on an ad hoc basis. Contact the project coordinator for details.

The future: expert panels

The need for an injection of technical skills into the design and planning framework was recognised in January 2009, when Government called for the establishment of an 'expert support network' of renewable energy experts to be set up in order to offer advice and support to planning professionals across England.

In 2006, the Government produced a long-term strategy in its consultation document *Building a Greener Future: Towards Zero Carbon Development*. This was released at the same time as the original consultation on the Code for Sustainable Homes.

In *Building a Greener Future* it was suggested that the Code for Sustainable Homes, and any non-domestic equivalent, would represent route maps for the evolution of building control, at least in relation to energy. So, in theory, by 2016 issues relating to the energy performance of new buildings could be dealt with entirely by building control officers. However, this leaves many other technical disciplines which are proving equally challenging and, in many respects, where poor performance is detrimental to the delivery of quality living environments. Technical and design review panels could provide a useful solution.

Project resources
A Planner's Guide to Carbon is available online:
www.nbtconsult.co.uk
www.natural-building.co.uk
www.goodhomes.org.uk
www.urbanbuzz.org (select projects)

THE ROOTSCAPE PROJECT: Leys Remix

Lead organisation
Oxford Brookes University

Project coordinator
Professor Georgia Butina Watson

Project start and end dates
February 2008 to December 2008

Total UrbanBuzz funding
£59,910

Total CIK
£13,571

Contact details
gbutina@brookes.ac.uk

- ● Environment
- ● Society
- ● Governance
- ● Planning/regeneration
- ● Infrastructure
- ● Design/housing

The context: youth-friendly design

It is widely recognised that child and youth-friendly urban design is central to the building of sustainable communities. No matter how carefully researched, current advice on child and youth-friendly design is articulated from adult perspectives. This project aimed to enable children and young people to experience and understand urban design in ways that they could relate to, and to equip them with the means to communicate their knowledge to designers.

Key project objectives

The project aimed to develop the capacity of children and young people from Oxford to articulate their everyday experience of their schools, estates and public spaces. Translating the innate knowledge of young people into positive action is a key focus of this project, which is as much about personal development as it is about urban design.

During confidence- and team-building exercises at a survival park, and visits to local community gardens, the groups have learned multimedia skills such as photography and video-making. The young project participants were also encouraged to develop a range of employment skills and business opportunities related to their individual interests and aptitudes. The project aimed to:

01 improve the young people's group dynamics and team skills through confidence-building exercises;

02 teach young people multimedia skills such as photography and video-making to help them present their design ideas;

03 bring teachers, pupils, residents, local authority staff, youth workers and Brookes' students together to ensure that the scheme is self-sustaining;

04 develop a DVD-based best practice toolkit and teaching resource for teachers, enabling them to incorporate built environment and design issues into school curricula; and

05 engage young people in Oxford in a live regeneration process to which they can contribute.

The project response

The first challenge for the project team was recruiting young people into the project. This was done in collaboration with schools and community groups in Oxford, which helped the team to make links with existing groups in the Blackbird Leys and Cowley areas of Oxford.

The aim was to have the same group of young people participating throughout the life of the project. This proved to be difficult, however, as a single group would not commit for the necessary ❯

Places remixed: hands-on design skills for young people

The young students involved in THE ROOTSCAPE PROJECT: Leys Remix have demonstrated just how readily they understand what makes a place good or bad – and how they can help to make changes for the better

The young people took part in consultations...

Team and confidence-building was a key aim

Sessions at Go Ape helped with facing challenges and developing trust and cooperation – as well as photo skills...

New recording skills enabled the young people to analyse the qualities of a range of sites

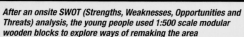
After an onsite SWOT (Strengths, Weaknesses, Opportunities and Threats) analysis, the young people used 1:500 scale modular wooden blocks to explore ways of remaking the area

'We made powerpoints and videos to express our ideas for design'

Discussions of 'urban design do's and don'ts' were the first moves towards developing design ideas

Hands-on design skills

Creating 3D designs...

for a new community centre

Visits to Oxford, London and Amsterdam

YOUNG TO HELP SHAPE ESTATE

'I think the biggest lesson that we all have learned is that we need to respect each other. Partnership working, and the engagement of different communities, including the young, is absolutely critical to the sustainability agenda. We need to work collaboratively in order to take some of the big decisions' Professor Butina Watson

Oxford Youth Works
Rev Patrick Mukholi
Project skills development co-ordinator

Helen Mukholi
Project pastoral care

Peers School
Teachers and staff
'As a teacher it was great to see these students enjoying themselves and being so positive about their work'
Ingrid Weaver, teacher

Oxford Brookes University
Professor Georgia Butina Watson
Project coordinator

Emeritus Professor Ian Bentley
Urban design training coordinator

Becky Kiddle, PhD student
Working with school pupils on design, presentation and ICT skills

Laura Novo de Azevedo, Regina Lim and Morten Geertje
Research and advisory roles

Oxford Brookes students from undergraduate programmes Cities: Environment, Design and Development and City and Regional Planning

Peers School
Young people
'It was great to have my family see my designs at the exhibition. I feel more confident and would like to study architecture'
Peers school pupil

Mayim Youth Group
School pupils
'There's a real need for youth projects that are sufficiently challenging to engage teenagers constructively over a long period' A parent

'The work has been about trying to engage young people in the way built environment is designed. This had to be done quite creatively, and we academics went through a huge learning process. They taught us a lot about how we need to engage with them, and how we might engage with university students in new, less didactic ways of teaching and learning' Becky Kiddle, graduate student

months. Eight young people were recruited via Youth Works at the start of the project, 12 young people joined the project from youth organisation Mayim, which joined the project in August 2008, and two classes participated (28 and 12 young people) via Peers School during May 2008. A key lesson learnt was that the recruitment and retention of students for voluntary projects can be difficult; working with local groups and schools can be useful so that learning can take place in organised situations such as classroom sessions.

The second key challenge for the team was the organisation of workshops. Initially these focused on 'learning by doing' activities, with an educational drive. Feedback from the young people highlighted the need for a 'fun' angle, as many saw the workshops as too much like school. In order to understand what motivates the different age groups, the team considered a range of strategies. Young people aged between 12-14 preferred to focus on short, focused mini projects, with additional 'play-time' activities to keep them engaged. Activities such as football and basketball were organised to supplement the workshops, and had the effect of bringing the group together. The team recognised that activities needed to be dynamic, offering a range of options.

Says Becky Kiddle, a PhD student from Oxford Brookes and a project participant, the work has been all about trying to engage young people. 'This had to be done quite creatively, and we academics went through a huge learning process as we found ways to keep the young people active and engaged. They were very sharp and quick to pick up on ideas, even though they're often dismissed and not listened to. They taught us a lot about how we need to engage with them, and how we might engage with university students in new, less didactic ways of teaching and learning.'

The project team organised two design-focused field trips: to a successful community-led housing regeneration project in Angell Town, Brixton, London; and to Amsterdam. The field trips were organised to encourage young people to think creatively about how spaces are designed are used, and how they made them feel. Alongside these trips, educational workshops took place, themed around urban design issues but with activities focused on developing IT, multimedia, design and crafts skills.

The young people were given the task of applying their newly-acquired knowledge and skills to several local design-related tasks such as regenerating a wildlife garden and the redesign of school buildings. They were given briefs, including design guidelines and site constraints, and came up with their own design options.

The project's growing profile within the Blackbird Leys community led to an approach from the Mayim youth group, which was involved with an empowerment programme aiming to set up a Youth Development Centre named Pulse. This involves the redevelopment of a derelict community centre in the Cowley area of the city.

Together, the two groups identified a common interest in working closely together on creating designs for this potentially live project. The young people conducted area analyses of the site, going out in teams to observe and critically discuss design options and possibilities.

Project impact

The project activities enabled the young people involved to develop a range of career-related, practical skills. Many team members acted as mentors to the young people, providing informal careers advice. The adult volunteers involved in the project also developed practical multimedia and presentation skills alongside the young people.

The project will be self-sustaining, taking on approximately the same number of participants each year, and with Oxford Brookes staff and students participating in summer schools and in teaching. The team also expects to progress the project through plans for the building of the Pulse youth centre: future Oxford Brookes undergraduate and graduate students and project partners will take this forward through a process of community service learning.

In this way, Oxford Brookes students will contribute to the project and, in turn, gain live educational opportunities to improve their own learning. 'The idea is that the young people that the project has trained will become leaders in new initiatives, and that they will mobilise their own colleagues and their friends in schools,' says project coordinator Professor Butina Watson, Oxford Brookes University.

Knowledge exchange

'I think the biggest lesson that we all have learned is that we need to respect each other,' says Butina Watson. 'Young people need to respect the elderly. Teachers need to respect students. This is key to partnership working and community engagement, and is absolutely critical to the sustainability agenda. We need to work collaboratively in order to take decisions.

'We were able to work with voluntary organisations, as well as involving students and teachers and the key players in the community, for example local councillors. Importantly, we were also able to connect with local schools, and to understand what young people are currently learning, and how new skills will fit in.'

The next stage is to take the project experience back to local schools and implement the methods and techniques developed with the pilot group, adds Butina Watson. 'This will enable teachers to talk with young people about urban design from the point of view of geography, history, citizenship, IT, art and through the various modules that are taught in local schools.'

All designs and workshop outputs were showcased at an exhibition held at Oxford Brookes, planned and organised by the young people, in November 2008. This showcased the work undertaken during the project, and served to disseminate the project to the wider community. A project 'storybook' has been created (see resources, below).

Education and training

Project team member Becky Kiddle will be using the knowledge and information collated in this project within a PhD thesis focusing on social learning spaces. Oxford Brookes students will be encouraged to get involved with future partnerships and project activities. The team is creating a 'toolkit' DVD that will outline processes for engaging young people, and focus on ways in which work created by young students can be taken forward by professionals. Contact the project team for more information on the DVD.

The future: live designs

The team is taking the designs for the new community centre forward, and is engaging with architects, designers and policymakers. 'We already have support from councillors in Oxford, as well as from developers and planning officers,' says Butina Watson. 'Working with the young people to implement their ideas will require skill and negotiation, but we're hopeful that there will be a successful outcome.'

Supporting this initiative, Oxford Brookes University is a leading partner in the Academy of Urbanism's UniverCities initiative that brings a city's public, private, academic and community stakeholders together to inform city development. Butina Watson aims to involve ROOTSCAPE participants in the UniverCities partnership to take the community centre designs forward, and to create 'a legacy of partnership working' in Oxford.

Project resources
www.brookes.ac.uk/schools/be/research/jcud/
urbanbuzz/rootscape.html

Details of how to get copies of the project storybook and the DVD toolkit can be accessed online, or by emailing gbutina@brookes.ac.uk

See also: www.urbanbuzz.org (select projects)

Lead organisation
UCL

Project coordinator
Dr Dejan Mumovic

Project start and end dates
December 2007 to July 2008

Total UrbanBuzz funding
£30,482.77

Total CIK
£17,474.76

Contact details
d.mumovic@ucl.ac.uk

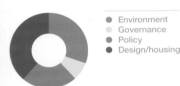

- ● Environment
- ● Governance
- ● Policy
- ● Design/housing

Building partnerships for sustainable schools

The design and performance of schools is being improved through knowledge exchange, post occupancy evaluation and shared understanding of how school buildings and systems work

The context: energy performance in schools

Reducing energy use in schools is a key step towards achieving 'zero carbon' performance levels in school buildings across the UK. To help achieve this initiative, the TOWARDS ZERO CARBON SCHOOLS project supported the formation of the CIBSE School Design Group, which aims to improve the delivery of sustainable, high-quality schools funded under the Government's £45 billion Building Schools for the Future (BSF) programme.

In terms of energy use, UK schools are responsible for 15 per cent of the energy used in public and commercial buildings. In the three years since the BSF initiative was launched, the issue of carbon has risen to the top of the political agenda. BSF aims to rebuild or upgrade all 3,500 secondary schools in England and Wales before 2020.

Key project objectives

The project aimed to raise awareness of the problems related to the design and operational performance of school buildings, and to instigate a cross-disciplinary dialogue focused on reducing school-related emissions. The project aimed to:

01 bring together a wide range of stakeholders involved in school design, from building services engineers, academics, architects and construction managers to planning officers and building users, many for the first time;

02 promote the use of computer-based simulation of school environments in research and practice, especially the use of modelling tools to prove compliance with building bulletins;

03 influence the implementation of the Government's £45 billion Building Schools for the Future (BSF) schools initiative by providing key sustainability information from engineering, computer simulation, energy, construction and ventilation and building services experts.

The project response

The CIBSE Schools Design Group was formed in April 2008 with support from UrbanBuzz; the group's launch event was attended by more than 60 professionals and academics. A range of issues relevant to the delivery of low-carbon schools was identified:

01 the need for technically well-defined post occupancy evaluation initiatives, and more emphasis on user understanding of school buildings and systems;

02 the need for detailed analysis of the PFI/PPP process and the delivery of innovation;

03 the realisation that knowledge exchange mechanisms within the consortia teams are fundamental to the creation of effective design, innovation and monitoring processes;

04 the need to clarify a framework for the modelling stage within the design process, and its conversion into availability criteria and payment mechanism standards;

05 the need to streamline the overall delivery process.

The CIBSE School Design Group will actively contribute to the International Building Performance Simulation Association (IBPSA) international building simulation conference, to be held at Strathclyde University in 2009.

Following the launch event, membership of the CIBSE Schools Design Group has reached almost 200 – with many joining as a direct consequence of the introduction provided by the project team, the launch event and the publication of the first *CIBSE Schools Design Group Bulletin*, also supported by the project. A second *Bulletin* was published in February 2009. ❯

Project partner Faber Maunsell's Northumbria University improved on 2002 building regulations regarding carbon emission requirements by almost 40 per cent

John Palmer,
Faber Maunsell
Applied researcher at
Faber Maunsell, and chair
of the CIBSE School
Design Group. Offered
technical support and
advice to the project team

Mott MacDonald,
Gordon Hudson
Offered technical
support and advice
to the project team

UCL

Mike Davies
Technical
supervision and
support

Dejan Mumovic
Project coordinator

Hector Medina
Production of
the CIBSE School
Design Group
Bulletin

'The CIBSE Schools Design Group is a forum for information exchange that's bringing together experts in a way that we haven't seen before. The Building Schools for the Future (BSF) programme has tended to focus on architecture, and we now need to create an appropriate balance between design and actual performance'
Dr Dejan Mumovic, UCL

CIBSE Schools
Design Group
Bulletin

CIBSE School Design Group,
the launch of which was
supported by UrbanBuzz,
is bringing together building
services engineers, academics,
architects, construction
managers, planning officers
and building users, many for
the first time, to collaborate on
design and maintenance issues
in schools

CIBSE
The Chartered Institution of
Building Services Engineers
is a professional body, and the
standard-setter and authority on
building services engineering.
It publishes guidance and codes
that are internationally recognised
as authoritative, and sets
the criteria for best practice
in the profession

Do schools such as the
Mossbourne Community Academy
in Hackney, London – designed by
Rogers Stirk Harbour + Partners,
and winner of a RIBA award in 2005
– create the right balance between
design and performance? The
Building Schools for the Future
(BSF) programme has tended to
focus on architecture rather than
performance, says Dr Mumovic, UCL

Project impact

'The CIBSE Schools Design Group is a forum for information exchange that's bringing together experts in a way that we haven't seen before,' says project coordinator Dr Dejan Mumovic. 'There are problems with many of the new schools created within the BSF initiative. The programme has tended to focus on architecture, and we need to create a balance between design and actual performance.'

Audience at CIBSE School Design Group launch event

1,000 copies of the first *CIBSE School Design Group Bulletin: Engineering Sustainable Schools*, were produced and disseminated at the launch event.

The second bulletin was published in February 2009

'Detailed results are beginning to come through on the first six or seven BSF schools,' says Mumovic. 'We're bringing together case studies with interesting aspects of technology and building practice to learn from, some of which feature in the first *CIBSE Schools Group Bulletin*.' CIBSE and the CIBSE Schools Design Group have collated the findings from discussions initiated with UrbanBuzz support and responded in detail to a consultation paper covering the remit and focus of the BSF Task Force. Going forward, the group will be providing key advice and support to the Task Force and its government delivery agent, Partnerships for Schools.

To make progress, the group believes that there needs to be better management of schools' facilities and equipment. Several issues may need to be addressed: new ways of gathering data on schools' energy use; refining the design of school buildings to lower energy demands (using more passive heating or cooling, and more natural light); creating 'champions' with responsibility for energy saving in schools. Other issues include integrating energy supply systems across local communities, and investing in renewable energy and shared heat supplies, along with off-site generation, where appropriate.

Knowledge exchange

The key to success in this sector is knowledge exchange, with partners from academia, private practice, the investment sector and Government reliant on joined-up planning in order to make progress. The long-term legacy of the CIBSE Schools Design Group is to foster knowledge exchange between all interested parties working on sustainable school design, to encourage cooperation between different professional bodies and institutions, and to initiate cooperation between academia and industry.

These professionals will share their experience of sustainable school design through a future programme of events, via website resources and in publications such as the *CIBSE Schools Group Bulletins*.

Education and training

Several academics involved in the TOWARDS ZERO CARBON SCHOOLS project plan to feed their shared experiences into new educational and training modules. The group is working on a publication on ventilation design for school buildings, promoting low-carbon ventilation design, and hopes to publish this during 2009. An evidence-based paper on sustainable school design, to be submitted to the Government's Task Force on Schools, is also being prepared. In February 2009, a second event, A Roadmap to Zero Carbon Schools, was held at UCL, and the presentations filmed and added to the Low Carbon Buildings Directory resource created by the E-POD project team (see page 116). The Low Carbon Buildings Directory is used to support both teaching, training and Continuing Professional Development.

The future: towards new behaviours

In the move to low-carbon schools, building occupancy patterns will need to be addressed alongside with design, construction and energy issues. The alliance forged via the CIBSE Schools Design Group and its partners intends to strengthen the knowledge networks needed to deliver expertise and innovation. Evidence suggests that even when buildings are designed to be energy efficient, they often do not perform as predicted. In some cases, energy use actually increases because of the combined effect of the equipment and facilities used within schools. For example, some schools leave the lighting on night and day for security reasons, and computers are often left on overnight and during school holidays.

In order to drive behavioural change, there has been a requirement from October 2008 for many schools to display details of their energy performance. Additional measures, such as smart metering, are likely to be required if the performance of schools is to be better managed.

Project resources
For details on future events and bulletins, and for further information, visit the CIBSE School Design Group website at www.cibse-sdg.org. The group plans to stage seminars and workshops covering a range of topics of interest to designing zero carbon schools for the 21st century

Visit www.lowcarbonbuildingsdirectory.org for multimedia presentations on low carbon school design and operation

VIBAT LONDON: Looking over the horizon: transport and global warming – Visioning and Backcasting for Transport in London

Lead organisation
Halcrow

Project coordinator
Dr Robin Hickman

Project start and end dates
May 2007 to December 2008

Total UrbanBuzz funding
£202,090.66

Total CIK
£299,378

Contact details
hickmanro@halcrow.com

- Environment
- Society
- Governance
- Policy
- Planning/regeneration
- Infrastructure

The context: transport sector emissions

The issues relating to climate change have risen to the top of the national political agenda, and the importance of transport in contributing to reduced levels of CO_2 is clearly evident. Transport has been highlighted as the sector that contributes least to CO_2 emission reduction targets. Within London, the transport sector is responsible for approximately 9.6 million tonnes of carbon (21 per cent) of total CO_2 emissions. Road transport accounts for most of this figure, generating about 80 per cent of the total.

Any future review of the Mayor's Transport Strategy and London Plan will need to set out and refine the strategic policy approach for the transport sector. The current forward-looking approach is set out in the T2025 document from Transport for London (TfL), 2006. The Greater London Authority (GLA) Act (2007) includes a duty of regard to address climate change. The new Mayor has also produced his own initial vision for transport in London (*Way to Go*, GLA 2008). The Climate Change Action plan (GLA, 2007) sets out a strategy for London.

A target has been adopted for a 60 per cent reduction in CO_2 by 2025. Much positive work is being carried out on this issue, yet the difficulty remains that the likely carbon reduction impact of potential behavioural change remains largely unquantified. Reducing emissions consistent with strategic aspiration remains a huge challenge.

Key project objectives

This project aims to quantify the carbon efficiency of the current transport strategy (the Mayor's Transport Strategy and T2025) in London and contribute to the development of a strategy for a 60 per cent and 80 per cent reduction in transport emissions by 2025 and 2050. The project team aims to develop the work carried out at the national and EU levels on this topic, but with a specific London focus. The key project objectives are:

01 to develop a 'backcasting' approach to transport planning in London from now until 2025 and 2050. Practically, this means outlining the incremental steps that London planners, policymakers and citizens need to take from now on if the 2050 target is to be met;

02 to provide a means of successfully communicating future lifestyle and behavioural choices to stakeholders and the public; and

03 to create an interactive scenario-testing tool that would allow stakeholders and the public to 'road test' the impact of potential policy packages. ❯

London's low-carbon transport challenges
The capital's transport emission reduction targets can be achieved only through a combination of behavioural change, technological innovation and robust policy implementation. The VIBAT project has highlighted the city's options

Development

Oxford University
Professor David Banister, Director of Oxford University's Transport Studies Unit
Direction and input, backcasting methodology, policy packaging and appraisal

Space Syntax
Development, input on urban planning and transport simulation development of TC-SIM 'front end' scenario-testing tool

Alain Chiaradia, Jorge Gil, Jasia Ward, Gavin Baily

Halcrow
Project management and direction

Dr Robin Hickman, Sharad Saxena, Olu Ashiru

Research, baseline and target setting, developing alternative visions of the future, and defining policy packages (PP) and modelling of scenarios, specification and modelling for TC-SIM

Greater London Authority (GLA) and Transport for London (TfL)
Advising on London transport policy, appropriate policy packaging, participation in workshops and feedback on the project and TC-SIM tool

A range of academics and practitioners
Peer review on reporting, playing the TC-SIM 'game' and providing feedback

Evaluation and dissemination

'Achieving large reductions in carbon emissions, while retaining economic and quality-of-life goals, is likely to be difficult. Add in the city's large population and planned economic growth and the task of reducing aggregate emissions becomes very ambitious... If an aviation figure is defined and included in London emissions, it is very unlikely that targets will be met' Dr Robin Hickman, Halcrow

The project response

The scenario building process used in the VIBAT project has progressed through three stages: baseline and target setting, the development of alternative images of the future, and the definition of policy packages (PP) and pathways that can move policy towards the adopted target.

Extensive research outlined the theory behind the backcasting methodology and the framework, determining the baseline for a 'business as usual' (BAU) scenario regarding London's transport emissions and policy development and implementation.

An inventory of potential measures, based on this research, was proposed to tackle CO_2 emissions. The team has used its extensive analysis to develop an interactive computer simulation, TC-SIM (transport and carbon simulator), that can be played as a 'scenario testing game' for quantifying the carbon efficiency of a range of transport strategies. 'Players' explore the policy pathways and the impact of their implementation by selecting policy package options. The pathways include behavioural and technological options such as choosing to walk or cycle, buying low emission vehicles and the introduction of road pricing regimes.

TC-SIM can be played in different user modes: for example as a 'free rider', a 'techno optimist', an 'enviro-optimist' or a 'complacent car addict', and there is also a free role. The idea is that, using the game, scenario testing will highlight the willingness of various sectors of the public, based on their perceived identities, to engage with the policy agenda. The simulation can also highlight the utility of entrenched policy positions – such as relying on technological change.

Users can select each policy package at 'low', 'medium' or 'high' levels of application. The team is assuming that transport emissions grow year on year as an extrapolation of recent trends under a BAU scenario. The current fully-funded investment strategy for TfL is also represented – approximately £2-7 billion per annum to 2025.

The game has been played and evaluated by a range of project partners including TfL and the GLA, with feedback incorporated into the game's policy matrix. Final reports have been published outlining the project methodology, the TC-SIM appraisal framework, an assessment of policy packages and a review of the acceptability and implementability of measures. ›

Zupa software development studio collaboration with Space Syntax and Halcrow to design the TC-SIM simulation model

'Scenario testing and backcasting offer real possibilities as mechanisms to assess and achieve trend breaks and targets over time. TC-SIM has great potential for raising awareness of complex issues and future lifestyle choices'
Robin Hickman, project coordinator

Project impact

The outcomes generated by use of the TC-SIM game, and the policy review on which it is based, will provide evidence for any review of the Mayor's Transport Strategy and Climate Change Action Plan, and build on the strategy of T2025 via project partners TfL and the GLA. The TC-SIM model will be used as a training tool for planners, students, developers and policymakers.

The outcomes from scenario testing so far suggest that a wide range of policy packages all need to be implemented to a 'high intensity' level of application – including new vehicle technologies, alternative fuels, pricing options, public transport, walking and cycling, urban planning, freight planning and ecological driving. If international air emissions are included in the calculations, relative to the current policy approach, then target achievement becomes impossible to achieve.

Knowledge exchange

TC-SIM is web-based and offers an innovative, and potentially very flexible, means of decision-making. It is a non-real-time collaborative experience where several individual users can interact within the same model and establish a dialogue about the decisions being made.

The 'game' draws on attitudinal theory, a field increasingly being applied to transport planning, and has brought experts from a range of disciplines including transport planning, urban design, planning, statistical analysis and behavioural theory together. Attitudinal theory suggests that, as there are variable attitudes among the travelling public, a single policy response is unlikely to encourage all travellers to change their habits.

Communication and participation tools, such as TC-SIM, applied to different contexts, could play an important role in testing different transport futures with a range of different users, including the public. In the end, a consensus will need to be achieved; and it is the public who will make the difference in choosing radically different (carbon efficient) future lifestyles.

The scenario testing and backcasting methodologies offer 'real possibilities as mechanisms to assess and achieve trend-breaks and targets over time,' says project coordinator Robin Hickman. 'TC-SIM has great potential for raising awareness of complex issues and future lifestyle choices. It could be used to raise awareness of the issues involved, or even as an opinion surveying and voting tool,' he says.

The VIBAT team has an active dissemination strategy and has presented at a wide range of conferences/workshops and contributed papers to more than 10 publications to date. A user group and a number of additional TC-SIM enhancements are under development, seeking to refine and transfer further the lessons and skills acquired during the VIBAT London project.

Workshops have been delivered to the GLA and TfL to disseminate the project conclusions, and to showcase the TC-SIM model and the ways in which it can inform learning.

The work from this project, and the previous VIBAT UK project, is already being built on. The methods developed are now being used in projects in India (Delhi) and Canada (Victoria, British Columbia).

Education and training

An ongoing training programme is being taken forward by Halcrow using the VIBAT methodology. This will continue to be promoted internationally. The project and TC-SIM are also being used as an educational tool during lectures to students at University College London and Oxford University.

The future: the use of enabling mechanisms

Even the most positive outcomes from the scenario testing suggest that further incentives or 'enabling mechanisms' may be required to help achieve the ambitious CO_2 reduction target. 'Oil price volatility has already acted as a catalyst in the switch to lower-carbon travel behaviour,' says Hickman. 'Critically, a carbon-rationing scheme may prove to be the only way to a low-carbon future.'

Achieving a low carbon transport system is likely to involve some very difficult political choices. London is providing a lead for other cities. The challenge now is to map out a variety of future pathways and to engage the public in the decision-making process. The years 2025 and 2050 may be a long way ahead, but the transition to a low carbon society needs to start now.

Project resources
www.vibat.org

A wide range of papers, presentations and other information is available on the project website

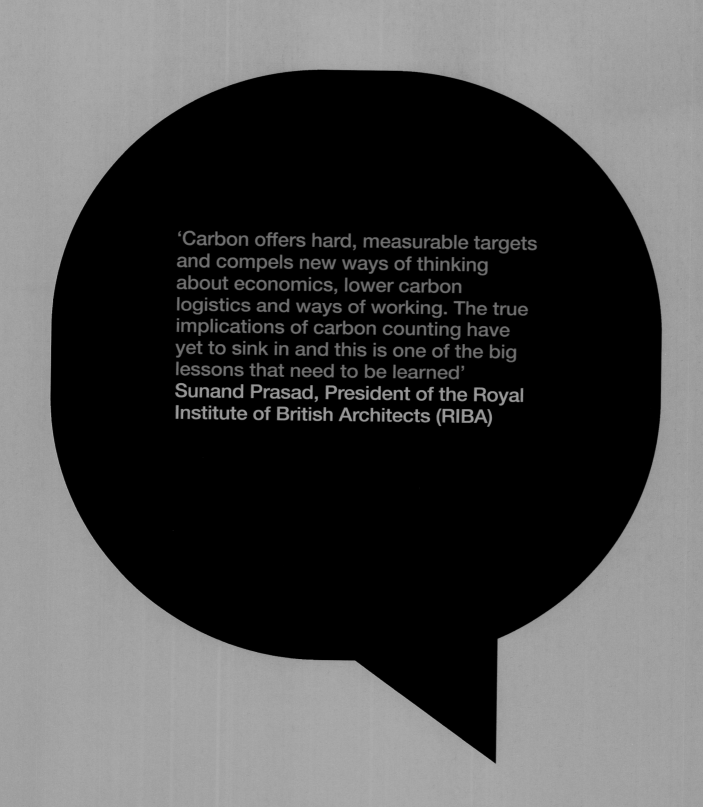

'Carbon offers hard, measurable targets and compels new ways of thinking about economics, lower carbon logistics and ways of working. The true implications of carbon counting have yet to sink in and this is one of the big lessons that need to be learned'
Sunand Prasad, President of the Royal Institute of British Architects (RIBA)

Thank you

Academia

Central St Martins
City University
De Montfort University
Goldsmiths College
Imperial College
Leeds Metropolitan University
Liverpool University
London School of Economics
Nottingham Trent University
Oxford Brookes University
Oxford University
Queen Mary University
Royal College of Art
Salford University
UCL Bartlett Architecture
UCL Bartlett Planning
UCL BSGS
UCL CASA
UCL Civil, Environmental and Geomatic Engineering
UCL Computer Science
UCL CSCS
UCL Development Planning Unit
UCL Geography
UCL Jill Dando Institute
University of East London
Univeristy of Brighton
University of Auckland
University of Cardiff
University of East Anglia
University of Leeds
University of Newcastle
University of Salford
University of Sheffield
University of West England
Westminster University

Public sector corporation / agency

Arts Council England
BBC
British Council of Offices
British Library B&IPC
Constructing Excellence
Construction Skills
Highways Agency
Housing Corporation
London Organising Committee of the Olympic Games
Planing Aid for London
South East England Development Agency
Sustainable London 2012
Transport for London

Industry or professional body/ consultancy / private sector

3D Reid
4M
Action Acton
Addictive TV
Aedas
Art2Architecture
ARUP
Atkins Civil Engineering
Audacity
AZ Urban Studio
BDP
Bio Mapping
Bircham Dyson Bell LLP
Body>Data>Space
BRE
Buchanan
BURA
BURA research associates
CABE
Capita Symonds
Child Graddon Lewis
CIBSE
City and Provincial PLC
City Mine(d)
Community Environment Associates
Construction Products Association
Cryil Sweett
DEGW
Design for Homes
drmm
EDAW
Faber Maunsell
Fletcher Priest Architects Trust
Foundation for Art and Creative Technology
Good Homes Alliance
Halcrow
Hamilton Architects
Hammerson
Haque Design+Research
Home Builders Federation
HOK
HTA Planning
JMP
Knauf Insulation
Lancefield Consulting
Landers Associates
Lengard
Mae LLP
Make Architects
Max Fordham
Meganexus
Mott MacDonald
RIBA
RPS
Savills
Skanska
Slider Studio
SmartSlab
Space Syntax
Tank.TV
Taylor Wimpey
Terra Cognita
Thames Water
AOC
The Douglas Stephen Partnership
Three Dragons
Urban Futures
Urban Initiatives
Volterra
WAND
XCO2

Local government

Bath & North East Somerset Council
CHCTRT (Canning Town Regeneration)
Deptford Council
Hants County Council
LB Barking & Dagenham
LB Barnet
LB Camden
LB Croydon
LB Islington
LB Kingston
LB Lewisham
LB Newham
LB Southwark
LB Tower Hamlets
Lewisham Council
Sutton Council
Thames Gateway London Partnership

Government

Department for Communities and Local Government
Department for Health
Department for Innovation, Universities and Skills
East of England Development Agency
Greater London Authority
Office of Government Commerce

Voluntary / social enterprise / association

Action Sustainability
AECB
Better Archway Forum
Creekside Community Forum
Development Trust Association
ECSC
English Heritage
Groundwork London
Groundwork North London
London 21
London Older People's Strategy Group (LOPSG)
LSx
National Trust
Oxley Conservation
Parity Projects
Pepys Community Forum
Sponge
The Princes Foundation
Transition Town Brixton
Women's Design Service
Youth Works Oxford

The Programme Board

Professor Tim Broyd, former chief executive of CIRIA and now Group Technology Director for Halcrow, chaired the Programme Board. Professor Broyd helped shape the board membership to ensure the broadest engagement of sectoral interests. The Board provided an excellent sounding board and a basis for discussing activities and options for programme management consideration.

Tim Broyd
Group Technology Director, Halcrow;
Halcrow Chair of Construction Innovation, University of Dundee

Jane Carlsen
Principal Planner, Greater London Authority

Pamela Gardner
(former) Head of Regeneration, East Thames

Susannah Hagan
Director MA in Architecture, UEL

Bruce Mew
(former) Director, Housing and Regeneration, Ernst & Young

Peter Morris
Professor and Head of School of Construction and Project Management, The Bartlett, UCL

Tadj Oreszczyn
Professor and Head of School of Graduate Studies, Director of Environmental Design and Engineering, The Bartlett, UCL

Nick Pollard
(former) Executive Vice President, PFI/PPP Skanska UK Plc. Now Chief Executive of Bovis Lend Lease UK

Genie Turton
(former) Director-General for Housing and Planning at ODPM, non-executive director Wates Group

Jean Venables
Director, Crane Environmental, Chair Thames Estuary Partnership and President of ICE (term of office started November 2008)

Elanor Warwick
Head of Research and Futures, Commission for Architecture in the Built Environment (CABE)

Tom Bolton
Research and Features. Advisor, CABE

Max Weaver
Chief Executive, Community Links

John Lock
Development Director, UEL

Ray Wilkinson
Development Director, UEL

Alan Penn
Professor of Adaptive Architecture, originator and lead academic, UrbanBuzz programme, The Bartlett, UCL

David Cobb
Programme Director, UCL

Sponsoring organisations

Alex Thompson (HEFCE)

Simon Whittemore (HEFCE)

Philip Purser-Hallard (HEFCE)

Abigail Tribe (HEFCE)

Adrian Day (HEFCE)

Andrew Shaw (DIUS)

Ashley Malster (DIUS)

Keynote speakers at the UrbanBuzz Conference, December 2008

Peter Bishop, LDA

Bob Kerslake, HCA

Roger Madelin, Argent Group

Simon Milton, GLA

Jean Venables- ICE

Nick Raynsford, CIC

Matthew Taylor, RSA

Sunand Prasad, RIBA

Paul Finch,
Architectural Review

Contributors and supporters of other key UrbanBuzz events

Anna Gagliano, RIBA

Owen Jenkins, CIRIA

Linda Gledstone,
Academy of Urbanism

Tim Stonor,
Academy of Urbanism

Tim Barnes, UCL Advances

Tim Williams, Navigant Consulting

Andrew Crudgington, ICE

Sean Fleetwood, BURA

Eddie Bridgeman, BURA

Stacey Toth, RIBA

Keith Snook, RIBA

Iara Iudicissa,
Capacity Global

Jackie McKeay, CEN

Esther Kurland, Urban Design London

Adam Dawson, SPONGE

Ray Phillips, LVSTC

Nicholas Watts, London Metropolitan University

Anna Walnycki, Islington Environment Forum

Carol Pummell; Ken Brine, CGI Ltd

Gloria Laycock, UCL JDI

Vaseem Khan, UCL CSCS

Herve Borion, UCL CSCS

Natalie Warner, UCL Geography

Matthew Gandy, UCL Geography

Mark Clapson,
Westminster University

Vesna Goldsworthy,
Kingston University

Ian Sinclair

Yolande Barnes,
Savills Research

Martin Davies,
Knowledge East

Rebecca Maguire,
Birkbeck

Outreach activities

Nadia O'Hare, UCL Bartlett Architecture Listing

Jenny Gimpel, UCL Media Relations Manager

Sarah Guthrie, UCL Development and Corporate Communications

Andrew Scoones, The Building Centre

Meghan Fernandes, The Building Centre

UrbanBuzz: spreading the word

Through events, partnerships, networks and sponsorship, the UrbanBuzz message has been spread far and wide. Programme Director David Cobb reflects on a personal journey that has taken UrbanBuzz to some unusual and unexpected places

Wishing to raise awareness of UrbanBuzz's innovative contribution to the creation of sustainable communities, the management applied creative thinking towards generating a wide-ranging and effective outreach programme.

In discussion with the Programme Board, the team developed a branding and awareness campaign to capture the attention of stakeholders. Thus, as the new tools and processes developed by the project teams began to emerge in late 2007, a proactive programme designed to penetrate numerous and diverse sectors in the public, private and academic domains was put in motion.

This included promotion at major events such as Ecobuild (February 2008), Sustainable Development UK (March 2008), Sustainable Communities (June 2008), Sustainability Conference (July 2008), the London Festival of Architecture (July 2008), the Royal Geographical Society Annual Conference (August 2008), Empowering Communities (September 2008), the National Environmental Crime Conference (October

(clockwise from top left) The UrbanBuzz choir (from Abbot's Hill School) in Graz, Austria, outside the famous Kuntshaus public galleries, co-designed by the UCL Bartlett's Peter Cook and Colin Fournier

UrbanBuzz, courtesy of David Cobb, reaches the the summit of Mount Aconcagua, Argentina, 22,841 feet above sea level

David Cobb (right) and UrbanBuzz marketing coordinator Daniel Gilbert at the Thames Gateway Forum, November 2008

Filming for Sky TV's programme on sustainable careers

multimedia presentations from a range of project teams, including insights into making high-yield, low-input urban agriculture work, reflections on creating a low energy Victorian house and reviews of community mapping initiatives.

Presentations and papers

Outreach went well beyond the UK at project and programme level. A dedicated 'conference fund' was offered to fellows who sought support to attend international events. Conference papers, based on UrbanBuzz project work and on its innovative knowledge-sharing model, have been presented at a number of international conferences: a range of papers, presentations and/or notes from these events are accessible from the project websites (see the project pages from page 76 onwards).

The UrbanBuzz community actively communicated both online and offline. Whilst the creation of a substantial virtual network comprising more than 3,000 registrants in just two years represents a valuable resource which augers well for future collaborations, UrbanBuzz also facilitated a number of 'professional and social' networking gatherings, often featuring influential guest speakers (see page 36).

UrbanBuzz in high places...

The desire to spread goodwill whilst generating awareness has taken UrbanBuzz in some unusual, and unexpected, directions. The programme has supported a local boys' football team and a girls' school competing at the World Choir Games in Graz, Austria. Finally, as the UrbanBuzz programme drew to a close in February 2008, UrbanBuzz reached the summit of Mount Aconcagua, Argentina, 22,841 feet above sea level. But, unlike the mountain expedition, the conclusion of the UrbanBuzz programme signals only the end of the beginning. I very much look forward to the next chapter: shaping UrbanBuzz's legacy in the real world.

2008), the Governance and Sustainability seminar (November 2008), and Sustainability in the Built Environment (February 2009).

The above represent mainly London-based conferences and seminars at which UrbanBuzz was promoted directly through exhibits and speakers. This proved an effective awareness-raising mechanism, successfully connecting the programme with many major event organisers whose cooperation will be valuable for future UrbanBuzz communications.

In addition to participation at events, UrbanBuzz connected with all the major professional institutions and 'umbrella groups' to discuss education, training and outreach activities post-programme. The programme supported a number of events under the auspices of the Royal Institute of British Architects (RIBA), which attracted both academic and practitioner sectors. Programme Board member Jean Venables, in her presidential address at the Institution of Civil Engineers in November 2008,

extolled the importance of innovative knowledge exchange mechanisms, citing UrbanBuzz as an exemplar programme in this respect.

UrbanBuzz media

The growing sustainability agenda is spawning job opportunities right across the 'green industry' supply chain, driving an increase in courses being offered in the education sector. Sky TV contacted UrbanBuzz early in 2008 to explore ways in which young people can develop and shape careers in the sustainability industry. UrbanBuzz was a natural portal for the enquiry, given the diversity of its community. Throughout 2008, project representatives, including myself, were interviewed and their reflections on sustainability careers have been screened.

Internet phenomenon YouTube has brought many issues and initiatives to the world's attention, and UrbanBuzz tapped into its global audience to raise awareness of the project teams' work. The online facility provides access to video and

Keywords by project

Antisocial behaviour	SEDUC
Attitudinal theory	VIBAT
Backcasting techniques	VIBAT
Building performance	DEI DEMONSTRATION, LEVH, TOWARDS ZERO CARBON SCHOOLS
Building physics	LEVH, E-POD, TOWARDS ZERO CARBON SCHOOLS, LC4R
Carbon emissions	CARBONBUZZ, VIBAT, LEVH, LC4R, DEI DEMONSTRATION
Census; statistics	EASY
Community; mapping	C-DG, EASY, ESP-SIM, MCSC, MOB-KNOW
Consultation processes	CD-G, CLOVIS, FEFUR, MOB KNOW, THE ROOTSCAPE PROJECT, GBE
Cultivation	ABUNDANCE
Density metrics	METRICITY
Deprivation	SEDUC
Development control officers	SUSTAINABLE TRAINING
Digital workflows	SSSP, EASY, SEDUC, i-VALUL, MCSC
Dwelling stock	EASY, i-VALUL, LEVH, LC4R
Economics and value	i-VALUL
Energy: performance; reduction	CARBONBUZZ, LEVH, LC4R
Evaluation framework	RETILE COMBEEP
External insulation	DEI DEMONSTRATION
Field trials	LC4R, LEVH, ABUNDANCE
Gender; equality	GBE
Green economy; networks	REBOPSE
Heritage and conservation	LEVH
Housing policy, design	MOB KNOW, ESP-SIM
Infrastructure; policy	EASY, METRICITY, i-VALUL, VIBAT
Low carbon living	DEI DEMONSTRATION, E-POD, TOWARDS ZERO CARBON SCHOOLS, VIBAT
Masterplanning	i-VALUL, SSSP, VIBAT, ESP-SIM
Night shutters	LEVH, DEI-DEMONSTRATION
Older people	MOB KNOW
Pattern book designs	ESP-SIM
Performance gaps	LEVH, LC4R
Placemaking	i-VALUL, THE ROOTSCAPE PROJECT, SSSP, SEDUC, FEFUR, CLOVIS
Planning processes; skills gaps	SUSTAINABLE TRAINING, ESP-SIM, i-VALUL
Planning policy	ABUNDANCE, CLOVIS, ESP-SIM, GBE, METRICITY, SUSTAINABLE CONSTRUCTION POLICIES, SUSTAINABLE TRAINING
Population count	EASY
Post-occupancy evaluation	LEVH, LC4R, CARBONBUZZ
Project evaluation	RETILE-COMBEEP
Recruitment; internships	LSTS, REBOPSE
Regeneration	FEFUR, i-VALUL, EASY, SSSP
Renovation; refurbishment	LEVH
Schools; youths	EASY, THE ROOTSCAPE PROJECT, TOWARDS ZERO CARBON SCHOOLS
Screens	SCREAM
Secondary glazing	LEVH
Security and crime	i-VALUL, SEDUC
Self-evaluation	RETILE COMBEEP
Simulations	E-POD, ESP-SIM, SSSP
Social enterprise	MCSC, REBOPSE
Social plannin; policymaking	SEDUC, ABUNDANCE
Spatial planning; GIS	EASY, SEDUC, MCSC, i-VALUL, SSSP
Students; interns	LSTS, REBOPSE
Thermal envelope	LC4R, LEVH, DEI DEMONSTRATION
Transport policies	VIBAT, METRICITY
Unemployed people	REBOPSE
Urban agriculture	ABUNDANCE
Urban layout	i-VALUL, SEDUC, SSSP, ESP-SIM
Windows; insulation	DEI DEMONSTRATION, LEVH, LC4R
Youths; schoolchildren	THE ROOTSCAPE PROJECT